W9-AQK-621

SIGN OF THE 76

Where the title comes from

Lyrics from a popular Union Oil commercial

SIGN OF THE 76

The fabulous life and times
of the Union Oil Company of California

Published by Union Oil Company of California, Los Angeles, California.

Library of Congress Card No. 76-39767

Printed in Los Angeles, California—January, 1977

The words, phrases and expressions used in this publication are those used in general non-technical conversation and do not necessarily express the legal characteristics of the matters, things and relationships discussed or described herein.

Foreword

This is the latest edition of the Union Oil Company of California story. The first—*The Black Bonanza*—was printed in 1950. And the most recent—*The 76 Bonanza*—was published a decade ago. They were the work of Frank J. Taylor and Earl M. Welty, both now deceased.

We thought it was time to update the story, because Union Oil and the world we live in have changed so dramatically over the past decade.

We call this new edition *Sign of the 76*. It reports the history of Union Oil from its 1890 beginnings through 1976. For the first time it chronicles the intriguing story of the early years of Fred L. Hartley's term as chief executive officer, starting in 1965 with the Pure Oil merger. During those years, among the most perilous in the company's long life, a world no one could see coming changed many of the rules by which we had lived.

These tempestuous years saw a severe challenge to the very survival of free enterprise, and particularly to the continued existence of integrated oil companies.

These were the years when the environmental movement flourished and often collided with the growing energy crisis.

In this period, too, Union Oil was rapidly changing from a regional to an international oil company, operating in nearly two dozen foreign countries.

This edition brings our adventure story up to date. You'll meet the people who led us through this decade of challenge.

Paul R. Waddell
Robert F. Niven

Contents

UNION OIL IN '76

THE EXCITING YESTERDAYS

THE CHALLENGE OF CHANGE

UNION OIL IN '76

If one picture is worth a thousand words, the full color family album that follows is a visual history of Union Oil.

Today.

And today is light years away from the company that began humbly in a two-story building at Santa Paula in the Santa Clara valley 86 years ago.

You'll see that building in this album.

You'll see more.

You'll see Union Oil's worldwide headquarters in Los Angeles and the Union 76 Division eastern headquarters under snow in Palatine, Illinois.

You'll see a drilling crew toiling for gas in Alabama and Union's crude being pumped to tankers in Indonesia.

You'll see a total family of Union products—all with a strong family resemblance.

You'll see Union Oil retail outlets that blend with their communities. And serve them in 45 states.

You'll see Union Oil in petrochemicals and a Union subsidiary working an open-pit uranium mining project in Wyoming.

You'll see a Unicracker that increases production of unleaded gasoline and POPCORN® sulfur sprayed from a nozzle. The little balls are used to convert soil into good farming land.

And more.

You'll see a Research Center where more than 600 scientists and technicians are at work and one of the 300 auto/truckstop "supermarkets" under the Union Oil flag.

You'll see Union's monopod platform in the Cook Inlet, Alaska, and Union at The Geysers field in northern California, the world's largest geothermal operation.

You'll see a portion of Union's 20,000 acres of prime oil shale land in western Colorado and a portion of Union's oil and product pipeline system.

You'll see Union's oil and natural gas finders at work in the Gulf of Mexico, Indonesia and around the world, and biologists testing the sea waters near the Santa Maria Refinery to insure conformance with environmental regulation.

And more.

As you turn the page and browse through this color album of Union Oil you realize something else.

Today the company can stand proudly tall: a fully integrated energy company doing business around the world.

That's a fair piece of growing in less than nine decades.

SIGN OF THE 76

Introduced in 1967, this Union logotype—a combination of the company name and the traditional 76 symbol—is used on all products, buildings, vehicles, signs, advertising and printed matter.

WHERE IT ALL BEGAN

In this quaint Santa Paula, California, building, three small companies consolidated on October 17, 1890 to form Union Oil Company. The first floor now houses the California Oil Museum.

EASTERN DIVISION HEADQUARTERS

A blanket of snow covers Union Oil's Union 76 Division Eastern Region headquarters in Palatine, Illinois, former home of Pure Oil Company.

UNION OIL CENTER

The center of Union Oil Company's worldwide operations, located in downtown Los Angeles, covers nearly five acres. It includes three major office buildings and a separate structure housing cafeterias and a large auditorium. The site is beautifully landscaped with native trees and plants.

76

SKELETON OF A GIANT

Assembled onshore, giant platforms such as this will later be towed to the productive oil and gas tracts off Louisiana. Workman climbing ladder indicates the relative size of the structure.

FO'C'SLE OF A STANDSTILL SHIP

A powerful floating crane hoists the crew's quarters atop an offshore platform under construction.

A PLATFORM IN THE GULF

Workmen construct an offshore drilling and production platform in the Gulf of Mexico. The giant legs in the foreground are anchored to the ocean floor to enable the platform to withstand hurricane forces.

INTERNATIONAL COOPERATION

A platform and support ship in background search for oil in the Attaka field, off East Kalimantan, Indonesia, as the workboat in the foreground flies the Indonesian flag and the Union Oil colors from a stern halyard.

NATIVE WORKMEN

Indonesian workmen rig a mud line on an exploratory drilling barge offshore East Kalimantan. Drilling is done through the large pipe on the right.

FILLING THE LINES

Huge 42-inch pipelines connect oil storage tanks to ship-loading facilities at Lavan Island, off the coast of Iran. The large capacity lines make it possible to load almost a million barrels a day of crude oil from the prolific Sassan field in the Persian Gulf.

EST VENTURE

THE MAKING OF A PLATFORM

Aberdeen, Scotland, serves as assembly point for this Union Oil platform (above) destined for duty in the Heather field off the British coast. Workmen make last minute checks (right) on the gargantuan legs that will make the platform over 600 feet tall.

RIG OVER TROUBLED WATERS

An enormous semi-submersible drilling platform, the West Venture, is used in Union Oil's search for oil and gas in the turbulent North Sea.

ONE-LEGGED NORTH COUNTRY CYCLOP

Union Oil's monopod platform in the Cook Inlet, Alaska, is designed to resist the extreme conditions of the area. The center trunk will accommodate the drilling of 32 wells.

TOILING FOR GAS

A drilling crew works on a well near Chunchula, Alabama, site of an important natural gas field discovered by Union Oil in 1973.

ENERGY AND OUR ENVIRONMENT

As a sea lion rests on an offshore platform in California coastal waters (left), beach goers enjoy a man-made oil development island off Long Beach, California.

GEOTHERMAL ENERGY: THE GEYSERS

Union Oil is the operator of The Geysers field in northern California, the world's largest geothermal operation. The company explores for, develops and produces the natural heat energy of the earth and sells it to a power company for conversion to electrical power.

THE PHILIPPINES

Operating for the Philippine government, Union Oil has discovered two geothermal fields on Luzon Island and electrical generating plants are being constructed.

OIL BEARING ROCKS

View of a portion of Union Oil's 20,000 acres of prime oil shale land in western Colorado, much of it acquired more than 50 years ago. Union is a pioneer in developing technology to extract shale oil, and research is being conducted for a prototype retort that would process 10,000 tons of shale per day.

ENVIRONMENTAL TESTING

Scientists collect meteorological and other environmental data to determine what impact, if any, large scale oil shale retorting operations might have on the western Colorado site.

TRANSPORTATION:
GETTING THE OIL THERE

From the San Francisco Refinery, above, to the 40-inch Capline running from Louisiana to Illinois, right, pipelines are an essential tool in delivering crude oil and petroleum products. Via tank trucks, below, gasoline goes to a network of more than 14,000 Union Oil service stations.

LOADING INDONESIAN OIL

Union Oil's Indonesian crude is pumped from onshore tanks through underwater pipes to the monobuoy, foreground, then through the hoses, floating at right, into tankers such as this one bound for markets in Japan and the United States.

WINTER WONDERLAND

Refinery operators, at left, flush a fire nozzle after a snowstorm at the Chicago Refinery. The ultra-modern facility was built in 1970 at a cost of more than $200 million.

PATTERNS OF STEEL

At the San Francisco Refinery, a Unicracker reformer complex makes it possible for Union Oil to produce unleaded gasoline.

NERVE CENTER OF A REFINERY

Union Oil's automated refinery near Chicago is operated from this central, computerized control room.

A STEEL GIANT
At the Los Angeles Refinery, workmen inspect the reactor columns of the Unicracker that increases production of unleaded gasoline.

PANORAMA OF ENERGY *A recreation park adjacent to the Los Angeles Refinery provides a carefree atmosphere for visitors, proving that energy and recreational pleasures do not have to clash.*

SULFUR RECOVERY UNIT

Developed by Union Oil and another company, this Beavon sulfur recovery unit at the Los Angeles Refinery recovers more than 99 percent of the sulfur in refinery effluents.

SYMMETRY OF TANKS

In Eastern Texas, the Beaumont Refinery is strategically located to receive crude oil from two pipelines, barges and ocean tankers.

CONSIDERATION FOR THE SEA

Biologists test the ocean near the Santa Maria Refinery in an effort to insure that the facility's outfall is pollution-free, and the water in better condition than when it was used in the refinery.

A MOUNTAIN OF GOLDEN SULFUR

Popcorn® sulfur, developed by Union Oil, is sprayed from a nozzle. The little balls that look like popcorn were once a petroleum pollutant. This sulfur is now recovered and used to convert alkaline soil into good farming land.

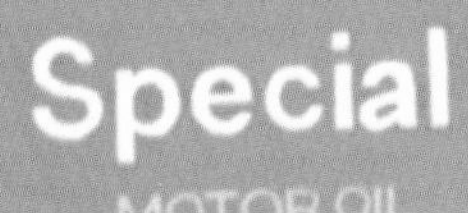

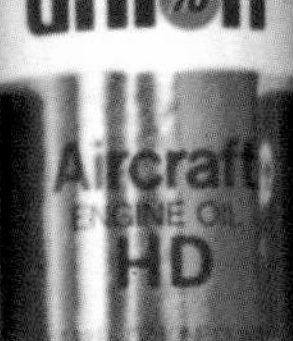

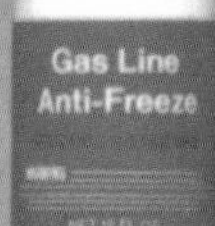

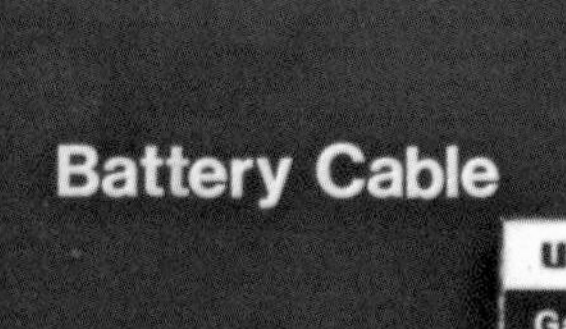

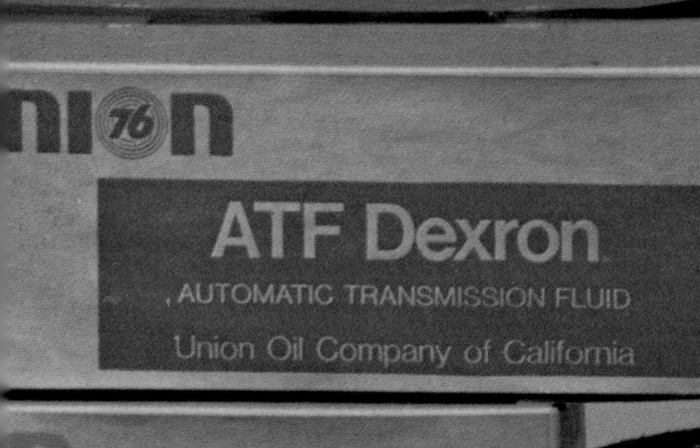

UNION 76
Special
MOTOR OIL
TWO U.S. GALLONS
Premium
Custom
MOTOR OIL
NET 32 FL OZ (ONE QUART)
Special
MOTOR OIL
ATF
Dexron
AUTOMATIC TRANSMISSION FLUID
Aircraft
ENGINE OIL
HD
Guardo
MOTOR OIL
Windshield De-icer
Sure Start
Reinforced Jiffy Patch
FOR TUBELESS TIRES
Oil Filter
SUPER HEAVY DUTY
Motor Vehicle Brake Fluid
ALL SEASON
Windshield Washer Solvent and Anti-Freeze
Gas Line Anti-Freeze
MP Automotive grease
Jiffy Patch
SELF VULCANIZING
Du-All Plugs
FOR TUBES AND TUBELESS TIRES
HEAVY DUTY
Radiator Flush
Cooling System Anti-Rust
Gasoline Filter
FIVE
★★★★★
STAR
EXTRA CAPACITY
Battery Cable
Gasoline Filter
PF 25
PF 7 OR PF 10
ATF Dexron
AUTOMATIC TRANSMISSION FLUID
Union Oil Company of California
ATF Typ
UNION ★★★★ FOUR STAR
Air Filter

HIGH QUALITY, DIFFERENT MOTIF

While the architecture may vary—from the airy, trim look in Forida, top, to the tile roof style of California—Union Oil service stations consistently maintain the high quality they have always been known for.

THE UNION LOOK

The consistent use of the Union Oil logo on all product packaging has established a high degree of brand recognition among customers and insures the user of the highest quality products.

ECONOMY ON THE GO

Union Oil conducted fuel economy tests of the most popular makes of foreign and domestic autos to inform the public of mileage differences.

AUTOMOTIVE SUPERMARKET

More than 300 of these nationally-known truck and auto stops throughout the country provide every service for truckers—be it a good night's rest or good, fast food or excellent maintenance facilities and quality fuels.

COLOSSAL POOL TABLE

Perched atop a brilliant orange 76 sphere in a field of many awaiting installation as service station corner pole signs, a young woman shows the spirit of 76.

76
UNION OIL
RESEARCH

FROM FERTILIZER TO SHALE OIL

While a scientist examines plants in a green house (left) to study the effects of fertilizers produced by a Union subsidiary, a team of researchers (below) inspects the latest oil shale run from the pilot retort plant at the research center.

RESEARCH CENTER

More than 600 scientists and technicians are at work in Union Oil's Research Center in Brea, California, where all the technological and research needs of every division in the company are served.

AGLOW

Night lights illuminate the Brea, California, ammonia plant of Collier Carbon and Chemical Corporation, a wholly owned subsidiary of Union Oil.

NORTH IN ALASKA

Located in the picturesque Cook Inlet of Alaska, Collier's fertilizer plant uses the natural gas from Union Oil's nearby onshore and offshore fields to manufacture ammonia and urea.

AMSCO OUT WEST

These modern offices in La Mirada, California, house the western regional offices of AMSCO, a division of Union Oil involved in manufacturing and marketing a variety of petrochemicals.

PROBING THE EARTH

A Union Oil subsidiary, Minerals Exploration Company, is working on an open-pit uranium mining project in Wyoming, one of many discoveries located by the company's geologists.

FAR EAST OPERATIONS

Unoco, Ltd., a Union Oil subsidiary, has a 50 percent interest in the Kyung-In Energy Co. steam generating and refinery complex at Inchon, South Korea, which provides electrical energy from petroleum products to assist in that nation's development.

MEETING WITH THE PRESIDENT

President Gerald R. Ford listens closely to Union Oil's President Fred L. Hartley during a tour of The Geysers geothermal field in April, 1975. President Ford was accompanied by Federal Energy Chief Frank Zarb. The party toured the facility despite a cold, wet snow flurry. Dr. Carel Otte, head of the geothermal division, (yellow jacket) participated in discussions on this alternate energy source.

WORKING GRASSHOPPERS— SMILIN' JACK

Oil pumping units, decorated to look like grasshoppers, break the visual monotony of an oil field near a busy highway in the oil-rich La Habra Hills in California. A Jack-O-Lantern, created each year by painters at the Los Angeles Refinery during the Halloween season, attracts kids of all ages during the night of ghosts and ghouls.

PASADENA'S FAMOUS GARDENS-ON-WHEELS

The world famous Tournament of Roses in Pasadena has seen the participation of Union Oil for more than 40 years. In 1970 Union Oil was awarded Grand Prize with this entry entitled "Indonesian Holiday" in the New Year's Day Parade, an event seen by millions.

GOOD WILL TOWARD MEN

An electric Christmas tree atop the Union Oil Center in Los Angeles reminds motorists of the hope found within all mankind.

UNION OIL'S EXCITING YESTERDAYS

THE FAR-FLUNG UNION OIL COMPLEX, with assets in 1976 of $4 billion, achieved its present position because of the dogged courage of its founders and early builders. Despite drilling dry holes and going broke repeatedly, they refused to be defeated, eventually finding the oil that made possible in a large measure the company's growth and success. The Union Oil pioneers were more than oil miners. They were builders with visions of an enduring company serving the public for decades to come. Time after time, the giants of the industry and of high finance tried to swallow up the independent company that battled successfully to preserve its independence. "Union Oil's Exciting Yesterdays" is the story of Union Oil's growth from puny infancy to stout, vigorous adulthood to the point of its merger with Pure Oil Company in 1965. The history of the enlarged and strengthened Union Oil begins with "The Challenge of Change."

DRAKE

CHAPTER ONE 1859-1883

Bible-quoting Wildcatter

RIDING HORSEBACK ALONG THE DUSTY TRAILS of the wooded Venango Valley in the northwestern tip of Pennsylvania, a solemn, keen-eyed youngster in his late teens kept a sharp eye out for mysterious seeps from which oozed a black, sticky "rock oil," as petroleum was called in the 1850's. The youthful horseback rider was not particularly interested in the black tar, which was collected in pits or skimmed from Oil Creek, flowing down the valley, and sold to apothecaries, who used the rock oil in medicines that "cured" almost anything. Spotting oil seeps was a means of taking his mind off a great personal problem.

Lyman Stewart's chore was collecting hides from farmers for his father's tannery in the village of Cherrytree. The boy hated the smelly hides, and he hated tanning, the trade chosen for him by his father, so much that he had decided to offer himself as a missionary. A wave of religious zeal, which he shared, was sweeping the country, and churches were calling young men to go forth and preach among the heathen. His hobby was preparing him for a date with destiny, which was to be a hunter of oil rather than a hunter of lost souls. All the rest of his life he was a "seep geologist," envied for his uncanny "nose for oil."

Young Stewart came by his piety and his evangelical urge quite naturally. His thrifty Scotch forebears, who had settled in the Venango Valley in 1802, were devout Presbyterians. His father, William Reynolds Stewart, had helped build the first Presbyterian church in the area. When weather delayed the circuit-riding pastor, Stewart was the pinch-hitting preacher. His mother, Jane Irwin Stewart, gathered her seven children, of whom Lyman was the second-born, about her each evening and read the Bible aloud, then ended each day with

AMERICA'S FIRST OIL WELL

People stopped laughing at "Uncle Billy" Smith and "Colonel" Drake when the well they punched into the ground at Titusville, Pennsylvania, yielded a flow of oil and started a mad land stampede.

WHERE OIL WAS DISCOVERED

Earliest map record of presence of petroleum in Pennsylvania was published in 1755 in Map of the Middle British Colonies *by Lewis Evans. Note word "Petroleum" shown near the present site of Oil City. Oil was known to Senecas, who used it for barter; was used by troops in Revolutionary War to relax sore muscles.*

prayer, just before the candles were snuffed out. Thus, almost from the day of his birth, July 22, 1840, Lyman Stewart felt a kinship with the Almighty. The lessons he drew from the Bible shaped his life, gave him the faith and the courage to take risks.

Though he probably knew the location of more oil seeps than anyone else in the valley, Stewart felt little urge to collect and sell rock oil, even to augment the saving of every hard-earned dollar he could accumulate to finance his missionary adventure. The oil was everywhere, but there was little demand for it. The most popular use was as "Seneca oil," an old remedy handed down from one generation to another by the Seneca Indians, who used petroleum for wampum in barter with other tribes.

There were many old pits around the valley into which the oil seeped. Supposedly they had been dug by the Indians or by the canoe-paddling French explorers. An early map of Pennsylvania, drawn in 1755, had the name "Petroleum" on it close to where Titusville later mushroomed into the world's first "oil capital." During the Revolutionary War, General Benjamin Lincoln's weary troops paused in the valley to bathe their feet and joints in oil they found floating on the creek. "This gave them great relief and freed them immediately from the rheumatic complaints with which many of them were afflicted," the general recorded in his journal.

For decades, visionaries had foreseen riches from oil, if somehow a market for the stuff could be found. As far back as 1802, President Timothy Alden of Allegheny College had written:

"This oil, called by the Senecas 'au nus,' might be collected so as to become a profitable article of commerce. The oil is much esteemed for its efficacy in removing rheumatic complaints. It burns well in lamps, and might be advantageously used for lighting streets.

"If by some process it could be rendered odorless, it would become an important article for domestic illumination."

But the thrifty, hard-working Stewart clan wasted no time dreaming about riches from oil. William Stewart labored hard at his trade, tanning, anticipating the day when young Lyman would finish school and carry on the family livelihood. Lyman's formal schooling was the best that the neighborhood and the times afforded. Cherrytree village consisted of four families, with other homes scattered in the surrounding woods. The tiny, single-room school offered three grades of reading, writing, and arithmetic. For the other five grades, Lyman and his brothers and sisters had to go to town. This meant Titusville, 10 miles distant, itself little more than a village. But Titusville had a school, three churches, two taverns, several stores along its muddy main street. Its population of 400 doubled or trebled on Saturday nights, when the farmers and lumberjacks boiled into town. The nearest railroad ended at Corey, 27 miles to the north via a rutty, almost impassable road.

During his school days, both in Cherrytree village and in Titusville, Lyman sat with several classmates whose names were to go down in oil history along with his own. One was John W. Steele, later known as Coal Oil Johnny. After inheriting an oil fortune and a daily income of $2,000, he rollicked off to New York to stage an orgy of spending that ended only when the wells ran dry. Steele returned to Titusville to spend the rest of his life as a baggageman. Another was Demetrius G. Scofield, who, like Stewart, learned the oil business in Pennsylvania and then migrated to California to head the concern that later became the nucleus around which the Standard Oil Company of California was built. Still another was I. E. Blake, a Titusville boy who, after working as a driller for Lyman Stewart, became a pioneer oil hunter in California and who later lured Stewart to the Golden State.

The first "oil millionaire" to make a fortune from petroleum seeping out of the soil was apparently Samuel Kier, the Pittsburgh druggist who bottled Kier's Rock Oil, exploited as a medicine to be used either externally or internally to cure practically anything. Another of his products, Kier's Petroleum Butter, was put up in boxes and sold for burns, scalds, and bruises. Druggist Kier shipped quantities of his "butter" to California gold miners, who were always banging themselves up.

Kier's thriving business set other promoters thinking. One of these was George H. Bissell of New Haven, Connecticut. Bissell had seen at Dartmouth College a sample bottle of Oil Creek petroleum sent in by a Titusville doctor, who asked the college chemists to analyze the stuff and determine its potential uses. Though the chemists were noncommittal, Bissell and his partner, Jonathan G. Eveleth, journeyed to Titusville, where they purchased 100 acres of land and leased an additional 112 acres, 2½ miles north of the town. The hopeful promoters employed Professor Benjamin F. Silliman, Jr., of Yale to analyze samples of their

THE FIRST "OIL MILLIONAIRE" *Samuel M. Kier, a Pennsylvania salt merchant, sold petroleum bottled as medicine, calling it "Kier's Rock Oil," lauded as a cure-all for internal or external ills. Another product, "Kier's Petroleum Butter," sold for burns, scalds, and bruises, was popular with California's gold miners, who "were always banging themselves up."*

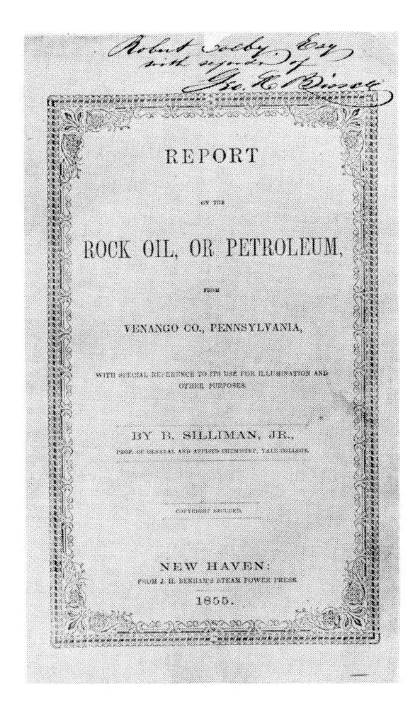
REPORT

ON THE

ROCK OIL, OR PETROLEUM,

FROM

VENANGO CO., PENNSYLVANIA,

WITH SPECIAL REFERENCE TO ITS USE FOR ILLUMINATION AND OTHER PURPOSES.

BY B. SILLIMAN, JR.,

PROF. OF GENERAL AND APPLIED CHEMISTRY, YALE COLLEGE.

COPYRIGHT SECURED.

NEW HAVEN:
FROM J. H. BENHAM'S STEAM POWER PRESS.
1855.

THE REPORT THAT KICKED OFF THE FIRST OIL BOOM

Glowing reports by Geology Professor Benjamin Silliman, Jr., of Yale started oil booms in Pennsylvania in 1855, and in California in 1864.

rock oil and to suggest commercial uses for it. The professor reported that a synthetic coal oil, or kerosene, could easily be refined from it for lighting homes, stores, and public buildings and streets and prophesied that many other useful by-products would eventually be extracted from petroleum.

The professor's report was all the Connecticut promoters needed to launch the oil age. With other New Haven financiers, they organized the Pennsylvania Rock Oil Company, soon superseded by the Seneca Oil Company, which took over the properties near Titusville that Bissell and Eveleth had acquired. Instead of digging pits near the oil seeps, the Seneca Oil Company directors decided to dig a well and try to tap the main source of oil underground. This might be a lake or a river; just what they might dig into nobody knew for sure. The well would be similar to those already drilled for salt water in the Titusville area.

Scouting for an "expert" to oversee the punching of the hole in the ground, Banker James M. Townsend, one of the Seneca Oil Company's more enthusiastic organizers, hit upon Edwin L. Drake, a retired railroad conductor. One of Drake's qualifications was that he could get free passes on the railroad to travel between the company's oil properties in Pennsylvania and the home office in New Haven. To give Drake prestige, Townsend, being a canny promoter, tagged him with the rank of colonel. Thereafter he was always known as Colonel Drake.

The colonel was a man of action. Arriving at Corey, he rode horseback to Titusville and inspected the Seneca Oil Company properties, decided where the hole should be drilled, then looked for a driller. The quest brought him in contact with Uncle Billy Smith, blacksmith and toolmaker, whom he promptly hired. When Smith began pounding the bit into the ground to tap oil, both he and Drake became the laughingstock of the valley. The operation was known, of course, as Drake's Folly. The name stuck until August 27, 1859, when the

THE COUNTRY'S FIRST OIL DRILLER

"Uncle Billy" Smith made his own bits and drills and punched out a hole in the ground at Titusville, using methods employed for centuries in probing for water. Heavy bits were slung from an elastic pole and raised and lowered by a combination of manpower and the whiplash of the pole. A good crew could drill three feet a day by this method.

hole was 69½ feet deep. On that Sunday afternoon Uncle Billy peered down into the stovepipe casing, an original idea hit upon by Drake to keep the sides from caving in, and saw a black substance floating only a few feet from the surface.

Despite all the ridicule, Drake had struck oil by drilling for it. This was the first time in history that oil had been found in that manner. The oil industry was born that day, among the trees lining the banks of Oil Creek. While the oil never flowed from that well, it was easily pumped out. The cry of "Oil, Oil!" spread like wildfire, and the peaceful valley was soon the scene of one of the maddest, wildest land stampedes in history. Everyone scrambled to lease ground around the discovery well. Oil was selling for $20 a barrel, and nearly everyone in the valley decided to get rich quick. But Drake, the discoverer, wasn't sharing the riches, because his rig and tanks were destroyed by fire soon after the pioneer well was drilled.

Before the month was ended, hundreds of oil-mad outsiders had poured into Titusville. Wildly excited, they milled about, buying, leasing, and selling land with such abandon that shortly nearly every acre on the valley floor was tied up. No one bothered to inquire about the seeps. Land was land, and few questions were asked by the excited oil-lease hunters.

This contagious oil fever failed to arouse Lyman Stewart unduly at first. Nineteen at the time, he had completed his apprenticeship and was entitled to practice the trade as a journeyman tanner. He hated the trade as much as ever, and still planned to become a missionary. To this end, he had saved $125, a lot of money in 1859 for a young fellow not yet of age. But as the oil madness spread, he was tempted to make a quick fortune before becoming a missionary—a decision that paradoxically enabled him eventually to endow churches and Bible schools on a magnificent scale.

"Living within a few miles of Titusville, it was natural that I should become interested in the new industry which was causing such excitement. My boyish enthusiasm became so strong I couldn't resist the excitement," he recalled, later.

On December 5, 1859, he invested his $125 in a one-eighth interest in a lease on the John Benninghoff farm. It took all of his capital. Unfortunately, his partners in the venture were strapped, too. By the time they had paid the $1,000 demanded by the cagey old German for the right to drill on his farm, the amateur promoters could raise no capital with which to finance a well. They lost their lease and all of their savings. Ironically, six years later when other oil hunters drilled on the Benninghoff farm, their first hole produced a 300-barrel-per-day well, and soon Benninghoff had an income of $6,000 a day from oil royalties.

This was Lyman Stewart's first plunge in oil. It was only the first of several oil fortunes to slip through his fingers. It took over a year of hard work at the trade he hated to save up enough for a second plunge. By this time the Venango Valley was literally crazy over oil. Derricks were going up everywhere, and holes going down. Steam engines huffed among the trees; great piles of barrels were stacked up along Oil Creek in which to ship the oil to market. The creek was so shallow that horses walking in the stream drew the oil-laden barges down to the river via which they floated to Pittsburgh. Hastily built hotels were crammed full of oil hunters, two in every bed. Mud had become the nightmare of the cursing, sweating teamsters who carted the oil barrels to the barges. Prices of land for leases soared to fantastic figures. Oil had dropped in price, but was still selling for $10 per barrel.

By 1861 Lyman Stewart had saved up enough for his second plunge in oil. He and several partners leased the Boyd farm near Petroleum Center; this time, profiting from experience, they held out $1,000 to drill their first well, which was a producer. But after it came in, with fortune again at their finger tips, other new wells likewise began spewing out more oil than the buyers could handle. The price of oil fell so low that Stewart and his partners could not afford to pump their well. Again, they lost their lease. Later the Boyd farm became one of the valley's rich producers. But not for luckless Lyman Stewart.

As oil production boomed, the market for oil became more and more uncertain. The Venango Valley had plenty of oil, but the public had not yet learned how to use it. The Venango *Spectator*, the valley's leading newspaper, commented in 1862:

"The great depression in the market prices of crude petroleum in the past year, while it has almost ruined all of the operators of limited means or forced them to seek more remunerative businesses, has also been the means of introducing the product to all parts of the world, and made it as much a necessity as any single article of human want. As an illuminator, it is beyond the reach of competition. Its brilliancy is unsurpassed, its cheapness unparalleled, even at double the present ruling prices."

Europe had become the major outlet for Pennsylvania oil, but the outbreak of the Civil War cut off this promising market. It also provided Lyman Stewart

"FOUNDER" OF UNION OIL AT AGE 19

Apprenticed as journeyman tanner, Lyman Stewart had little interest in oil at age 19, intending to become a missionary. Saving $125 toward his escape from tanning into missionary life, he plunged it into an oil gamble to increase his capital, but lost every cent. It took him a year to accumulate enough money from his tannery work to make a second plunge, and by then he was caught by the oil fever that never left him.

with an escape from the tannery. Putting aside his dreams of riches, he joined a group of volunteers and enlisted in the 16th Pennsylvania Cavalry in September, 1862. For the next three years the young tanner-promoter served with the rank of private as a valet to horses. His one claim to military distinction was that his unit was at Appomattox Courthouse when General Robert E. Lee surrendered to General Ulysses S. Grant, thus ending the war.

When he returned to Titusville, in 1865, Stewart could scarcely believe his eyes. A bustling boom town of 6,000 inhabitants had mushroomed in the heart of the Venango Valley. The 13 hotels were so crowded with guests that most of them had only half a bed, an entire interest in a bed being something unknown in the oil fields. There were three banks bulging with oil money in their vaults. Titusville had an opera house, which attracted a constant stream of lecturers, singers, and musicians. The railroad had built south from Corey and extended its line through Titusville to Oil City on the Allegheny River.

The tough, cursing mule skinners whose teams formerly transported oil over the muddy roads were gone. Pipelines now moved the oil to the waterways. Shallow Oil Creek had been dammed. When the spillways were opened, fleets of flatboats and barges carrying from 1,000 to 3,000 barrels of oil floated down to the river on the crest of artificial freshets. At Oil City steamboats picked up the oil and transported it to Pittsburgh. The railroads had invented tank cars to haul the oil products of the refineries, largely kerosene, to the Atlantic sea-

HORSES PULLED THE FIRST OIL BARGES *Oil was hauled to market in horse-pulled flatboats in shallow Oil Creek, Pennsylvania, the main artery of transportation in the early oil fields. During months of low water, artificial freshets were created by releasing dammed water.*

board. A forest of derricks dotted the valley, and thousands of wells were spewing out oil faster than the market could absorb it.

The returned veteran had no capital to plunge into this heady oil rush, but he was more determined than ever to shake loose from the life of a tanner. Stewart decided to round out his meager education with a hurry-up commercial course at Eastman's Business College in Poughkeepsie, New York. He had saved up enough money to stay in college for six months. By deep concentration, he managed to absorb a course in bookkeeping and finance, which stood him in good stead all the rest of his life.

Returning to the Venango Valley in 1866, he opened a tiny office in Pioneer Run not far from Titusville to negotiate oil leases. Now his boyhood experience in tramping over the hills, collecting hides and delivering leather, became an unexpected asset. He knew where the seeps were better than any other operator. His luck took a turn for the better. He had hardly opened his office when a Pioneer Run wildcat well came in for 600 barrels a day. Speculators, promoters, financiers, and drillers rushed in. Stewart was ready for them. Negotiating quick leases with the farmers, he began to make money.

OIL FIELD ROADS HAD THEIR SHORTCOMINGS

Muddy bottomless roads through early Pennsylvania oil fields near Lyman Stewart's home so impressed him he later spearheaded a drive to cover the nation's highways with asphalt.

Then came the strike at Pit Hole, where a wildcat well gushed in one midwinter morning, flowing 250 barrels a day. Again the oil-well hunters stampeded in, and by the following September Pit Hole field was producing 6,000 barrels per day. A ramshackle boom town sprang up, with banks, hotels, the third largest post office in the state, and a population of 15,000. As suddenly as it came in, the field ran dry, pumped out by wells crowded so close together that there was barely room for the derricks. The exodus started. In a few months the new homes, the banks, the hotels, and other structures were vacant. Pit Hole had become a ghost oil city. From Pit Hole Lyman Stewart learned a lesson in shoestring financing, one that he practiced the rest of his life.

"The practice during the Pit Hole excitement was to sell interests varying from 1/64th to 1/4th, each interest entitling the purchaser to a pro rata share in the profits from the well," he explained later. "Speculation and excitement ran very high and men often bought interests in wells without first taking the precaution to determine whether the owner had not oversold the allotment of interests. It was not uncommon for a hundred interests to be held in a single well, each entitling the owner to a 1/32nd of the oil produced."

Stewart began buying one-sixty-fourth interests in wells, thus spreading his limited but growing capital over a maximum of chances. Later he was able to

PENNSYLVANIA BOOMTOWN *Pioneer Run, about the time Lyman Stewart settled there to begin buying and selling leases, aided by knowledge of the countryside gained as tanner's apprentice. Hills were stripped of trees and covered with derricks, wastefully jammed together.*

increase this to one-thirty-second interests, and finally to one-eighths. But he and his older brother, Milton, with whom he often operated in partnership, always tried to spread their risks. By 1868 the Stewarts were well-established operators. They also had a unique reputation that set them apart from the typical, rough-and-ready oil-boom promoters.

"The Stewarts even then were known as gentlemen," recalls one of their contemporaries. "They dressed immaculately. They were courteous and soft-spoken. A profane word never came from their lips. Milton was not much of a mixer. He stuck close to the financial and refining end. Lyman could go out into the roughest and toughest field and mix with the most foul-mouthed scum

STEWART'S FIRST HOME

Lyman built this family home in Shamburg. Mrs. Stewart is seated on steps while her husband holds their son, William, destined to succeed his father as president of Union Oil. The family was forced to give up this home and move back to Titusville because of financial reverses.

and riffraff and command the respect of everyone. He was never a hypocrite. He carried his faith with him, and the roughest character seemed to respect him, not only for his knowledge of oil but for his cleanliness and downright decency. All of the Stewarts were Christian gentlemen, and of them all Lyman was the most respected and beloved."

An incident in 1867 not only illustrated Lyman's character but also affected his fortune. With Frank W. Andrews, one of the more businesslike operators in the area, and several others, the Stewart brothers were watching a new well being dynamited to increase the flow of oil. As the explosive cut loose, it sprayed most of the spectators with foul-smelling petroleum. While others cursed and fumed, Milton turned to Lyman, gazed at his brother's drenched white suit, and quietly began to rub the oil off the clothing.

"Quite a bit of oil," commented Milton.

"Yes, and it's good oil," replied Lyman as he fingered it and smelled it. "This well should be a good producer."

Neither brother said a word about his oil-bespattered suit. This composure so impressed Andrews that a little later, when he formed the Claremont Oil Company at Petroleum Center, in 1868, he invited the Stewart brothers in for an interest. Claremont Oil made them a substantial quick fortune. Later Andrews offered them an opportunity to buy a five-eighths interest in the 112-acre Tallman farm.

"In four years we got 1,750,000 barrels of oil from the 24 wells on the 30 acres of proven territory on this lease," Stewart recalled in an interview.

The brothers were riding high. It appeared that nothing could go wrong with their plunges in oil. In the six years from 1866 to 1872, Lyman Stewart piled up $300,000 in cash in the bank. He and Milton were holders of shares in hundreds of wells; Milton had branched out into a small refinery. Lyman stuck to the producing end. He was also head of Lyman Stewart Company, a family partnership consisting of himself and two brothers, Milton and W. B. Stewart; two sisters, Eva and Lydia Stewart; John Irwin, a cousin; Alexander Waldie, a friend; W. J. Chichester, a Presbyterian minister. The partnership participated in numerous profitable oil deals. One of their wells, the Lady Stewart, became the largest producing well in the Shamburg area.

To be nearer to the scene of his most productive oil field, the Tallman farm, Lyman Stewart built a two-story, frame house in Shamburg in 1870. By this time he was a substantial family man, having married, on May 2, 1867, Sarah Adelaide Burrows, a devout and religious young New Yorker whose family had settled in Cherrytree a decade before. In this house, Will, the second of their children, was born—likewise "to oil."

About this time an apparently insignificant incident changed the whole course of Lyman Stewart's life. While the brothers were riding the crest, Milton Stewart suggested to Lyman one evening that they go to the meeting of the Mendelssohn Society in Titusville, which had plunged into culture in a big way. Unfortunately Lyman had promised to meet a man; so Milton and several friends, after their evening of music, decided about midnight to organize a small oil company to take over a small lease that Milton knew he could get. They called

OIL TOWN OF THE 1870's *Muddy main street of Shamburg, Pennsylvania, where Lyman Stewart moved to be closer to his investments in the nearby Tallman Farm. Stewart home was located a few hundred yards back of drug store.*

their new venture the Octave Oil Company. With this musical beginning, the company made some money. But none of it went to Lyman. He was overlooked when the Octave deal was set up.

Lyman Stewart had spent the evening with a persuasive visitor to Titusville, a promoter with a glib tongue and a big idea. He proposed to establish a factory to build and sell agricultural machinery. Stewart and another newly rich oil friend agreed to underwrite the project. This he felt he could well afford to do; he had an income of around a thousand dollars a week and over a quarter of a million cash in the bank. He was a charter member of the Titusville Oil Exchange, the first of its kind in the world. He had been a leading figure in the Producers Committee to study oil conservation and to find a means of solving the problem of overproduction. He was known in the field as "a man who knows oil." Had he stayed in oil, he would have saved himself years of financial heartbreak. The agricultural-implement business turned out to be a complete financial fiasco. When the two backers had paid their debts, Lyman's bank account was washed up and he had lost not only most of his leases but his home as well.

"This mowing machine proposition was engineered by a man who was a clever financial schemer," he explained later. "My partner and I didn't have sense enough to accept our losses and get out. We went into it in 1869, and for nearly three years we paid—paid until the very last nickel was expended. It took every cent I had made in addition to what I was even then realizing as an oil operator. I lost my home in 1872. I was flat broke, and for several years was compelled to work for a salary to take care of my family."

For the next five years Lyman Stewart was a wage earner, trying desperately to save a new nest egg. Before he had accumulated a new stake, Lady Luck unexpectedly befriended him again.

Back when he was in the $1,000-a-week bracket, Stewart had helped a number of younger men, among them two brothers, James and Harvey Hardison from Maine. The Hardisons had hired out as laborers to get drilling experience. Eventually they became experts at fishing for lost drilling tools. Several times they had come to Stewart's home to discuss mechanical problems with him. Even then he had revealed an engineering knowledge surprising for a man with no technical education. When the Hardison brothers needed money, Stewart dug into his bank account to help set them up in a business from which he never profited financially. But helping the Hardisons paid off in friendship.

"It was an example of the scriptural injunction to 'Cast thy bread upon the waters,' " Stewart often said.

Another Hardison brother, Wallace, had gone out West and made a fortune cutting ties for a transcontinental railroad. Returning East in 1877, he stopped off in Titusville to look things over and to get acquainted with the man who had befriended his brothers. The exciting activity of the Venango Valley soon afflicted Hardison with the oil fever. He proposed that he and Lyman Stewart buy up some oil properties on a partnership basis. Stewart explained his embarrassing financial condition and regretted that he could not join in the enterprise. Wallace Hardison brushed aside the protests.

WORLD'S FIRST
OIL EXCHANGE

Early dealers in oil kept few records, quoted inconsistent prices, worked without knowledge of amount of oil on market. Titusville Oil Exchange, created to bring buyers and sellers together, systematized the marketing of oil. Building at right—designed to "do honor to Titusville"—was opened in 1881.

DEPOT OF "OIL CREEK RAILWAY" TITUSVILLE.

"You know oil and I don't," he said. "I have the money and you don't. We'll be partners. I'll put up the money and you put up the experience."

With only a handclasp to seal the agreement, they launched a partnership that was never put in formal written agreement until many years later in California, when bankers insisted upon a contract on paper. The dignified partners always addressed each other as "Mr. Hardison" and "Mr. Stewart" throughout their long association.

This new toe hold in the oil boom restored Lyman Stewart's old confidence. Once again he was ready to plunge into the hunt for oil. Another man whom he had befriended in his plush days was Captain J. T. Jones, the largest producer in the newly developed Bradford oil field. When the Bradford strikes began attracting attention, Stewart mentioned them to Hardison, saying that Bradford looked like a promising area. Describing this turning point, Stewart said years later: "It looked like a good proposition to me, as I had thus far made but little progress toward regaining the ground lost by failure of the mowing machine investment. I strolled over one night after supper and told Mr. Hardison about it. He said, 'We'll saddle up the horses in the morning and look the country over.'

Early next day they were off on the rugged 100-mile ride to Bradford. Still grateful to Stewart, Jones granted them leases on some of his best acreage. They got in just ahead of the big rush. The Bradford area quickly became the most spectacular oil field of the decade, with 7,000 wells producing 100,000 barrels daily. In 1881 the field produced four-fifths of the country's oil.

Unfortunately Hardison and Stewart made only a modest fortune from their Bradford plunge. The prodigious production of the field led to a glut of oil. Prices fell steadily as more big-yielding wells came in, inundating the market with oil. Big operators, particularly the group John D. Rockefeller had organized, held a strangle-hold on distribution facilities. They controlled the pipelines, the railroads, the exchanges, and the markets. Eventually they forced the price of oil down to 8 cents a barrel at the well, less than the cost of pumping.

"Mr. Hardison and I were getting pretty tired of working under those conditions," Stewart recollected. "He was figuring on moving out to Kansas and I wanted to go even farther west where there were reports that extensive oil lands could be had for practically nothing in California. The idea of the new, open country, with the opportunity for unhampered effort, appealed to me very strongly."

Fed up with the cutthroat competition, Lyman Stewart and Wallace Hardison decided to sell out. Hardison had branched out into politics, banking, and farming; he had served a session in the Pennsylvania Legislature, where he fathered the new law that made pipelines common carriers. He owned a bank and farm lands in Eldred. Hardison had become a man of many interests.

Lyman Stewart, meantime, was looking at greener pastures. He was intrigued by reports from California of potential oil fields to be developed. When I. E. Blake, the former Titusville boy who had become a pioneer oil hunter in California, visited his home town and told of the great petroleum deposits

STEWART "MEAL TICKET" WELL *Lady Stewart Well in Shamburg was partially owned by Lyman Stewart. Its dividends helped pay family bills in California when finances were at lowest ebb. Probably named for Lyman's mother, Mrs. Jane Irwin Stewart.*

beneath Southern California soils, Stewart longed to investigate them firsthand. Recalled Stewart: "Mr. Blake approached me with a proposition to go to California. He offered me all the territory we could drill up, and stated his company held leases extending over 65 miles from Newhall to Santa Barbara."

Stewart proposed to Hardison that they transfer their operations to California. Hardison was unwilling to return to the Pacific Coast but agreed to sell out and divide the returns from their oil investments. They realized about $135,000 from the sale. Dividing the money, they parted, Hardison heading for Kansas, Lyman Stewart for the land of promise, Southern California.

Thus it was that, in the spring of 1883, a veteran oil operator, seasoned by twenty-four years in the school of hard knocks, boarded a train from Titusville for the Pacific Coast. Mrs. Stewart stayed in Titusville until her husband could size up the opportunities out West and provide a home for the family.

"What I was to find in the West I knew not," said Lyman Stewart later. "Except that it was opportunity, and that was all I asked. With me I carried a small Bible Mrs. Stewart had given me years before. That Bible was to be my guide and protector, my inspiration during the hectic and discouraging times ahead."

CHAPTER TWO 1857-1883

California's Oil Argonauts

THE LYMAN STEWART WHO STEPPED OFF THE TRAIN in Los Angeles in the spring of 1883, accompanied by his round-faced teen-age son, Will, looked more like a Quaker than a daring oil-field wildcatter. Conservatively dressed, with black hair, thin face, and long black beard, Stewart was eager to tap California's hidden petroleum deposits for a new fortune, but he was determined to move cautiously. At forty-three, in the prime of life, he had made his first million and lost most of it. Out of his successes and debacles, he had salvaged roughly $70,000, plus a modest interest in his family's oil holdings in Pennsylvania. After weathering lean periods when he was flat broke, he vowed that he would never again risk his all on a hole in the earth—unless it was a sure thing. Stewart decided to take his time finding the sure source of plenty of oil.

In this search, he had ample help. Old friends from Titusville, now veterans in California's shaky oil boom, which was contemporaneous with Pennsylvania's oil strikes, were already on the ground. One of them, I. E. Blake, greeted the Stewarts, father and son, at the depot in Los Angeles. Blake's California Star Oil Company had lands in the vicinity of Newhall under lease, including acreage in Pico Canyon, where General Andreas Pico and his nephew had dug alongside seeps and operated the first commercial tar pits in California. While visiting Titusville the year before, Blake had promised Stewart all the land he wished to drill for oil.

Eager to make good his promise, Blake took Stewart up to Newhall, which was on the Southern Pacific Railroad. He pointed out the seeps and the oil wells his company and several others had drilled there. It was mighty exciting! Seeps were something that Lyman Stewart understood. But after his first survey of

EARLY CALIFORNIA PRODUCER

Foot-of-the-Hill well found oil at a depth of 1,000 feet in Tar Creek and proved to be one of the company's best producers prior to incorporation.

STEWART & SON FACE WEST

Fed up with conditions in Pennyslvania and lured by rumors of an oil boom in California, Lyman Stewart came West in 1882, with his son, Will. The pair was destined to serve the California oil industry for a half century.

CALIFORNIA'S PIONEER REFINER

Whale-oil refiner, George Gilbert, built a small refinery near Mission San Buenaventura that produced "liquid bitumin and asphaltum" in 1857, two years before Drake's pioneer well in Pennsylvania.

Pico Canyon, caution overwhelmed the plunger in him. He returned to Los Angeles to think it over, also to find out, if possible, why the California oil boom, puny compared with that of Pennsylvania, had collapsed as flat as a pancake in the late sixties and was now barely coming to life again.

What he learned about the scramble for oil in the Golden State was intriguing, but it also made him hesitate. As was the case in Pennsylvania, the Indians were the first users of oil in California. For a century or more they had collected the sticky "chapapote" at natural tar pits near scores of seeps scattered from Los Angeles to Eureka. They had used the stuff to waterproof canoes, baskets, and their shelters. They also used it to mend utensils, to fasten spearheads to shafts, and to make medicines. Some coastal Indians swapped tar with interior tribes for skins and spearheads. Thus oil was an item of commerce before the white men arrived.

The padres who founded the California chain of missions and the early Spanish Californians knew about the tar, which they called brea, from their contacts with the Indians. They made little use of brea, though at some of the missions the padres and their Indian workers did distill a light oil which they used in lamps in place of whale oil, then quite scarce. Only at San Fernando, Santa Barbara, and Ventura missions did these primitive distilling operations grow to commercial ventures.

As early as 1846, Thomas A. Larkin, United States consul at Monterey, then the capital of Mexican California, had reported "several places throughout California where a bituminous pitch is used to cover the house roofs." Larkin suggested that the black, sticky water-proofing material might have some commercial use. His observations went unnoticed in Washington. At the time oil had not been officially discovered.

About 1855, General Andreas Pico, brother of Pio Pico, the last Mexican governor of California, set up a crude still at San Fernando that extracted axle grease, lamp oil, and medicine oil from the tar he and his nephew hauled out of the hills near Newhall. This was the feeble beginning of California's oil bonanza, unnoticed because more venturous fortune seekers were still digging for gold and silver in the populous northern part of the state.

A year or so later, an enterprising druggist from San Francisco, Charles Morrell, set up a small distilling plant near the Carpinteria seepages, which were well known to the padres and the Indians of the Santa Barbara Mission. Morrell managed to refine an illuminating oil but could not sell his smelly product. Candles were cheaper, and they gave off less smoke.

A Brooklyn whale-oil dealer, George Shoobridge Gilbert, who had joined the gold stampede to California in 1851, saw the possibilities that Consul Larkin had suggested. Gilbert, a native of Kent, England, had come to America as a boy. After he arrived in California, he left the pursuit of gold to others and started the Phoenix Oil Works, refining and marketing whale oil. Fascinated by the rock-oil seepages in Southern California, he investigated them. In 1857, two years before Drake's discovery well was drilled in Pennsylvania, Gilbert was refining "liquid bitumin and asphaltum" at a small refinery near San Buenaventura Mission. There the first year he managed to refine about four hundred barrels of marketable oil, which establishes Gilbert as the first commercial petroleum refiner in California.

Soon after Gilbert got his little refinery into production, he had a visitor, A. C. Ferris, a Brooklyn, New York, whale-oil refiner and dealer. Ferris was sure he could sell Gilbert's rock oil in the East in competition with whale oil. So Gilbert consigned 100 small kegs of his product, shipping it by boat to Panama, where it was to be transported by muleback to the East Coast, and transshipped to New York. Unfortunately the muleteers found the cargo too hard to handle on the Panama trails, and they jettisoned it in the jungle, where the kegs of oil were found many years later. This, too, occurred before the Drake discovery well kicked off the Pennsylvania oil boom.

Gilbert continued to produce lamp oil for the small West Coast market at his Ojai refinery, so named because it was located on the Rancho Ojai. In 1864 he had another visitor, Professor Benjamin Silliman, Jr., the same Yale savant who had tested samples of the Titusville petroleum in 1855 and who had forecast great commercial possibilities from the refining of rock oil. The professor's prophecy had come true in the Pennsylvania oil boom. Now he was eager to check reports of California's fabulous oil seeps for some of his friends, who had hit it rich in the Pennsylvania oil fields.

OIL SEEPS MISLED EARLY DRILLERS

Oil seeps fooled many of the early drillers and even the expert, Professor Silliman, who concluded that they indicated a plentiful reservoir of oil close to the surface, as would have been the case in Pennsylvania, but found after drilling one duster after another that surface indications could not be relied upon in California. The well at the right was one of Bard's early disappointments; he drilled 5 dry wells before his backers called him off.

Landing at Ventura, site of the mission, Professor Silliman heard from the townspeople about Gilbert's refinery up on Rancho Ojai. He hired a horse and headed up a dusty trail. Delighted to have so distinguished a guest, Gilbert described his refining process and pointed out his sources of crude, the several seepages along the San Antonio Creek and on the slopes of Sulphur Mountain. All Gilbert had to do was dig pits and scoop up the crude oil. Professor Silliman was fascinated. For several days he rode back and forth over the area, checking the seeps. Hardly believing his own eyes at first, he finally was overwhelmed with such enthusiasm that on July 2, 1864, he wrote the letter that, in effect, sparked California's first oil boom, just as in 1859 his report on the Titusville samples indirectly launched the Pennsylvania stampede. This time he wrote to his friend, Thomas R. Scott of Philadelphia, describing the oil seeps of Rancho Ojai:

"The property covers an area of 18,000 acres of land in one body, on which there are 20 natural oil wells, some of them of very large size. The oil is struggling to the surface at every available point, and is running down the rivers for miles. Artesian wells will be fruitful along a double line of 13 miles, say for about 25 miles in linear extent. The ranch is an old Spanish grant of four leagues of land, lately confirmed and of perfect title. It has, as I have stated, 18,000 acres of land well watered by four rivers, but its great value is in its almost fabulous wealth in the best oil."

The professor even went out on a limb to estimate a net profit of $1,365,000 could be made from drilling 10 wells on the property. How he arrived at that figure, he never explained.

Tom Scott was a man of action. Vice-president of the Pennsylvania Railroad, Assistant Secretary of War in Lincoln's Civil War cabinet, he was one of the plungers who had profited fabulously in the Pennsylvania oil boom. Calling in a group of friends, he spread out a map of California, read Professor Silliman's letter to them, then pinpointed the areas where he thought they should buy land quickly, while it cost only a few cents per acre. With enthusiasm unlimited at the opportunity to get in on the ground floor, the group formed a syndicate that snapped up 277,000 acres of land, sight unseen, including eight ranchos in Ventura County and 12,000 additional acres in Los Angeles and Humboldt counties. Three companies were incorporated to handle these deals. One, the California Petroleum Company, was capitalized for 10 million dollars. Its prospectus, dated 1865, stated that "one-tenth of the stock has been reserved for working capital." Like many oil companies of the period, it was nine-tenths water, one-tenth oil.

Too preoccupied to come West himself, Scott called in two nephews, Civil War veterans just out of uniform. They were Thomas R. Bard and D. C. Scott. In poor health, Bard had been forced to give up the study of law. He welcomed the opportunity to go to California and live an outdoor life. So did young Scott. To counsel the inexperienced young men, Scott sent along J. A. Beardsley, an oil-field veteran from Titusville. Well heeled with the syndicate's money, the trio visited the Titusville and Bradford fields to buy drilling equipment, including the first steam drilling rig shipped West, and to hire drillers. Late in 1865 Bard unloaded his machinery and men at San Pedro, from which point the heavy drilling tools, casings, boilers, and engines were laboriously carted a hundred miles over the plains and hills to Rancho Ojai. Ironically, young Bard did not know it, but he was hauling his rigs across and away from the richest oil field in California, the Los Angeles Basin.

Without wasting time to check on others who had already drilled for oil in California, Bard began "making hole" with his steam drilling rig near the tar beds on the east bank of San Antonio Creek. At 500 feet depth, he abandoned his first hole, which yielded more water than oil. On his second try, 5 miles up creek, he hit oil, but in too small quantities for production. Bard was learning the hard way, like others who wildcatted California's jumbled formations, both before and after him. Drilling into California's oil caches was far more difficult than tapping Pennsylvania's.

By 1867, when the petroleum boom in California collapsed, 70 oil companies, capitalized at 45 million dollars, had drilled 60 wells. It cost them a million dollars to produce 5,000 barrels of oil worth $10,000 at the prevailing prices.

The first well in California to produce "coal oil" was drilled in Ferndale, Humboldt County, in 1865. This well belonged to the Union Mattole Oil Company, organized by San Francisco promoters. Union Mattole shipped its crude by steamer to San Francisco camphene works owned by the Stanford brothers, Josiah, A. P., and Charles. The Stanfords quietly began buying up Union Mattole stock until they controlled the source of their crude. Unfortunately other wells drilled on the company's property were poor producers, and the Stanfords had to go south to Ventura for additional crude.

Josiah Stanford was a mining man. Intrigued by the seepages on Sulphur Mountain, rising behind the riverbed along which Bard was drilling, Stanford decided to "mine for oil." He drove 30 tunnels into the mountains, slanting them so that the oil flowed out by gravity into tanks at the entrances. Each tunnel yielded from 1 to 20 barrels per day. Stanford had both economical and steady production and became for a time one of the state's top oil producers. Some of his old tunnels were still yielding crude oil a century later—for Union Oil Company of California.

While Stanford "mined oil" successfully, Bard continued to drill for it. For his third well, he chose a site some distance from the tar seeps. He boldly planned to drill to 1,500 feet, but by this time the backers in Philadelphia were grumbling at his failure to find oil where Professor Silliman had reported it "flowing down the rivers." They sent out two geologists to check the syndicate's property and Bard's drilling. The geologists arrived when his third well was at the 520-foot level. The experts advised abandoning this hole and drilling

FIRST REFINERY IN NEWHALL

Original Still of the Scott & Baker refinery in 1875, one of several in operation before the Stewarts arrived.

SOUTHERN CALIFORNIA OIL METROPOLIS *This was the Los Angeles of 1883 where Lyman Stewart, following the trail of forerunners from Titusville, hoped to re-enter the oil business.*

on another site, which likewise was abandoned at 400 feet. Then the geologists proposed drilling shallow holes near seepages. This could be done by the old spring-pole method, much cheaper than steam drilling. The next well produced oil at 100 feet—not much, but 6 barrels a day, which was oil to sell.

But Bard and young Scott still believed that they should drill deeper. Racing against time while their backers grew more restive, Bard drove his crews overtime, hoping to prove his deep-well theory before orders came to cease drilling. At 550 feet, far short of his 2,000-foot goal, the bit struck oil sands yielding 20 barrels per day. This was the best well anyone had drilled anywhere in California to date.

Unfortunately he struck oil in commercial quantities late in 1866 just as the bottom dropped out of the market. Eastern refineries were dumping oil on the Pacific Coast market for less than it cost to refine California's heavy black crude. The post-Civil War depression had set in. Bard had spent $200,000 hunting oil on lands where it reputedly bubbled out of the earth. Out of six wells, he had two producers, but no market for his oil. From Philadelphia came orders from Colonel Tom Scott to cease all drilling immediately. This touched off similar retrenchment by other operators. The California oil bubble had burst.

Disillusioned, Bard turned to agriculture until two decades later, when Lyman Stewart rekindled his enthusiasm for the oil hunt. After 1866 nobody showed any interest in California's oil bonanza for four years. Then in 1870 Sanford Lyon rigged up an inexpensive spring-hole outfit at the head of Pico Canyon and punched a hole that proved the oil was still down there under the soil. Others moved in, drilled, and got a little production, but not enough to arouse great excitement.

In 1873, C. C. Mentry, a husky, heavy-bearded derrick builder from Titusville, Pennsylvania, drilled in Pico Canyon, where leases were "a dime a dozen," and got 6 barrels a day at a depth of 76 feet. He drilled another hole across the canyon and got another small producer. His third well was a dry hole. This might have ended Mentry's role in the California oil dream, but for the timely arrival of another Titusville veteran, D. G. Scofield, Lyman Stewart's old classmate. Scofield had opened a paint and hardware store in San Francisco but after three years as a merchant was unable to resist the lure of the oil gamble. Scofield began scouting the Southern California oil seeps.

Impressed with Pico Canyon and the Mentry properties, he reported his findings to a group of influential San Franciscans, who promptly organized the California Star Oil Company, with Scofield as president. They took over the Mentry leases, employed Mentry as drilling superintendent, outfitted him with a steam rig, and ordered full-speed drilling of Pico No. 4. In 1876, at a 600-foot depth, Mentry struck an oil flow of 150 barrels a day, the best and most spectacular oil well drilled up to that time in the Golden State. Pico No. 4 proved that real oil production was possible in California. It also inspired another newcomer from Titusville, J. A. Scott, a prosperous refiner, to erect an up-to-date refinery alongside the Southern Pacific tracks at Newhall. To bring crude to this refinery from the wells drilled on the Mentry leases, Scofield built a 5-mile pipeline 2 inches in diameter, the first oil pipeline on the Pacific Coast, laid in 1879.

Another oil hunter got into the game. W. E. Youle, a successful Pennsylvania driller, joined Scofield in checking oil seeps in Moody Canyon, 60 miles south of San Francisco, the big market for oil on the Pacific Coast. While they were tramping Moody Gulch, still another Pennsylvanian, R. C. McPherson, grabbed the leases they wanted for the newly organized San Francisco Oil Company and the Santa Clara Oil Company, owned by a Colonel Boyer. One day McPherson and Boyer fell into a violent disagreement. Boyer pulled out a six-shooter and "invited" McPherson to sign over his half interest in the Moody Gulch leases. Persuaded, McPherson signed.

Boyer next employed Youle, with Scofield's consent, to drill the gulch. Youle got together a crew, only one of whom had ever helped drill an oil well. Youle's description of his efforts to assemble a rig records a revealing picture of the driller's problems at the time.

"I ordered lumber and rig timber sawed at a mill in the Santa Cruz mountains, some miles away. I purchased a boiler engine and tools that were stored in San Francisco—a secondhand outfit but in very good condition. The largest bit was eight inches; the rig had originally been used to drill a deep water well. I purchased several sizes of pipe from George W. Gibbs, an iron merchant of San Francisco. Then I located a 1,500-foot coil of drilling cable and sandline—they were Manila. The bits I had made by Charles Oester, on Mission Street, San Francisco, and it was certainly some job to make the forgers understand what oil tool work required."

Meantime, Scofield had taken a group of San Francisco capitalists, among

OIL FIELD ADONISES

Two handsome drillers, David Swartz and Hall Proudfoot, were imported from Pennsylvania to work for Hardison & Stewart Oil Co. in 1883. They are posing in the derrick house of a well at Tar Creek, California. Equipment from this well has been preserved in the oil museum at Santa Paula.

STEWART SCHOOLMATE—FUTURE COMPETITOR

A schoolmate of Lyman Stewart's and a veteran oilman from Titusville, D. G. Scofield came West, resumed career in oil, and became a strong competitor of the Stewart interests.

them United States Senator Charles M. Felton and Lloyd Tevis, president of Wells Fargo Bank, to both Pico Canyon and Moody Gulch. They came back enthused. With their backing, Scofield formed the million-dollar Pacific Coast Oil Company—a merger of the California Star Company, the San Francisco Oil Company, Boyer's Santa Clara Oil Company, and several smaller concerns—which became the giant of the Western petroleum industry, and eventually the Standard Oil Company of California. Senator Felton became president, with Scofield the active executive.

The several wells they drilled in Moody Gulch soon ran dry. The expensive pipeline and other facilities installed to bring the oil to San Francisco Bay were useless. Scofield returned to Pico Canyon and nearby Wiley Canyon, where production rose to 200, then 300, and finally 500 barrels per day. The crude was shipped by rail to a new 500-barrel-per-day refinery Scofield built at Alameda Point on San Francisco Bay, whence products were transshipped to Pacific Coast ports from British Columbia to Mexico, and even to Hawaii. By 1880 the Pacific Coast Oil Company accounted for the bulk of the state's production of 40,552 barrels of oil.

Compared with the East, the Pacific Coast was a skimpy market. Sleepy Los Angeles, the nearest outlet to the Newhall and Ventura oil fields, had barely 14,000 population in 1882, fewer than Sacramento or Oakland. Only San Fran-

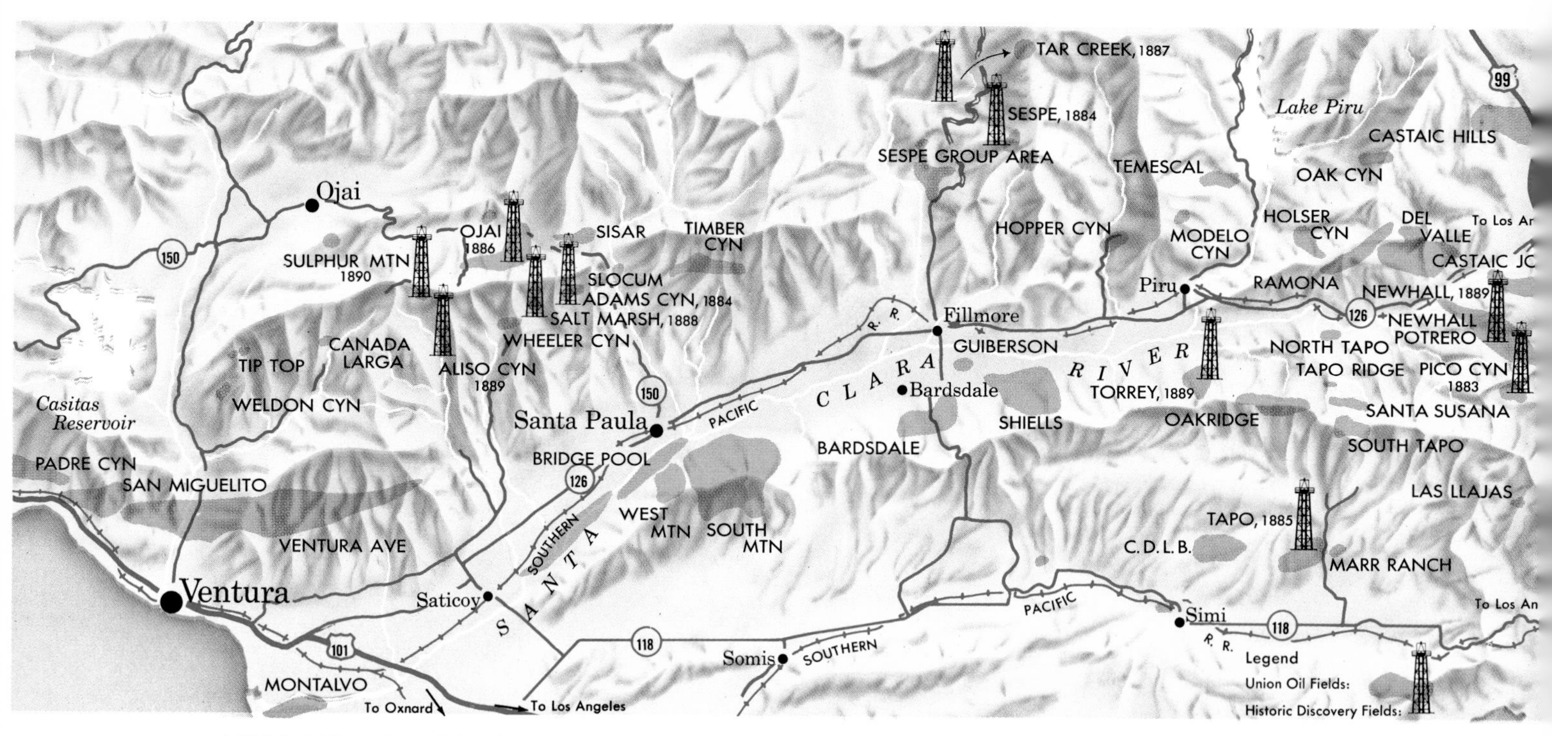

UNION OIL FIELDS IN VENTURA COUNTY

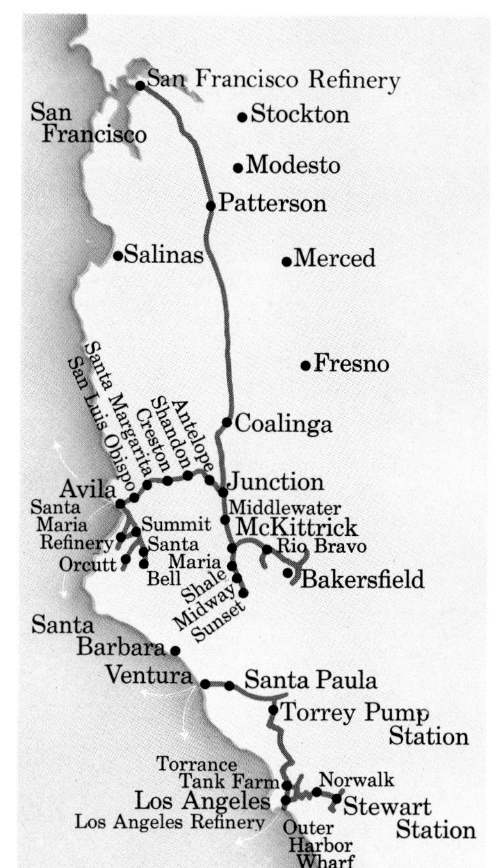

PIPELINES *1906 – 1976*

CALIFORNIA'S VENANGO VALLEY

Pennsylvanians felt right at home when they tramped the hills of southern California. Superficially, the terrain resembled their own Venango Valley, a complex of valleys and mountains in northern Pennsylvania. Similarities ended, however, when the drills probed for oil. The Easterners soon found the tortured, rocky substrata of California tougher to penetrate and more unpredictable than the oil lands at home. The early oil ventures of Stewart and Hardison centered on Pico Canyon, Adams Canyon, Ojai, and other areas marked on the map. A network of pipelines grew up in California to serve the expanding needs of Union Oil, as shown in the map at right.

cisco of all the Pacific Coast cities had a quarter-million population. All of California had fewer than a million people.

To move the Pico Canyon crude to the San Francisco Bay refinery, Scofield bought 50 tank cars. These failed to solve his transportation problem. The oil producers were forced to pay prohibitive railroad freight rates. Scofield waged a vigorous campaign to persuade the Southern Pacific to reduce "excessive rates on petroleum." The little refinery at Newhall had been shut down, and Scofield was now at the mercy of the railroad to get his crude to the refinery near San Francisco.

Then one day Southern Pacific officials learned that Felton and Scofield had secretly ordered many miles of pipe and were running a line from Newhall to Ventura on the coast, from which point they could move oil by water to San Francisco. At first the railroaders thought the oil men were bluffing. The latter continued to lay pipe. The strategy worked. Before many miles of pipeline had been laid, the railroad had "rechecked figures" and found that freight rates on oil could be cut in half. Felton and Scofield never completed their pipeline or built the tankers they had designed to handle the oil when it reached the ocean end of the pipeline. The distinction of laying the first pipeline to tidewater and building the first tanker to sail the Pacific awaited another oil pioneer from Titusville who was trying to make up his mind whether or not to risk his all by drilling holes into the rocky soils of California.

GENERAL PICO'S LEGACY TO UNION OIL

If it were not for Star No. 1 well in Pico Canyon—named for the Mexican general (left) *who first extracted oil there in 1855—Union Oil Company of California might never have been born. After a series of dusters, in 1884 Stewart and Hardison finally brought in Star No. 1, a prodigious producer that saved them from financial collapse.*

CHAPTER THREE 1883-1890

Seven Years of Famine

AFTER HIS THIRD TRIP TO PICO CANYON in the spring of 1883, Lyman Stewart's newborn caution could no longer hold his plunger's enthusiasm in check. There was oil up there in the hills, and he was itching to drill for it. His old Titusville friends, Scofield, Blake, Mentry, Youle, and Scott, had cut themselves in on the bonanza yielding around 500 barrels per day from shallow wells. Stewart was sure there was more oil down deeper. Blake, who was transportation manager for the newly merged Pacific Coast Oil Company, the West's first oil combine, still held out his offer. Stewart could sub-lease and drill on any of the company's extensive unproved lands.

Stewart picked a promising drilling site on Christian Hill in Pico Canyon. Then he wired his former partner, Wallace L. Hardison, describing the prospects in glowing terms. Hardison, busy with two banks and several farms in Kansas since he and Stewart had dissolved their oil-hunting partnership, was in Pennsylvania winding up his affairs there. "Mr. Hardison replied immediately in his usual crisp manner, merely stating the date he could come out and commence operations," recalled Stewart. Without another scrap of paper, Stewart and Hardison resumed their partnership as oil hunters.

Hardison's faith in Stewart's judgment was demonstrated in another way. Before he left Pennsylvania, he ordered two heavy drilling rigs and other equipment, costing around $70,000. He also recruited two crews of experienced drillers from Bradford, 35 men in all, guaranteeing their wages for six months. Between them, Stewart and Hardison raised a total capital of $135,000, including the drilling rigs, to launch their California venture. For their drilling

FIRST REFINERY CREW

The refinery crew at Santa Paula in 1887 managed to turn out fair quantities of asphalt and fuel oil, but rarely a barrel of gasoline. After a damaging fire parts of the refinery were shipped to Oleum.

superintendent, they brought out John Irwin, a veteran Titusville driller and a cousin of Lyman Stewart. For headquarters they rented a single small room in Newhall. It served as the "home office" for four rugged years.

Hopes were high, late in May, 1883, when the heavy-mustached Pennsylvanians started punching down Hill No. 1, so named because of its location on Christian Hill. Slight, tidy Lyman Stewart and huge, robust Wallace Hardison were present, brimming with optimism. The Pennsylvanians soon found that drilling was more difficult in California. They had trouble keeping the hole straight through the rocky upthrusts. They were drilling deeper than they had ever punched holes in Pennsylvania. Nevertheless, they made hole with enthusiasm until they hit the 1,850-foot level, deep drilling at the time. There they ran into real trouble, losing their drilling tools. "Fishing" failed to recover the bit. All the way down there had been no showing of oil of any kind; so the partners decided to chalk it up to experience. Hill No. 1 was abandoned, their first dry hole in California.

Moving the rig 475 feet to the east, they started down again. Hill No. 2 was a replica of Hill No. 1, except that the trouble began at 1,050 feet, where the drilling tools were lost again. The partners abandoned this well without seeing a trace of oil. For Hill No. 3 they moved 700 feet west of Hill No. 1 and pushed a hole to a depth of 1,650 feet. Here they found signs of oil, but nothing more; so Hill No. 3 was written off as another dry hole. Hill No. 4 was also a duster.

SOME PRODUCTION—BUT NOT ENOUGH *Some of Union's best producers were on Tar Creek in Ventura County, but even these were disappointing. By the end of 1887, the company had to sell mules, boilers, and other gear to stay solvent.*

FIRST HEADQUARTERS *First home of the predecessor of Union Oil was this little shack in Newhall, California, occupied from 1883 to 1886.*

Funds were running low. "This certainly can't go on," said Hardison. "The law of averages, if nothing else, should work in our favor pretty soon." The partners spudded in Hill No. 5. It, too, was a dry hole. Disaster faced the partnership. After paying drilling crews following duster No. 5, they had a few thousand dollars left, enough for one more try. Where to drill was the question.

They moved from Christian Hill, which had swallowed most of their cash, figuring that, over on Tar Creek or on Santa Paula Creek, they might find more promising spots. This time they had to be right. They decided to take time picking the site for this final hole, and asked their drillers to work for a short time at road builders' wages instead of the higher pay commanded by drillers. They had paid the crews' fares from Pennsylvania, and had guaranteed them six months' work. The six months' guarantee period was over, and the partners figured the crews would be willing to cooperate to that extent. To their surprise, in the midst of all their other troubles, the drillers walked off the job, refusing to work for lower wages, even temporarily. So the partners had to continue the higher wages and watch their capital dwindle day by day, while they negotiated the lease for drilling their sixth well on Tar Creek, known as Smith Farm No. 1.

The original logbook bears mute testimony to the anxiety of the twain while that well was being drilled. It reads:

"July 20, 1883. Smith Farm No. 1, Crew: John Irwin, superintendent; David Swartz, George W. Fleisher, William Esner, David Brown. Commence work July 20, 1883. Commence spudding in the pools July 31. August 6, cased with 119 feet of 8 5/8-inch casing. We had a good deal of hard drilling and lost lots of time with crooked holes. At 672 feet, we struck oil rock, and went through at 1,338 feet and got sulphur water that flowed over the top. We tubed the well and pumped for a week, getting lots of water and about 1½ barrels of oil per day. We pulled the tubing and started to drill again. The total depth reached was 1,520 feet. The sides caved badly. There were 282 feet of black slate. The rope broke and left the tools in the well, and it caved in on them. We fished for three weeks and couldn't recover them. We abandoned the well on December 31, 1883, leaving 100 feet of 8 5/8 casing in it."

In the meantime, Stewart had returned to Pennsylvania and brought out his family in November, 1883. New Year's Eve ended a year of stark financial disaster for Lyman Stewart and W. L. Hardison in California. They had drilled six wells and had yet to produce their first barrel of salable oil. They had spent just about every cent they owned. They still had their drilling rigs and plenty of courage, plus the optimism that goes with oil fever. They needed it.

In desperation the partners moved the rig over to a spot on Santa Paula Creek. Oil simply couldn't elude them any longer, they figured, forgetting that one of their Pennsylvania friends, Captain J. T. Jones, of Bradford, had once drilled 13 consecutive dry holes along Oil Creek. They couldn't stop now. Their new well, Santa Paula No. 1, was another dry hole, the seventh in a row for these veteran Pennsylvania oil men. The partners took stock of the situation.

"It looked as if the whole structure we had labored to build up was about to be destroyed," Stewart explained later. "We had worked feverishly, but only failure had resulted. We owed a total of $183,000 with no cash on hand to meet the current bills which were pouring in. We had used up our personal resources and had borrowed wherever we could."

They were in dire straits. Hardison, who had organized two small banks, one at Eldred, Pennsylvania, the other at Salina, Kansas, had borrowed up to the hilt. He had drawn so many checks on the Eldred bank that the cashier was protesting in almost every mail and warning that the depositors were getting wind of his overdrafts. On May 8, the cashier wrote: "We have had a run on the bank." A few days later he warned: "We must have some funds from some source soon. We have about $10,000 falling due this month, $7,000 of which is yours, due on the 25th. The stockholders who are borrowers must come to the front, and do that quickly, or we shall follow in the grand collapse."

Stewart went to his friend Blake and laid their troubles on the table, holding nothing back. He pointed out that so far they had drilled on territory yet to be proven as oil lands, costly wildcatting with seven failures to their record. He asked Blake for a chance to drill in some proven territory, if they were able to scrape together enough wages for one more try.

TRANSPLANTED PENNSYLVANIANS

Among the early employees of Hardison & Stewart Oil Company were these imported Easterners: Back row: Briggs Dougherty, Ed McCray, John Millard, David Swartz, O. C. Parker, and George Fleisher. Center: F. E. Davis, C. N. Baker, John Irwin (cousin of Lyman Stewart), and Lewis Hardison. Bottom: T. O. Toland, Charles Hazelton, Dick Whitten, E. Wiseman, Link Gilger.

Blake, who had initiated the whole venture through his glowing tales of the California oil strike during his visits to Titusville in 1882, was sympathetic. He knew both Hardison and Stewart were substantial, hard-working oil men who had simply run into an extraordinary period of bad luck.

"The Star lease looks like it might be a sure thing," said Blake. "Suppose you and Hardison drill over there for your next well."

This lease was also in Pico Canyon, but some distance from the site of the first five dusters drilled by the partners. Stewart took a sublease on a small site barely large enough for a single well. It was their last chance. If this failed, they were through. They spudded in a well, known on the logbooks as Star No. 1—an important well in California oil history, because without it the Union Oil Company of California might never have been founded.

Desperately racing against time, the partners watched as the bit chipped its way down. At 1,620 feet they hit oil. For 30 feet more the bit continued through the impregnated oil sands. When they pulled out the drilling equipment and put the well on the pump, it produced 75 barrels per day. They had oil, in an unusually good well for those days in California. They took out more oil in a day from that one well than they had discovered in a year in seven other holes. Again the Stewart luck had changed.

"We were elated. We had finally struck oil," recalled Stewart later. "But that was about all. Our resources were gone. We didn't have enough funds left to develop the oil we had found in Star No. 1."

The partners asked for more proven land on which to drill more wells but were turned down. If there were any more producers like Star No. 1 in the area, the California Star Company was going to drill them. The management offered in turn to buy Star No. 1 outright from Stewart and Hardison for cash. It was a hard bargain, but the partners had no other choice but to take it. Having no money either to develop this well or to drill, they sold out to get more capital to make a new start.

As it turned out, they didn't make a bad bargain. Later when the California Star Oil Works Company pushed Star No. 1 down to 1,675 feet, the production fell to 35 barrels per day, one-half of what it was when Hardison and Stewart sold. Other drilling in the area proved that Star No. 1 was on the extreme northern limit of a pool formed by a fault that extended down Pico Canyon. Had they sunk more wells on the lease, Hardison and Stewart might have gone broke right there in 1884.

The disillusioned partners learned one important lesson from the Star No. 1 job, namely, that they should own the land on which they drilled good wells,

OIL THAT SMELLED TO HIGH HEAVEN

When the new-born Union Oil Company of California was chartered in 1890, Adams Canyon accounted for 84,421 barrels of crude for that year, flowing from 26 wells. The crude was a heavy, smelly asphalt, half of it waste.

LAST WELL BEFORE THE MERGER

Robertson Well No. 1 at Bardsdale in 1890. Standing, left to right: Ed Scholl and two children, John Millard, Ben Robertson, Ed Elkins and an unidentified visitor. Seated, left to right: E. E. Chamberlain, Charley Millard, unidentified, Robert Cruson and son, Tom.

so they could make more hole later if they chose, without asking permission of anyone. Stewart, the seep hunter, scouted for lands which they could buy. The broad valley of the Santa Clara River, which flowed through the little hamlet of Santa Paula, reminded them, except for its lack of trees, of the Venango Valley in Pennsylvania. There were hills similar to those along Pennsylvania's Oil Creek. There were oil seepages. Here they felt at home. With their Star No. 1 returns, they made the down payment on mineral rights on several other small properties in Ventura County. What they lacked in capital they made up in daring.

Using the land on which they had made down payment as collateral, they borrowed money to get together a stake to drill again. They managed to drill a dozen wells in 1884, but hard luck still plagued them. One of their best sites was Adams Canyon. Adams No. 1 came in for a small production. Encouraged, the partners spudded in Adams No. 2, 100 feet south of Adams No. 1. When No. 2 was put on the pump, it drained all of the oil out of No. 1. Then they drilled No. 3, still farther south. It drained No. 2 and made the first two wells unproductive. At this rate they were getting nowhere.

The Adams Canyon wells produced a heavy sluggish oil with a small kerosene content. The kerosene from this crude had a repulsive odor. The oil yielded small quantities of gasoline, but this was a by-product for which there was little demand, other than for cleaning fluid. Half of the oil, a heavy asphalt, was

STRONG MEN AND HEAVY DRILLS *Hand-forged, heavy drilling equipment was made and kept in repair at the Santa Paula shops of Union Oil in the 1890's. Some of this equipment has been preserved in the California Oil Museum.*

ADAMS CANYON ENCOURAGED PARTNERS

Adams Canyon field, first drilled in 1884, encouraged partners to go ahead. Adams 1 (left) came in for small production. But Adams 2 drained all the oil out of No. 1. Then Adams 3 drained Adams 2. Adams 4 was actually a tunnel dug into the hillside.

largely waste, although some asphalt was being used for saturating roofing paper, for coating iron pipes, and to surface roads.

At Ojai and on Smith Farm the other wells they drilled were hardly more promising. What small production the partners were able to pump they delivered to a little refinery at Santa Paula, operated by E. A. Edwards. After drilling a well in Adams Canyon in 1876, Edwards had abandoned drilling to go into the refining end of the business. In 1884, he bought 2,661 barrels of Hardison and Stewart oil, all that they produced that year. The oil brought only $2.50 a barrel. The income was far from enough to meet the expenses of one drilling crew, much less make payments on their debts. Only the occasional dividends from oil leases back in Pennsylvania, in which both men had small interests, kept them afloat.

In 1884, one of their old Titusville associates, W. E. Youle, had made a discovery that probably kept Hardison and Stewart from going completely broke. Youle had been employed by two promoters, W. R. Rowland and William Lacey, to drill at Puente, not far from Los Angeles, near tar seepages. Shallow wells drilled earlier had produced a heavy, almost useless oil at the 100-foot depth. Youle talked his backers into letting him drill farther away from the seepages. At 1,600 feet he struck oil, 150 barrels a day, suitable for fuel without refining. This was the first definite proof that deep drilling in California would pay off in high-gravity crude.

Hardison and Stewart visited the Puente fields and speculated on why Youle got more and better oil at the deeper depths. Petroleum geology was an almost unknown science at the time. They were their own by-guess-and-by-gosh geologists. They decided that the tar springs and the heavy oil from the shallow wells were by-products pushed up by pressures from larger oil deposits deeper down in the earth. Youle's discovery caused Hardison and Stewart to do some deep thinking about the geological formations along Adams Creek. They concluded that their new drilling sites should be located after careful study of the geologic faults and anticlines, many of which could be traced from the outcroppings. John Irwin, their first field superintendent, agreed with them.

"Go up into Adams Canyon, and see how deep drilling works out," they told him.

Late in 1884 and during 1885, Irwin's crews drilled several deep wells ranging down to nearly 3,000 feet, producing from 5 to 300 barrels per day. There were some dry holes, too. But the depths of Adams Canyon yielded Hardison and Stewart their first commercial production and pointed the way to further deep drilling. In the entire year of 1885 they were able to produce only 4,806 barrels of oil.

Brooding over the cost of drilling, Stewart hit upon an idea that revolutionized industry, not only in the oil fields, but throughout California. At the time it was the practice to use coal to fire the boilers that provided steam for the drilling-rig engine. The cost of coal was $30 a ton, delivered in the oil fields. Stewart asked: "Why shouldn't we burn some of our oil, just as it comes from the well?" This had never been done; the only burners available were those used for kerosene.

They soon clogged with the heavy crude. Stewart had his crews try dripping the oil into a bed of rocks. Later they blew it into the firebox in a spray. This didn't work. Then the shop mechanics built a nozzle that successfully fed a continuous flame, when properly placed in the firebox. Soon all oil-field engines were equipped with oil burners. Stewart became the apostle of oil fuel throughout California. His crusade for oil burners doubled the potential market for California crude.

Restless Lyman Stewart next hit upon another idea that proved a shot in the arm for the feeble oil industry. He and Hardison had laid small pipelines to deliver their crude from the wells to the little refinery at Santa Paula, but that failed to solve the bigger problem of getting their oil to market. Refinery products had to be pumped into tank cars or into barrels and hauled by rail to Los Angeles or to San Francisco. It cost a dollar per barrel to ship the oil by rail to San Francisco. Without risking a dollar, the railroad made more from a barrel of oil than the oil men did from finding and producing it.

When the Southern Pacific refused to lower rates, Stewart determined to build a pipeline from the oil field to tidewater. Putting C. A. Burrows, another Pennsylvania oil man, in charge early in 1886, he and Hardison launched what was a stupendous undertaking for two already hard-pressed wildcatters. Undaunted, they brought 4-inch pipeline around the Horn to Ventura and hauled it by wagon to the mountainous oil fields. Across the deep barrancas, the pipe-

SECOND HOME OF UNION OIL
This tiny one-story office in rough-and-ready Santa Paula was shared with Mission Transfer Company as headquarters, 1886-1890.

CALIFORNIA'S TITUSVILLE *Oil Center of California, Santa Paula spread out over a wide valley in 1888. Mission Transfer Company refinery is at extreme left.*

line was suspended by cables. Constructing the pipeline was backbreaking labor, but by the end of 1886 it was completed. Oil flowed 40 miles from Newhall down to Ventura, where it was put in barrels and shipped by water at less than half the rail rate to San Francisco. That year Hardison and Stewart were able to increase their production to 35,350 barrels, roughly one-tenth of California's output.

At last the hard-luck partners felt they had a going business. Moving from the tiny room in Newhall to the thriving town of Santa Paula farther down the valley, they established headquarters in a one-story frame building. At the time Santa Paula was a frontier agricultural community into which a number of unwelcome Wild West gun-toting characters had moved in the wake of the oil strike. The latter were not only heavy drinkers but quick shooters, who terrorized the 200 inhabitants of the town. Santa Paula boasted the dubious distinction of having a saloon for every seven families. One, directly across the street from the Hardison & Stewart headquarters, pained Lyman Stewart particularly, because the drilling crews came to town, drew their pay, and made a beeline for the swinging doors. After watching them come out on anything but a beeline, Stewart persuaded Hardison that the partnership should put up a new office on Main Street, on a site that faced no saloon. But soon after they finished the building, an enterprising tavern keeper placed a brace of swinging doors directly across the street.

Numerically, the large Hardison and Stewart families made an important addition to the community. The partners plunged into the task of making Santa

COFOUNDER OF UNION OIL

Half of the firm of Hardison & Stewart Oil Company, Wallace L. Hardison became one of the cofounders of Union Oil and its first treasurer when the new firm absorbed Hardison & Stewart. A man of many interests, he promoted horticulture in Santa Paula Valley, helped make the town an agricultural center as well as an oil headquarters.

Paula a good place to live, just as they and their kin had helped transform Titusville from a rip-roaring oil town into a sedate, cultured little city. The Stewart clan consisted of Lyman, his wife, Sarah Adelaide Burrows, sons Alfred C. and William Lyman, daughters May and Eva, plus various relations who had joined them in the Western trek. Wallace Hardison had a son, Guy, two daughters, Augusta and Hope. Soon after the firm was established, several of his brothers and their families came West. Though he was the youngest of 11 children, Wallace Hardison was the dynamic leader of the family. A stocky, rugged, robust 200-pounder with a springy step, black mustache and hair, Hardison was an outdoor man who loved horses, politics, and farming. A born promoter, he immediately began transforming the semi-desert around the little town into one of California's rich agricultural areas, renowned for its citrus and walnut crops.

Lyman Stewart's interests were more concentrated. They were oil, his family, and the Presbyterian Church. A smallish, slender man of great dignity, natty even when out in the oil fields, Stewart, with his carefully trimmed beard, was an incongruous figure among the shabby, swearing drilling crews. Stewart worried about the drillers, their profanity, their chewing and drinking, and their unsaved souls. Yet the men liked him and drove themselves under his prodding. One of his first acts in building up Santa Paula as a community was to raise money for a Presbyterian church.

Hardison, though not a zealot like his partner, was likewise a religious man. He helped organize the Santa Paula Universalist Church, to which he gave liberally. Before long the Hardisons and Stewarts were competing by investing in stained-glass windows, by underwriting the expenses of visiting preachers, and by importing culture in the form of music, lectures, and reading to Santa

Paula. This was the first sign of rivalry in the rare business relationship between Wallace Hardison and Lyman Stewart, who, although they were trusting partners with unlimited faith in each other, were never close friends. Even after all their ups and downs together, they were still Mr. Stewart and Mr. Hardison to each other. Hardison's interest in their joint oil venture decreased in proportion to its success, and he turned to new enterprises. Stewart's enthusiasm grew apace with the business.

Until late in 1883, Hardison and Stewart had run an informal and purely verbal partnership. When they began to borrow money frantically, the bankers insisted, in 1884, upon a written agreement, in which Lyman Stewart and his family owned 51 per cent, Hardison and his friends 49 per cent. The firm was known simply as Hardison & Stewart. Stewart was still head of Lyman Stewart & Company, the family partnership which included two brothers and two sisters, plus John Irwin, his cousin, and W. J. Chichester, a Presbyterian minister. Alexander Waldie also owned one per cent. Spasmodic income from this family partnership kept the Lyman Stewart family in food and clothing during the lean early years in California.

Desperately needing money in 1885, Lyman Stewart journeyed to Los Angeles to try to talk I. W. Hellman, the town's leading banker, into lending the partnership $30,000. Stewart and Hardison already owed Hellman several thousand dollars. The banker pointed out that their financial position was not particularly strong, which was putting it mildly. He was sorry, but he could not let them have the $30,000 they needed. But before Stewart left the bank, Hellman asked for a statement in full of the Hardison-Stewart affairs. The thought of drawing up a statement made Lyman Stewart shudder, but he got it together and submitted it.

"I didn't sleep any that night, I can tell you," Stewart said later. "Hellman called me into his office the next day. As I entered, he was holding the statement in his hand, and didn't speak for what seemed a long time, although it was only a minute, I guess. He shook his head, then said, 'Stewart, this doesn't look as good as I'd like it to, but draw checks for $10,000 and I will approve them.' It wasn't what we wanted, but that $10,000 was just enough to spell the difference between failure and success. It tided us over that period when everything else had failed. It was just one of those cases when the last lift was needed to get over the top of the hill," recalled Stewart.

A short time later the partners got some unexpected dividends from oil wells back in Pennsylvania that pulled them through another crisis. But before long, Stewart was writing to Hardison: "The financial problem is serious. I have nothing available to sell excepting my town lot, but even that I could not turn in time to meet the emergency." They decided that if they were to make a real success of the oil business in California, they would have to go after big money. The richest man in Ventura County at the time was Thomas R. Bard. After drilling unsuccessfully on the vast ranch acreage which Tom Scott and his friends had bought as a result of the enthusiastic report of Professor Silliman, Bard had turned to buying up distressed properties for the syndicate. This proved

UNION'S FIRST TANK CARS *Lined up on the track alongside the facilities of Mission Transfer Company is a string of tank cars, some of the first purchased by the company. Union bought its first car in 1888, shortly after bringing in its first wells, and owned a fleet of 55 within two years.*

highly profitable. Bard had made a lot of money from these ventures. He was already in oil again through an interest in a small business known as the Mission Transfer Company, which owned several thousand acres of land in the Rancho (ex-Mission) San Buenaventura. Mission Transfer had tanks, pipelines, and a small refinery. It made money transporting and marketing other producers' oil.

Bard had already sold a one-half interest in Mission Transfer to the Pacific Coast Oil Company, Hardison & Stewart's big competitor. Much to their surprise, he agreed to sell the other half to them on easy terms. Bard also listened receptively to the idea of launching a new oil company to drill in Sespe Canyon on proven lands which Hardison & Stewart controlled. Thus on November 10, 1886, the Sespe Oil Company came into existence with Bard as president and "angel," although Hardison and Stewart got the majority of the stock in exchange for their leases. Dan McFarland of Los Angeles, a well-to-do friend of Bard, came in for a one-fifth interest in Sespe. Soon after this deal was consummated, Hardison and Stewart were able to acquire the rest of Mission Transfer Company from the Pacific Coast Oil Company. Bard agreed to serve as president of Mission Transfer, although the control and management were entirely in the hands of the Hardison & Stewart partnership. This transaction put them into the refining and marketing business for the first time.

The partners concluded that they were getting into such involved financing that it could be handled better by a corporation. The Hardison & Stewart partnership was terminated. The Hardison & Stewart Oil Company was incorporated on December 28, 1886, with a capital of one million dollars, consisting of 10,000 shares with a par value of $100 each. Lyman Stewart became president, Hardison vice-president and general manager. The other incorporators included Bard, McFarland, Walter S. Chaffee, Alexander Waldie, John Irwin, I. H. Warring, and Casper Taylor, all personalities who were to figure prominently in the bitter feud for control of an embryo oil empire. Stewart and Hardison were the controlling shareholders in the "million-dollar corporation."

Despite the rosy picture on paper, four years after they started hopefully to drill their way to riches, Lyman Stewart and Wallace Hardison were still marketing too little oil to meet their overhead, much less make payments on their debts. In 1887, they branched out and drilled in Tar Canyon, an offshoot of the Little Sespe. This improved their production, but still not enough. In fact, the situation became so desperate that by the end of the year they were forced to sell mules, boilers, engines, and miscellaneous equipment to meet the more pressing demands for money. But they managed to boost production that year to 50,000 barrels, approximately one-seventh of the entire California output.

Desperately in need of capital, Stewart dropped his work in the field, where he was continually prodding his crews to more production, to plead with I. W. Hellman, the Los Angeles banker, for another loan. This time Hellman was adamant. Hardison and Stewart already owed him $140,000. When the banker turned a deaf ear to his plea, Stewart was at the end of his rope. Luckily Hardison managed to raise several thousand dollars from Eastern sources in the nick of time. "It is another providential deliverance," Stewart wrote when Hardison reported about the money he had borrowed. Yet that year Stewart found time to carry on a $14,400 drive to raise money for the Y.M.C.A. in Santa Paula.

"I have had a hard week raising money for our Y.M.C.A. lot. Have not entirely succeeded yet, but hope to get through all right. I could not endure it, or rather would not, were it not that I believe it is for 'Him who giveth us all things to enjoy,' " wrote Stewart.

It was a time to try men's mettle. Eastern competitors were in the Los Angeles and San Francisco markets with a better, clearer, less odorous illuminating oil, which they sold for less than it cost to produce kerosene in the California refineries. Kerosene was the profitable end of the business. Although they were barely able to keep their heads above the financial waters, Hardison and Stewart decided, with characteristic brashness, to erect at Santa Paula a new refinery with which they aimed to produce a competitive illuminant. The refinery had a capacity of 14,000 barrels a year. In a memorandum to Hardison, Stewart wrote: "We should put on our bill heads that we are 'Producers of and Dealers in Petroleum Oils, and Dealers in Oil Well Supplies, Hardware, Pipe, Pipe Fittings, Paints, Oils, etc.' "

Early in 1888, luck changed for the better for the hopeful partners. In January, Adams Canyon Well No. 16 came in with a roar. It was California's first gusher. Their good fortune is indicated in their log, which reads:

"Adams Canyon Well No. 16, which was completed in January at a depth of 750 feet, is the largest flowing well ever struck in California. The oil shot up to a height of nearly 100 feet, and flowed at the rate of 800 to 900 barrels a day. Before it could be controlled, it sent a stream down the canyon for a distance of seven miles. After a lapse of nine months, it continues to flow at the rate of 500 barrels daily. At the present time it is producing sufficient gas to run all the works and machinery in the canyon."

The log of the first gusher partially compensated for some of the more dismal entries in the Adams Canyon logbook, such as these:

"Adams Canyon No. 23. At 1,580 feet we drilled for four days on iron which was put in the hole by someone."

"Adams No. 35. Drilled the well to 50 feet and shot for a crooked hole. Too much explosive and wrecked the derrick badly."

"Salt Marsh No. 6. Dry as dust."

That year, Lyman Stewart with Dan McFarland, another Hardison & Stewart director, took an independent flier on a wildcat well alongside the Brea tar pits west of Los Angeles. Though the heavy tar was seeping out of the ground around the well, it was another duster.

Even with the oil from the Adams Canyon gusher flowing into their refinery, the Hardison & Stewart Oil Company was still in danger of financial collapse. Bankers were cracking down on the firm. In San Francisco the Wells Fargo Bank demanded settlement on old notes, saying: "We expect immediate payment." The Santa Barbara National Bank turned Hardison down cold on a loan. At the Hellman bank a check for $5,000 was protested because of lack of funds, and at the Farmers and Mechanics Bank in Los Angeles several small checks bounced. Alexander Waldie, secretary for the company, warned Hardison that "the Mission Transfer's balance, at this moment is between $500 and $600 and the amounts coming in may not be here in time to take up our notes for $5,429.75, which mature Monday next."

Back in Pennsylvania, Milton Stewart, trying to raise money for Brother Lyman, was having his own troubles and protesting to Hardison & Stewart that he had already "advanced over and above my assessment, $4,500, on which I think there should be some adjustment." Even the wealthy Bard was using up all his connections and influence to raise dollars to keep the company afloat. But sales were good, and the partners figured that if they could only tide themselves over the immediate emergency, they could survive.

Lyman Stewart's personal finances were in even worse shape than those of the company. From a sickbed he wrote to the treasurer of Hardison & Stewart Oil Company, asking for "$200 or $300 to enable me to meet my more pressing demands." The company treasurer was able to spare only $100. A week or so later Stewart was still pleading for a couple of hundred dollars. "Sometimes I think I am engaged in a losing battle," he wrote. "During the past three weeks

SANTA PAULA REFINERY, 1887-1896

Above: *The plant erected by Hardison and Stewart had a capacity throughput its first year of about 14,000 barrels, turning out such products as asphaltum, greases, lubricants, and illuminating oils. Destroyed by fire in 1896, it was never rebuilt.*
Below: *One of the first "chemists" employed by Union Oil is believed to be the test-tube holder, who was a member of the first refinery crew.*

I have probably lost 20 pounds of my surplus flesh—well, hardly the surplus, for I didn't have that amount."

While lying in bed, Stewart had plenty of time to think, not only about debt and money shortages but overhead in general. One of the company's heaviest outlays was for freight to San Francisco, their main market. It was costly to ship oil in barrels to California markets, and the Southern Pacific adamantly refused to cut the tank-car freight rates. Stewart asked Hardison and Bard to come to his bedside. He outlined a scheme for a wooden tanker, a steamer with auxiliary sail to have a capacity of around 6,500 barrels of oil in steel tanks. A tanker could move oil from their pipeline at tidewater to San Francisco at half the prevailing freight rate. Hardison and Bard agreed that Stewart had the solution to much of their financial troubles. They approved the construction of the *W. L. Hardison*, the first oil tanker ever built, which was launched and ready for trial runs by midyear of 1889.

At this point they ran into a new difficulty. Because of several accidents on smaller craft using oil for fuel, the steamboat inspector in San Francisco refused to certificate a steamer using oil as fuel. Lyman Stewart was equally determined that the *Hardison* should use oil as fuel. Bard, who had political influence in Washington, persuaded officials there to overrule the inspector. The oil made a satisfactory and less expensive fuel for steamers. It was a revolutionary step, one that launched Lyman Stewart on a tremendous crusade to switch practically all of the Pacific Coast's shipping over to oil burners.

The *W. L. Hardison* did what was expected of it. As soon as it began operating, the rail rates dropped from $1 to 30 cents a barrel, and just in time, too. Shortly after midnight on June 25, 1889, a Chinese cook spilled a pan of burning fat in the galley of the *W. L. Hardison* as it was moored to the wharf at Ventura. Fanned by breezes, the blaze spread. The ship was cut adrift. By morning the fire had burned out the hulk, and the first oil tanker was a total loss.

In spite of their financial pains, known mainly to insiders, the Hardison & Stewart Oil Company looked good to outsiders. On December 31, 1888, the company's achievements were summed up by the Los Angeles *Times* in a story which read:

"The Hardison & Stewart Oil Company is now actively engaged in developing their interests up in Ventura County. During the past year several new and productive wells have been drilled, and production is up to 236,703 barrels, as against 121,355 barrels for 1887. The following shipments have been made: Los Angeles, 71,775 barrels; San Francisco, 119,706 barrels; San Diego, 17,491 barrels. During the past year the company has erected expensive refining works at Santa Paula, in which about 14,000 barrels have been manufactured into gas, oil, lubricants; machine oil, illuminating oils; asphaltum, and so forth.

"The company has large tanks at Hueneme, Santa Paula, Ventura, San Diego, and San Francisco. It has 90 miles of pipeline connecting the various oil tanks of the county. It also has 60 miles of telephone wires in operation. It has built 52 oil tank cars, and an expensive $40,000 steamer with a capacity of 6,500 barrels is about completed and will receive her cargoes of oil at Hueneme. The

NOTICE!

THE STEAMER

"W. L. Hardison"

As she now lies on the beach at San Buena Ventura, together with the Machinery, Engines, Boilers, Steam Winch, Tanks, Anchor Chains, Rigging and material on board of or attached to said Steamer, also seven or more large Oil Tanks on the beach, will be sold at

PUBLIC AUCTION

For account of concerned, at the

Merchants' Exchange, S. F., Monday, July 8th, '89

At 1.30 O'CLOCK. P. M.

By Order of Underwriters.

S. L. JONES & CO., Auctioneers.

WORLD'S FIRST TANKER GOES UP IN SMOKE

A pan of burning fat in the galley set fire to the pioneer tanker, W. L. Hardison, *at Ventura in 1889 soon after it was put in service. So shaky were firm's finances that a second tanker could not be built for 11 years.*

writer believes that the oil interests of this county (Ventura) are in their infancy and that the near future will develop untold wealth in this direction."

One month later, on January 31, 1889, Lyman Stewart was writing to Hardison: "Now one of two things are absolutely imperative, we must put more capital into our business, or promptly get a substantial increase in our production, failing to do either of these our business will be permanently ruined, and the directors individually bankrupt, as they are all endorsers of our paper. We had better look this matter squarely in the face and then get to work promptly to avert, if possible, impending disaster.

"To say that we have lots of property is no answer to meeting the requirements of the situation, as without substantial production the valuable property simply becomes 'junk' and would hardly sell for enough to pay the cost and interest . . . . I do not write in a spirit of criticism nor from the standpoint of one who has the blues, but in a spirit of candor, impelled by an earnest desire to protect our mutual interests and also those that have been committed into our hands as trusts."

The constant expansion and continuous debt to which Hardison and Stewart had become hardened was anything but good medicine for their new associate, Thomas R. Bard, who was vice-president of three of their other companies, the third being the Torrey Canyon Oil Company, organized in May, 1889, with a capitalization of $30,000, to drill on lands owned by the Bard interests. Though Bard was ready to drill for more oil, he urged curtailing other overhead, even to the point of closing the new refinery. It quickly became apparent that Bard and Stewart were at opposite ends on company policies. Stewart was forever on the lookout for a new oil lease and always experimenting with new products for new markets. He considered the refinery the key to the oil business and argued that only by refining an illuminant as good as that produced from

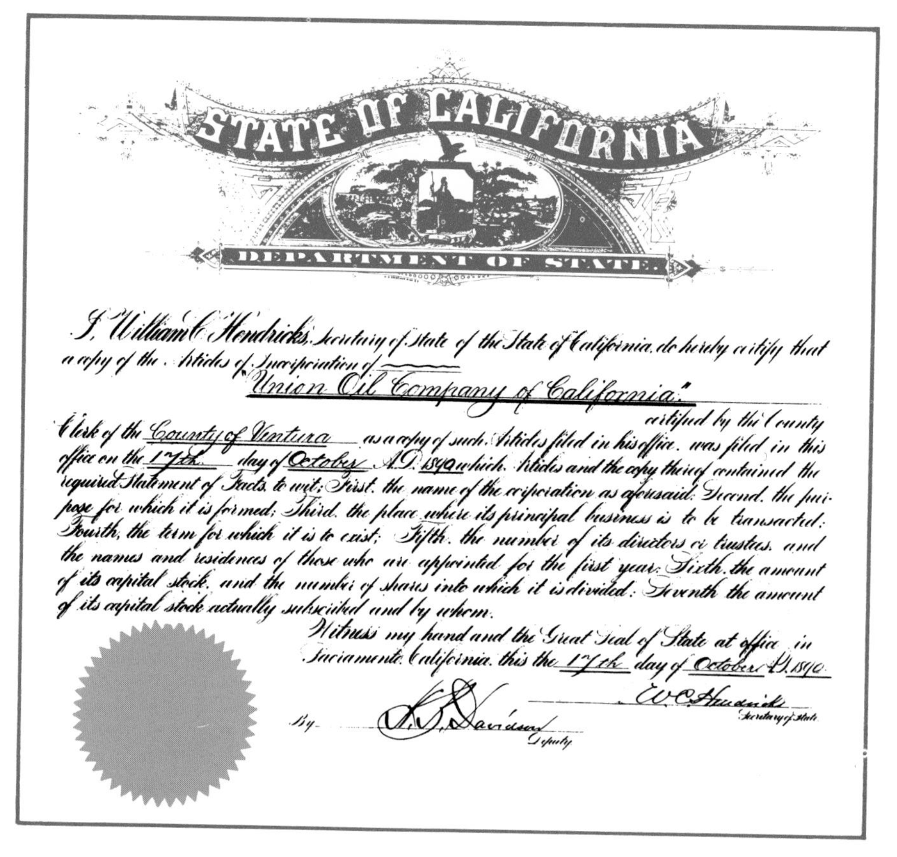

STATE OF CALIFORNIA

DEPARTMENT OF STATE.

I, William C. Hendricks, Secretary of State of the State of California, do hereby certify that a copy of the Articles of Incorporation of "Union Oil Company of California" certified by the County Clerk of the County of Ventura as a copy of such Articles filed in his office, was filed in this office on the 17th day of October A.D. 1890 which Articles and the copy thereof contained the required Statement of Facts, to wit; First, the name of the corporation as aforesaid; Second, the purpose for which it is formed; Third, the place where its principal business is to be transacted; Fourth, the term for which it is to exist; Fifth, the number of its directors or trustees, and the names and residences of those who are appointed for the first year; Sixth, the amount of its capital stock, and the number of shares into which it is divided; Seventh the amount of its capital stock actually subscribed and by whom.

Witness my hand and the Great Seal of State at office in Sacramento, California, this the 17th day of October A.D. 1890.

W. C. Hendricks
Secretary of State

By A. D. Davidson
Deputy

BIRTH CERTIFICATE OF UNION OIL COMPANY

Three already interlocked companies were combined and incorporated to form Union Oil Company of California on October 17, 1890. Officers of the 5-million-dollar firm were Thomas Bard, president; Lyman Stewart, vice-president; W. L. Hardison, treasurer; and I. H. Warring, secretary.

Pennsylvania crude could the Western oil producers compete on equal terms with their Eastern rivals. Bard's policy was to produce and sell the crude petroleum, leaving the refining and manufacturing problems to others.

Hardison by this time had branched out into agriculture and was one of the state's leading citrus growers. He was also being urged by influential politicians to accept the nomination for state senator. Although tempted by the offer, he turned it down and again tackled the job of raising money for the Hardison & Stewart Oil Company. While Hardison hunted money, Stewart, when he was able to get up from his sickbed, was out in the fields, driving the oil crews harder than ever.

Despite financial distress, the business was growing. On June 10, 1889, Hardison recapitulated in a letter to F. G. Babcock of Hornellsville, New York:

"Our oil business has grown very rapidly. We now have a very large scope of territory, have over 100 miles of pipeline with terminal facilities at Hueneme, San Buenaventura, and San Francisco, and have a finely equipped refinery at Santa Paula. We have 54 new tank cars, each with a capacity of 3,800 gallons, and have a new steamer designed especially for carrying oil in bulk. We have our own teams and supplies. In fact, we have the best equipped arrangement for producing and marketing oil that I know of, not excepting the Standard Oil Company. The oil business in this state is peculiar. We have worked up an excellent market, but are unable at the present time to supply the demand at handsome prices. We hope, however, in the near future to have more territory developed and be able to supply the increasing demands. We are now getting for our oil $2 and $2.25, delivered at San Francisco and Los Angeles. The cost of delivery to Los Angeles is about 30 cents a barrel, and to San Francisco, where our steamer runs steadily, the cost will probably not exceed 12 to 15 cents per barrel."

Nevertheless, by December, 1889, after almost seven years of hunting oil under California's canyons and hills, Lyman Stewart and Wallace Hardison were still broke. In a letter remarkable for its restraint under the existing conditions, December 7, 1889, Stewart wrote to Hardison: "I saw Mr. Bixby today and he wants some money from me on account of what I owe him, in time to use it in payment of his taxes. Can you help me out to the extent of $750? I am not very well; my head has given out again."

But Stewart's fighting heart hadn't given out. In spite of their financial difficulties, he and Hardison were highly respected as businessmen. Eastern interests had been watching the growing California company. Early in December, 1889, an Eastern syndicate offered to buy 49 per cent of the three companies, namely, the Hardison & Stewart Oil Company (which owned the Mission Transfer Company outright), the Sespe Oil Company, and the Torrey Canyon Oil Company. The syndicate controlled a new refining process developed by Dr. Frederick Salathe, a distinguished Swiss chemist. Stewart and Hardison, plagued by debts, granted an option on 49 per cent of the stock they held to Daniel Dull of New York and Ambrose C. Burdick of Chicago. Dull and Burdick guaranteed that the new refining process would double the amount of water-white kerosene extracted from California's crude. If successful, it would revolutionize the West's oil business.

Part of the deal was that the three companies be merged into one corporation, which would own all the properties, including the Mission Transfer Company and the marketing facilities. On Christmas Day, 1889, Lyman Stewart ordered an appraisal of all their properties. Not only Hardison and Stewart, but others as well, were amazed at the value of the business that had grown from their many borrowed shoe-strings. The companies were all fresh out of cash, as usual, but the properties were appraised at $1,800,000. Dull and Burdick did not exercise their option, probably because the claims they had made for their process proved extravagant and they were unable to live up to their part of the bargain. But Stewart, Hardison, and Bard decided to merge the three companies anyway, with Thomas R. Bard as president, Lyman Stewart as vice-president, W. L. Hardison as treasurer, I. H. Warring as secretary; John Irwin, Alexander Waldie, Dan McFarland, W. S. Chaffee, and Casper Taylor were directors. The new company was capitalized at $5,000,000. At the start, Stewart, Hardison, and their friends controlled 53 per cent of the stock.

Thus, on October 17, 1890, the Union Oil Company of California was born.

CHAPTER FOUR 1890-1900

A House Divided

THOUGH LAUNCHED AT AN AUSPICIOUS HOUR in the Oil Age, the Union Oil Company of California seemed born to trouble. Hardly had their signatures dried on the incorporation papers than President Thomas R. Bard and Vice-president Lyman Stewart became involved in a smoldering rivalry for control of the destinies of the infant company. The basic complication was that, of Union's three key executives, only Lyman Stewart, the oil hunter, the land buyer, and the petroleum producer, was willing to go out and call on prospective customers for the company's products—fuel oil, kerosene, greases, and lubricating oils and asphalt. Bard, busy with his land interests and politics, was for selling Union's crude in bulk to oil merchants in Los Angeles and San Francisco at ridiculously low prevailing prices, $1.25 to $1.50 per barrel. Hardison had become more interested in citrus trees than in oil wells.

The nub of the controversy between the founders was their conflicting ideas about the potential of the company they had founded. To Bard, an oil company was a mining operation, to be exploited for dollars to invest in other enterprises. This was the prevailing idea among most petroleum venturers at the time. Oddly enough, it was regarded as the conservative approach to oil-field exploitation. Union Oil started life with 26 producing wells, which yielded 84,421 barrels of oil in 1890, one-fourth of California's production. Bard was for pumping more oil out of the earth as fast as possible and selling it as crude. Stewart's policy was exactly the opposite. His ambition was to accumulate potential oil lands, build up reserves, and develop a long-lived company that would recover the oil slowly, refine it, and market its products for generations to come. Bard wanted

BIRTHPLACE OF UNION OIL

Incorporation papers for Union Oil were signed in 1890 in the corner office of the second floor of this building in Santa Paula, the third headquarters of the company. The California Oil Museum now occupies first floor.

RIVALS FOR TEN YEARS *Two strong-willed men, Thomas R. Bard and Lyman Stewart, guided the destinies of Union Oil for ten quarrelsome years after it was founded. Adherents to differing business philosophies, they feuded as often as they worked together.*

quick profit; Stewart sought long-time investment. Stewart also sensed the financial advantages of merging the four properties into one integrated company that could produce, refine, and distribute on even terms with larger competitors.

Though Bard was less enthusiastic about the merger, he agreed to go along when Stewart and Hardison offered him the presidency of the Union Oil Company. Bard continued as president of Mission Transfer Company, the marketing unit which he had sold to Hardison & Stewart Oil Company. He was also head of the Sespe and Torrey Canyon companies. Stewart was still president of Hardison & Stewart Oil Company, and he and Hardison together owned a majority of the Sespe Oil Company stock. Bard held a controlling interest in the Torrey Canyon Oil Company. These corporations were continued, and each shared the stock of the new Union Oil Company in proportion to the respective appraised values. The net result of this maze of interlocking ownership was that Lyman Stewart and Wallace Hardison and their families and friends controlled 53 per cent of the shares of the Union Oil Company of California. Unfortunately for these families, this did not mean that they had actual control of Union Oil. Ostensibly Bard, though president, would bow to Stewart and Hardison on a showdown of policy, because he and his friends controlled only 40 per cent of the shares.

Hardison and Stewart assumed that Bard would leave management of the Union Oil Company to Lyman Stewart, whose every dollar was tied up in oil properties and who lived and breathed oil. Hardison, whose enthusiasm was waning, was gradually selling his interests in the oil companies to the Stewart family as rapidly as the Stewarts could find money to buy. Bard did not see the picture in this light. By mutual agreement he was allowed to name the majority of directors on both the Sespe and the Torrey boards. Each of these companies named two directors to the Union Oil board. These, with Bard, gave him a five-to-four majority on the Union Oil board, which made the policy decision. The Union Oil board soon split into two factions. One, known as the "Bard camp," consisted of President Bard, Secretary I. H. Warring, and Bard's friends, Dan McFarland, W. S. Chaffee, and Casper Taylor. The four-man "Stewart group" included Vice-president Stewart, Treasurer W. L. Hardison, Drilling Superintendent John Irwin, a cousin of Stewart, and Alexander Waldie, secretary of Hardison & Stewart Oil Company.

Asked why he had supported Bard for the presidency when he and Hardison held stock control, Stewart later explained: "Mr. Bard was a man of great wealth and influence. We all regarded him as a multi-millionaire, while all the rest of us combined could not have approached a million at the time."

Ironically, the Union Oil board voted its rich president a $5,000 a year salary, while hard-pressed vice-president Stewart drew only $5 per day for his full-time services. Stewart managed to support his family only by means of occasional dividends from his Pennsylvania oil ventures.

Stewart was forced to divide his time between wildcatting for oil and "wildcatting for new markets" if Union Oil were to survive. Employing the same ingenuity and originality that made him an outstanding field operator, he became a familiar figure in the marts of the small but growing industrial areas of Southern California, carrying his satchel filled with small bottles containing samples of Union's petroleum products. Salesman Stewart soon found that, to market Union's wares, he had to offer the customers quality products as good as those of competitors, or better. One of his first resolutions, passed by Union's board of directors, authorized the expenditure of $2,500 for a research laboratory to try to find ways to extract clear, nonsmoking kerosene from California's evil-smelling crude oil.

A clash between Bard and Stewart developed almost immediately. When Stewart was out in the field scouting for more oil land or in the city peddling oil, Bard in Santa Paula ran the company with a high hand. When Bard was away, Stewart made decisions arbitrarily, often committing the company for sizable expenditures for land purchases, pipelines, or refinery equipment. He did this over the inevitable protests of Secretary Warring, who was Bard's man Friday, detailed by Bard to curb Stewart's spending sprees. Born near Santa Paula, Warring had started as a bookkeeper for the Mission Transfer Company when Bard first organized this concern. A busybody, Warring relished snooping on Stewart and Hardison and reporting to Bard whatever they did. He rapidly developed an animosity toward Stewart, frequently reversed Stewart's orders. This kept the company headquarters and refinery in a state of turmoil.

As time passed, Warring poisoned Bard's opinions of Stewart's policies to a point where genuine reconciliation between Union's two strong-minded leaders was out of the question. The board meetings at which Stewart sought confirmation for policies he had, as a rule, already put into effect soon degenerated into showdowns of strength, which, surprisingly, Stewart often won. These showdowns were only rounds in the knockdown drag-out struggle to control the destinies of Union Oil. Later, when asked "Wasn't it that you thought Mr. Bard was too conservative and he thought you were too bold and venturesome to be safe?" Stewart answered that he "guessed this was about the situation."

Devoting full time to Union's business, Stewart became the company's first general manager. Serving without title at the beginning, he drove the drillers to make hole faster in the field; he prodded the salesmen and the dealers; he angled for lower freight rates, crusaded for oil as the logical fuel for West Coast industry; he wangled loans to pay the bills; exhorted the refinery people to turn out better products and more of them. Although he was usually broke and was drawing no salary for his services, he favored pouring more of the company's earnings into oil lands, pipelines, refinery facilities. He argued eloquently for spending at least $2 for lands for each $1 paid out as dividends. As he put it later:

"The aim of this company and its predecessors, reaching as far back as 1883, had consistently been to use the profits in obtaining a control of as much available oil territory as possible by the purchase of fee or oil rights, by lease or by locating upon oil lands under mining law, rather than distribute the earnings in dividends."

Not a trained geologist, Stewart was one of the first oil hunters to sense that Nature, in the course of millions of years, had hidden vast pools of petroleum under California's broken hills and valleys. His nose for oil enabled him to smell petroleum even where there was no surface sign of it. He persuaded the Union directors to accept his policy of acquiring promising oil lands while they were available and cheap. On December 30, 1890, they authorized him to buy lands "for not over $5 per acre." Stretching this authority, Stewart picked up acreage as most men pick out neckties, foreseeing that the day of cheap land—$2 to $5 per acre—would soon pass. He bought oil lands on his own hunch, then told his associates in Union about it after he had already committed them. His buying and leasing kept the struggling company on the brink of bankruptcy.

Even Hardison deserted him on his mania for land buying, complaining: "I think it is about time we looked after our own households. It has now been eight years since we commenced to make our investments and began putting our time in this business, and we have not received in dividends one cent."

TUNNELING WITH MIRRORS

Following system used by ancient Egyptians when they tunneled tombs under the Libyan mountains, Union engineers used mirrors to reflect sunlight into the tunnels in Sulphur Mountain to guide the diggers.

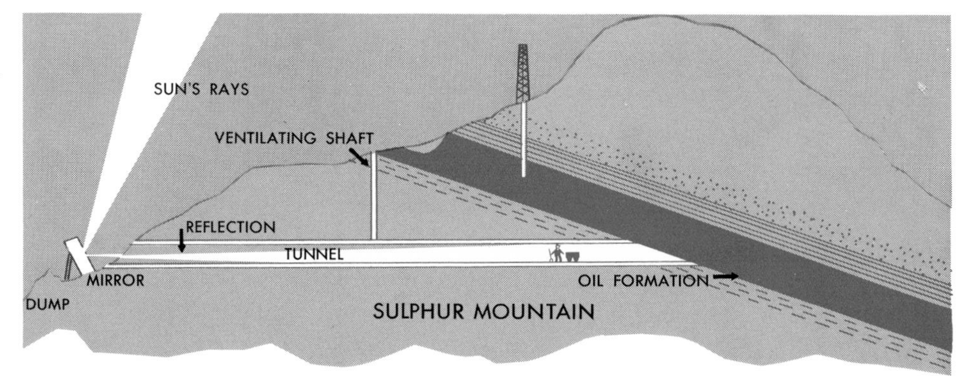

FROM WHALE OIL TO FUEL OIL *Pacific Steam Whaling and Arctic Oil Works in San Francisco was agent for Union Oil from 1894 to 1904, at which time the company bought the whale oil refinery on Potrero Street and converted it to a sales base for fuel oil distribution.*

In 1890 Stewart's resourcefulness in tapping oil sources was dramatized by the tunnels he had crews dig deep into Sulphur Mountain, which formed one of the walls of Adams Canyon, while Union's drillers were sinking deeper wells in the valley below. Sulphur Mountain's cliffs were too precipitous on which to perch derricks and engines. The earlier tunnels of Josiah Stanford had proved that there was a huge deposit of oil-bearing sand inside the mountain. When the sands were tapped by horizontal holes sloping slightly down to the cliff sides, the oil trickled slowly out by gravity into tanks.

Adams Tunnel No. 4 was known as the Boarding House Tunnel, in the vernacular of the oil-field crews. Harvey Hardison, brother of Wallace, was the boss on that tunneling job. By April 4, 1890, the diggers had pushed the Boarding House Tunnel 950 feet into the mountain. Early that morning an explosion deep in the hole shook the area. Two men at the mouth were slightly burned; two more inside were more seriously injured. Wallace Hardison, arriving on the scene, ordered workers to stay out of the tunnel after the injured men were rescued. While he was taking them to the hospital, Brother Harvey and three other workers decided to make an inspection. When they were 700 feet inside the tunnel, another explosion rocked the mountain, killing Harvey Hardison and two companions. Despite this tragedy, Union's crews finished the Boarding House Tunnel and 30 other tunnels, some of them 1,600 feet long, deeper than most "deep" wells of the day. Several of these old tunnels were still trickling oil three-quarters of a century later.

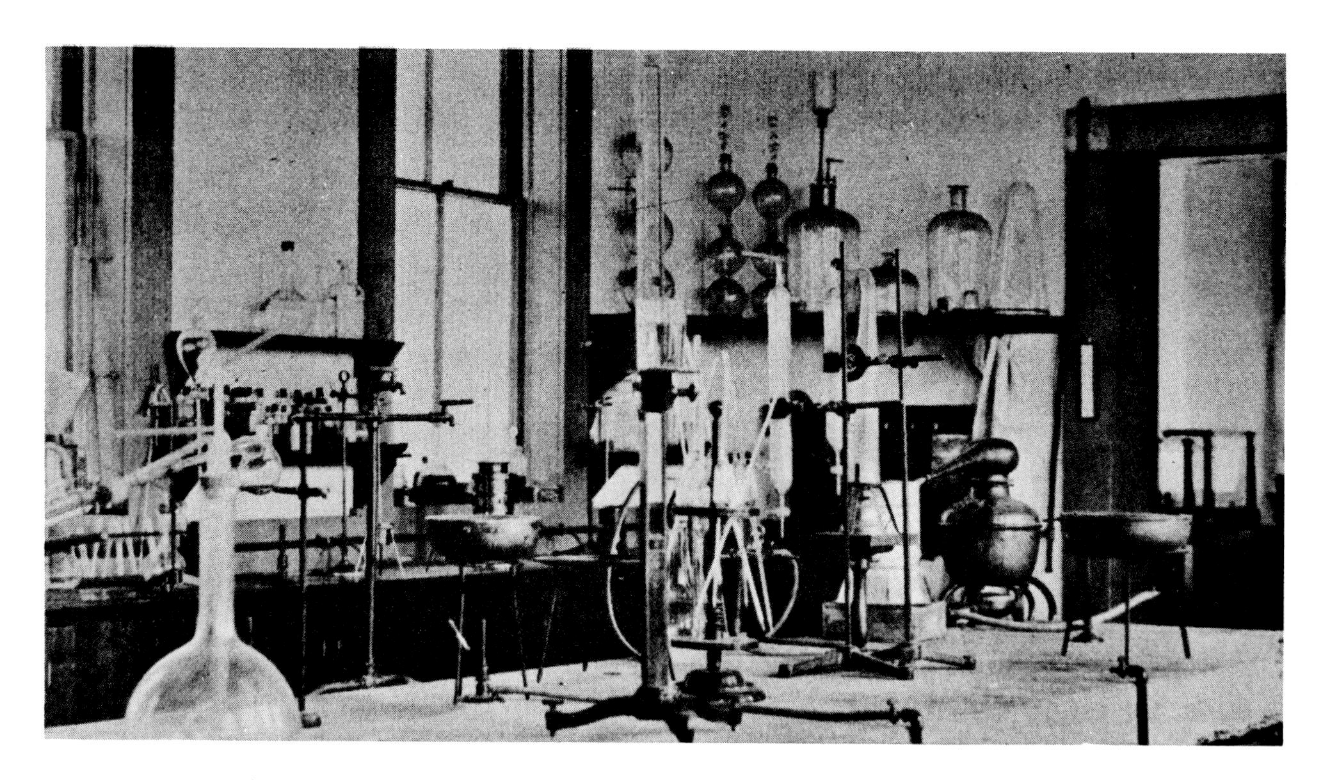

WEST'S FIRST PETROLEUM LABORATORY *Union Oil built this first petroleum laboratory in the West in 1891 at the Santa Paula refinery. Here the distinguished Swiss chemist Dr. Frederick Salathe began his study of Western oils in an endeavor to produce a water-white kerosene from California crude.*

In the hectic scramble to tap the deep-down pools of oil, Union's crews drilled furiously under the relentless nudging of unexcitable Lyman Stewart. They tossed up derricks and made holes faster because he asked them, in gentleman's language, to do it. They wildcatted wherever Stewart's intuition told them there might be oil beneath the barren hills. In 1890 they drilled as far afield as Coalinga, Union's first venture into the San Joaquin Valley.

The fight for markets was growing hot, particularly in San Francisco, largest outlet for oil on the coast. There, Eastern competitors were offering kerosene hauled across the country at prices lower than the cost of making and delivering illuminating oil from California crude. T. J. Cochrane, manager of the Mission Transfer Company's San Francisco office, reported: "The Standard are preparing for a war west of the Rockies, and soon there will be firing all along the line. There [in Chicago] they are building the largest oil refinery in the world, with a view to furnishing the Far West. Being 600 miles nearer the market than any other oil manufactured by their competitors, they will get a lower freight rate. They will, of course, get the usual rebate. Taking it all along, they will cut the life out of our prices within a year. Some of the Standard men are here now."

To gird for this threat, Lyman Stewart introduced a resolution at the next board meeting authorizing that "immediate steps be taken to secure the services of a competent analytical and manufacturing chemist." Stewart had the man, S. J. Carmen of Bradford, Pennsylvania, an experienced and practical oil chemist. But President Bard ignored Stewart's suggestion and hired instead Dr. Frederick Salathe, the Swiss chemist who had been hailed as the discoverer of the process by which Dull and Burdick had hoped to extract a much higher percentage of kerosene from California crude. Bard paid Dr. Salathe a then fabulous salary of $10,000 a year, plus a bonus, and put him in charge of the Santa Paula refinery as well as Union's pioneer research laboratory. An experimenter, rather than production man, Dr. Salathe soon had the refinery operation in a complete state of confusion. One of his first acts was to cancel the daily production reports to the marketing staff. Neither Lyman Stewart nor Union's dealers knew what the company had to sell. One of Dr. Salathe's enthusiasms was an improved sewing machine oil. He made up 300 barrels of his new product, enough to supply California for years.

Instead of restraining the temperamental doctor, Bard decided suddenly, early in 1891, to shake up the marketing branch of the company's operation. The first to get the ax was Cochrane, the San Francisco agent who had built up an excellent trade in the Bay area. Sales fell off so much that the company had to shut down the refinery at Santa Paula for a period. The board of directors sustained Bard over Stewart's protests. Bard next canceled the contract with the Los Angeles Oil Burning & Supply Company, which had handled Union's products exclusively in the Los Angeles market. The Los Angeles Oil Burning & Supply Company promptly built a refinery and became a competitor instead of an outlet. As a result, Union was confronted with a sharp drop in business in both of its major markets simultaneously.

But, paradoxically, for once there was money in the bank. Stewart wanted to use this cash to buy more oil lands, to expand the refinery, and to build a pipeline from Ventura to Los Angeles. His old partner, Hardison, supported Bard, who persuaded the directors to vote cash dividends of $10,000, plus a stock dividend of $30,000. These dividends, in May, 1891, were the first returns that either Hardison or Stewart had received in the eight years since they launched their oil hunt in California.

Late in 1891, Union found itself menaced on a new front. A bill introduced in the state legislature at Sacramento proposed to establish new and richer specifications for kerosene, which Western refiners could not meet. The bill, sponsored by Eastern oil interests, was a sleeper. If it passed, the illuminating oil market would become a Standard monopoly. Fortunately Bard and Hardison were influential enough in political circles to persuade the legislature to defeat the bill.

Hardly had this threat been eliminated when a new one arose. This was a lawsuit by a San Francisco firm calling itself the Union Oil Company, which claimed exclusive right to the name. The San Francisco concern was a partnership which had never been incorporated. Bard saved the day by pointing this

ANOTHER UNION OIL COMPANY

Among the many companies named Union Oil was one in Titusville, Pennsylvania. A flourishing and profitable concern founded in 1870, it was later absorbed by a competitor.

out and persuading the San Franciscans to call off their suit. At the time there was still another Union Oil Company back in Pennsylvania, a flourishing and highly profitable concern founded in the 1870s, which later was absorbed by a competitor.

In 1891 President Bard entered into negotiations with J. B. Livingstone, president of the Standard Paint Company of New York, who proposed to organize a new company to take over Union's refining and marketing activities. The deal provoked another bitter clash between Bard and Stewart. Nothing came of the negotiations, and the final showdown between Bard and Stewart was postponed again.

The infighting between the two camps was carried to the company's new subsidiaries. One was the Santa Paula Hardware Company, bought by Union Oil to provide tools and equipment at manufacturer's prices. Another was the California Ink Company, organized on November 18, 1891, by Lyman Stewart, W. L. Hardison, Thomas R. Bard, Alexander Waldie, and I. H. Warring, with a capitalization of $200,000. The ink company was the enthusiasm of Hardison, who had invented a process for making printer's ink from petroleum. On the afternoon that the ink company was founded, Union Oil Company bought it, along with its patents. Although the ink was manufactured at the Santa Paula refinery, California Ink operated as a separate concern. Union agreed to advance money, not to exceed $10,000 from time to time, to help the ink company get on its feet. To finance this deal, Union had to borrow from three banks, much to Bard's annoyance.

Stewart continued to buy and lease acreage. Acquiring land became an obsession with him. These land deals were invariably made over Bard's protests. Union's president also became increasingly irritated over the cost of the experimental work in the refinery. Stewart, on the other hand, was convinced there was a lot more in a barrel of oil than fuel oil, kerosene, asphalt, and grease. Late in 1891 the Standard Oil Company offered to contract for all of Union's naphtha and gasoline output. So little was made the year before that when one customer, A. D. Williams of Santa Barbara, tried to buy a drum of gasoline from the Mission Transfer Company, he was informed that "just at this time we have none in stock, and it will probably be several days before we make any." It was a month before the refinery was able to report that "we expect to make at least a drum of gasoline by Thursday of next week."

Stewart crisply turned down the Standard Oil proposal in a letter saying: "We are expected by our customers to fill orders for all kinds of our refinery products, and we cannot believe that it would be to our advantage to ask you to handle for us our entire output of any one of a few of our products, especially such as meet with so ready a sale at a satisfactory price as do our naphthas and gasoline."

Unable to induce the directors to vote the Union Oil Company out of the marketing business, Bard focussed his attack on another "Stewart hand," Refinery Superintendent F. H. Dunham, who suddenly found himself receiving petty and annoying memos, such as the following:

"It will be your duty to keep the gates of the refinery under lock at all times. You will report once a week the names of the persons admitted to the yard. You are enjoined from imparting to anyone any information relating to the work of your own or any other department of the company's business, except as you may be permitted to do so under special written instructions."

In June, 1892, Bard informed the directors he had decided to discharge Dunham, and with diabolical finesse he delegated Vice-president Stewart, who had backed Dunham to the limit in various clashes with Bard and Dr. Salathe, as a committee of one to notify Dunham that he had been ousted.

The 1892 annual report revealed that Union's wells had produced, the year previous, 101,901 barrels of oil, more than one-third of California's output that year. To gain this remarkable production, Stewart had moved the company's

NO GASOLINE IN STOCK TODAY

So little gasoline was refined by Union in 1890 that a driver from Santa Barbara was told at the Santa Paula refinery that there was none in stock and it would be several days before any would be made.

HISTORIAN'S DREAM *Ten early wells in Torrey Canyon pumped by lines running from a single eccentric wheel. Even today in other nearby fields, jacklines powered by a single source continue to operate pumps in wells drilled generations ago.*

drilling rigs away from lands controlled by the Hardison & Stewart Oil Company and had put down eight productive shallow wells on the property of the Torrey Canyon Oil Company, controlled by the Bard camp. These wells alone brought in 70,000 barrels per year. This production made Union Oil quite dependent on Torrey Canyon and provided Bard with a new weapon over the Stewart group. But the Torrey Canyon wells vindicated Stewart's judgment; they provided inexpensive oil needed to meet the competition in the San Francisco area.

By the end of 1892, Stewart was picking up oil lands so fast that the directors were obliged to appropriate funds to hire a temporary assistant for the Ventura County recorder to keep the land records straight. He was also acquiring land in Kern and Santa Barbara counties and early that year persuaded the directors to buy the Los Angeles Oil Company, which held 800 acres of promising oil land in the Los Angeles Basin. One Los Angeles well yielded 15,000 barrels of crude oil in its first year of production.

This expansion called for more money than the company was earning, and Stewart was forced to borrow wherever he could find lenders. This he did over Bard's opposition. Hoping to interest Eastern capital, the directors granted an option to Colonel J. M. Marble, a Los Angeles broker, who proposed to sell, within three months, 15,000 shares of preferred and 30,000 shares of common stock to a newly organized Union Oil Company of New Jersey. This subsidiary was an inspiration for financing the company's growth without upsetting the existing balance of power among its owners. The scheme never materialized, but it was the forerunner of stock-juggling devices that confused the Union Oil monetary picture for two decades.

WILD BILL CANYON JACKLINE

A revolving eccentric wheel alternately pulls and releases cables that pump a dozen or more wells, some a long distance away.

Luckily the Eastern money was not needed. On February 28, 1892, Adams No. 28 came in with a roar, showering oil all over the vicinity of the drilling rig. This was California's biggest gusher yet, pouring out 1,500 barrels per day. Catching the drillers by surprise, the oil shot over the derrick, filled all of the tanks and sumps, and flowed down the canyon into the Santa Clara River and thence to the open sea. Here was the "river of oil" Professor Silliman had predicted a quarter-century before. Irwin and his crew frantically dammed up ravines to catch the oil in open pits. Adams No. 28 gushed out 40,000 barrels of crude before it settled down to a steady 200 barrels a day.

Here was the oil strike men had dreamed of and had risked their lives to get. It eclipsed all other drilling jobs up to that time in California and changed the whole petroleum outlook, multiplying the state's potential a hundredfold. It touched off a new oil stampede as hectic and reckless as the eager struggle for quick riches in Pennsylvania's oil boom had been back in the sixties. It fired men with the spirit of the Gold Rush. This time prospectors were combing California for liquid black gold, battling not only Nature but each other for fortune. Hundreds found it; thousands lost it—sometimes by striking too much oil.

An example of the latter was the sensational Los Angeles City oil stampede, which for a time threatened Union Oil with disaster, despite the wave of optimism that swept the company following the Adams Canyon strike. In 1893 Edward L. Doheny, with a pick and shovel, dug a wildcat hole, a shaft 4 by 6 feet, on a city lot just west of downtown Los Angeles. At a depth of 46 feet he dipped up 4 barrels of oil a day. This remarkable hand-dug discovery well launched a wild scramble for oil under city lots. Not only Doheny but everybody else who could scrape together a few hundred dollars to buy or lease a lot began

OIL IN THE HEART OF LOS ANGELES *Los Angeles City Field about 1895 had "wells as thick as holes in a pepper pot" and the estimate of 3,000 wells in a narrow strip of land only 4½ miles long seems not far wrong. This boom was touched off in 1893 by Edward L. Doheny who dug a successful wildcat in the downtown area.*

digging or punching oil wells. They were shallow, cheap wells, the average cost being around $1,500, including tanks and pumps. A good many of them were put down by the old spring-pole method. By 1899 there were more than 3,000 wells in a 4-mile area west of downtown Los Angeles. (Six decades later, the Union Oil Center towered above the last of these old downtown oil wells.)

The eager oil hunters drilled so enthusiastically that the City Council was forced to declare town oil wells a civic nuisance. The city fathers forbade all oil-well drilling within the municipality's limits, whereupon everybody who had a lot on the west side of town discovered that he needed water, badly and right away. The council couldn't forbid the citizens from drilling wells for water to keep their gardens green. If the well happened to produce oil instead of water, that was just fate and luck. In 1893, a depression year, prices fell to 25 cents per barrel for crude in Los Angeles. Union was hard-hit. Booming Los Angeles, whose population had quadrupled since Lyman Stewart's arrival, was the company's second largest market.

Stewart's Scotch blood curdled at the thought of paying city-lot prices, $1,500 for a 25-foot city lot, for a drilling site in the new Los Angeles field. He urged

Union's directors to authorize him to build a pipeline from the company's Ventura fields to Los Angeles.

"With a 2-inch pipeline to Los Angeles harbor, we could reach the world with our products," he argued. They turned him down. The wells of Union's subsidiary, the Los Angeles Oil Company, were shut in, because it was cheaper to buy oil than to pump it in Los Angeles.

Within an unexpectedly short time, the shallow Los Angeles wells tapered off, then almost petered out. The scramble for new oil quickly shifted to the San Joaquin Valley fields, then to Lompoc and Santa Maria valleys. (Ironically, neither Stewart nor the eager drillers who moved their rigs north dreamed that they were leaving behind them the greatest oil lake of all under California. This was the Greater Los Angeles Basin, covering an area 22 miles wide and 46 miles long, south and west of the city and extending out under the ocean, a bonanza that yielded a later generation of oil hunters millions of barrels of crude from zones 2 miles deeper down than the shallow discoveries of the nineties.)

In an effort to recoup in the Los Angeles market, Stewart opened a small sales office downtown on Third Street. It was little more than a hole in the wall, but the office became a bone of contention. Secretary Warring, convinced that the $15-a-month rental was a waste of the company's money, made such an issue over the office that Stewart finally appealed to the board. The directors sustained him. But even this clear-cut decision failed to smooth out the differences between the Bard and Stewart camps. The feuding frequently cost the company badly needed business. For example, Stewart had induced General M. H. Sherman, president of the Los Angeles Consolidated Railway Company, to switch from coal to oil in the railway shops. The experiment was working smoothly when Bard, prodded by Warring, sent a sharp letter to the fiery old general, who was having his own financial troubles.

"We thought we had fully explained to you that it was impossible for us to deviate from our uniform rule of collecting in full monthly," wrote Bard. "While we hope to continue to enjoy your custom, we certainly shall decline your orders unless we can be insured against inconvenience occasioned by dilatory payment."

The angry general promptly switched his custom to one of Union's competitors.

During the financial panic of 1893, which occurred just as the wells of the Los Angeles City fields began pouring out their flood of crude, oil operators failed right and left. Union was forced to retrench severely. On one black day the company had to borrow from several individuals and from the estate of a recently deceased friend of the company. To make matters worse, Dr. Salathe chose this particular day to go out on a buying spree for new laboratory equipment, committing thousands of dollars that the company did not have. Warring resumed his sniping at Stewart, becoming so belligerent that he wrote to Bard: "I am inclined to think that we made a serious mistake when we employed Mr. Stewart to look after our fuel business, for the reason that he is too anxious to sell his burners."

Stewart's "aerated oil fuel burner" was one of the devices with which he hoped to weather hard times. The burner had been developed by Union's shop mechanics. With it, Stewart hoped to switch potential customers from coal to oil. Stewart offered to donate sample barrels of oil for the purpose of testing the burner in the customer's furnace. Both Bard and Warring heartily disapproved this "giveaway" of Union's oil. Unfortunately the quality of the fuel oil coming out of the refinery at Santa Paula, where Warring had taken over direction, deteriorated so seriously that steamship owners whom Stewart had persuaded to try oil complained that water in the fuel made the fires go out under their boilers. When Stewart protested that poor products were losing Union's best potential customers, Warring replied: "If you wish to take the position, as intimated in your letter, that the writer is sole manager of the refinery and as such manager is responsible for every barrel shipped, then it will be necessary to change the management of the refinery."

This was the moment for which Stewart had waited. Dr. Salathe's contract had expired, and not even Bard wanted to renew it. Taking Warring at his word, Stewart persuaded the board to "change the management at the refinery." Professor S. F. Peckham, experienced University of California chemist, was put in charge temporarily. The professor launched a cleanup, and the quality of Union's fuel oil and other products improved immediately.

With business picking up, Union needed a new refinery, which Stewart proposed to build close to markets either in the Los Angeles area or in the San Francisco Bay region. He attempted unsuccessfully to buy the Los Angeles Oil Burner & Supply Company, which was rapidly capturing much of Union's business in Southern California. Then he surveyed both the Los Angeles and San Francisco areas for refinery sites. This expansion program, which most of the directors approved, was so distasteful to President Bard that he presented his resignation as president of Union Oil early in 1894. On Stewart's motion, the board declined to accept the resignation, and Bard stayed on.

At this same meeting, Stewart resigned as sales manager in Los Angeles. Ten years had passed since he left the Pennsylvania oil fields, and he wanted to make a trip East on family affairs. Before departing, he arranged for son Will Stewart, who had worked as a roustabout for drilling crews during his summer vacations from studies at the University of California, to learn something about refining and marketing by starting on the lower rungs at the Santa Paula refinery at $75 a month. When Will reported for work, Secretary Warring took charge of his education. Several weeks later, Lyman Stewart returned from his trip to discover that his son had done nothing in the meantime but cooper barrels. Warring had issued instructions that Will was to be kept outside the refinery itself. Furious, Lyman Stewart assigned Will to a field crew, as a driller's helper.

The cofounders of Union Oil soon had it out in heated argument, in the course of which Bard stated that he intended to do everything in his power to defeat the ambitions of the Stewart family. Bard almost made good his promise at a board meeting on July 24, 1894, when both Hardison and Stewart were absent. Bard persuaded the board to accept his resignation and to elect his man, D. T. Perkins, as Union's new president, with Warring as general manager of the entire operation. Neither Stewart nor Hardison had any inkling of this maneuver.

Realizing that the time had come for a showdown, Stewart began lining up voting strength. Three months later, at the annual meeting in October, 1894, he was ready. When the new officers were chosen, he was named not only president but general manager as well, at the annual salary of $5,000 that Bard had previously drawn. However, Stewart continued to draw only $5 a day for two years more. The upheaval made him boss of the company which Bard had run for four years. Bard came out of the meeting and said to Stewart: "Well, you have us where you want us now."

Stewart responded with the conciliatory move of offering to let Bard name five of the nine Union directors, provided the former president would agree not to hamper the new management. This good will gesture merely set the stage for another showdown.

In the driver's seat, temporarily at least, Stewart lost no time in launching a new marketing program. Calling a special meeting of the board, he asked the directors to listen to some unpleasant truths from Professor Peckham, who was working on a new illuminant, with which Stewart hoped to compete on equal terms with Eastern lamp oils.

"The trouble with California oil is, no one knows anything about it; we do not know what we are working on, and the results of our labors thus far have been thrusts in the dark," the professor told the directors. Impressed, on Stewart's motion they asked Peckham to stay on with the company as long as he could do so at a salary of $333 per month. This was the real start of Union

UNION OIL'S SECOND PRESIDENT

D. T. Perkins, named president of the company when Stewart was absent from a board meeting, was promptly replaced in the post by Stewart himself after a showdown battle. Perkins' brief term ran from July to October, 1894.

Oil's research in petroleum. Peckham also took over temporarily as superintendent of the refinery. Union's products quickly improved in quality. To get them to market, Stewart ordered a new barge with a capacity of 5,000 barrels. Later he persuaded F. H. Dunham, the efficient former refinery superintendent who had been fired by Bard, to resume his previous position.

As a result of these vigorous measures, 1894 proved something of a milestone for Union Oil. The Los Angeles *Times* reported that oil was being used for baking bricks, for smelting, and in fact for any of the mechanical arts in which a high heat was necessary. The *Times* even tossed a neat editorial bouquet, reporting that: "Union Oil has long been known as 'Old Reliable.' Union makes it a special business to introduce oil for any new work wherein oil has not been used before, and puts forth every effort to make a success of the same."

Since four out of every five barrels of oil were sold as fuel in the early nineties, coal was petroleum's great competitor. This was particularly true of the Pacific Coast, where coal from the British Isles and even Australia was brought in as ballast and dumped at low cost by sailing ships which picked up return cargoes of California grain and lumber. Though the coal was cheap at tidewater in San Francisco, it skyrocketed to $30 a ton by the time the railroads hauled it to other California cities. Stewart redoubled his drive to sell his aerated oil burner, which had evolved out of trial and error; at first Union experimenters had tried spreading oil on bricks or cobblestones to burn it like coal, an idea that ended in failure; next, they saturated wood with oil, but that proved too cumbersome; then Stewart hit on the idea of spraying oil into the firebox, mixed with steam, which improved combustion. Stewart encouraged everyone who had an idea for a better oil burner, even inspiring editorial writers to take pen in hand, as did the editor of a Bakersfield paper: "The inventive genius of someone will someday confer a benefit on California, where coal for domestic uses is scarce and high priced, by devising a contrivance that will burn crude oil successfully in ordinary stoves. The future burner must act without steam and must be simple and easy to operate."

In his tussles with the coal merchants for the fuel market, Stewart discovered that he had one decisive advantage. The sailing ships that brought the coal as ballast arrived irregularly. Neither the coal merchants nor their customers could ever be sure of delivery. Oil Merchant Stewart was always ready to guarantee delivery on schedule.

One of the more promising markets was steamships. Stewart's first marine venture was the steamship *Pasadena*, whose owner installed an oil tank on top of the deckhouse, from which the burners in the furnace could be fed by gravity. The oil was atomized by steam, which necessitated a wood-and-coal fire to start the oil burning. Once the oil was ignited, the coal fire could be allowed to go out. Though this was a cumbersome operation, the owners were pleased with the test. Their satisfaction was short-lived. Soon after the *Pasadena* sailed on her maiden voyage, the oil fires went out because of too much water in the oil. Completely out of steam, the ship wallowed helplessly in the swells until she was rescued by a tug. Oil Man Stewart had to do some persuasive talking to avert a damage suit. He finally convinced the steamship man that in the future the Santa Paula refinery would deliver more dependable fuel.

Next he induced the owners of the tug *Waterwitch* to convert to oil. An unfortunate explosion forced the temporary abandonment of this craft. This event gave oil another black eye. Next the ferryboat *Julia*, plying between Port Costa and Vallejo, which had been converted to oil, was rocked by an explosion that ripped her apart, killing several people. The steamboat inspectors at San Francisco immediately canceled all permits to use oil as fuel. This forced even the *Pasadena* to switch back to coal as fuel. The steamboat inspectors even refused to allow Union to use oil as fuel on the company's first tanker, the *W. L. Hardison*, until the combined political influence of Bard and Hardison in Washington persuaded the authorities to overrule the local officials. Then, to cap the series of misfortunes, the *W. L. Hardison* burned.

Despite this bad start, which made the outlook for oil as a marine fuel seem bleak, Stewart persisted. One after another, shipowners agreed to try his burner. By perseverance, Stewart opened up a vast new outlet for the company's products. He celebrated the victory over coal by hanging on the side of the oil-burning tug *Rescue*, which the company had chartered to tow barges between Ventura and San Francisco, a huge sign proclaiming: "We Burn Union Oil for Fuel." This was the first advertisement for oil as a marine fuel.

Stewart won other converts to his oil-for-fuel gospel by donating hundreds of barrels of oil for experimental purposes. When the Los Angeles Iron and Steel Company was organized, the owners agreed to try oil on two conditions. One was that Stewart install burners for the tests at Union Oil expense. The other was that payment for the fuel be made in stock, of which Los Angeles Iron and Steel had plenty, rather than in cash, of which it had little. Stewart agreed. The steel company reported that oil cut its fuel costs to half. This convincing testimonial helped sell other industrialists. The directors of the Whittier State School agreed to try oil if Union would wait a year for payment, which had to be approved by the state legislature. The tests were a great success, and eventually the legislature appropriated the funds. In the years that followed, Union sold thousands of barrels of oil to the school and to other state institutions.

Next, Stewart turned his attention to the railroads. The railroaders were harder nuts to crack, because they hauled coal from the East and from Utah

OIL VS. COAL *Conversion of ships from coal to fuel oil was slow in evolving. Early installations proved faulty, and a tragic boiler explosion aboard the ferryboat* Julia *prompted an official ban on fuel oil for marine use that delayed the inevitable conversion for months.*

to California at a big profit. They refused to test oil burners in their engines. Union had become one of Southern Pacific's big customers, and it galled Stewart that the locomotives which hauled his oil to market used coal for fuel. But he was turned down every time he tried to get the Southern Pacific executives to try oil in just one locomotive. The persistent oil merchant then tackled E. H. Wade, the general manager of the little Southern California Railway Company, which later became part of the Santa Fe system. Wade pointed out that his company was small and had no money to spend on experiments. Anyway, his engines were doing all right with coal for fuel.

"Lend me a locomotive and we'll do the experimenting," offered Stewart. Figuring that he had nothing to lose, Wade promised to send a locomotive to the Union shops at Santa Paula. Stewart had mechanics make up an oil tank for the tender. Wade tried to back out of the deal on the grounds that he couldn't spare a locomotive. Stewart pleaded and cajoled. Some weeks later an old engine puffed painfully onto the spur track of the Union Oil shops in Santa Paula. Though the old locomotive had almost given its last wheeze, the mechanics went to work with zest, trying first one scheme, then another, for feeding oil into the firebox. But when the showdown test was made, the locomotive barely managed to move itself along at a snail's pace. The railroad men loaded up with coal and steamed back home.

[RAILROAD RECORD.]

PROVED A SUCCESS.

The Oil-burning Locomotive in Practical Use.

A Run from San Bernardino to Santa Monica and Return Without a Hitch.

The Los Angeles and Salt Lake Road Discussed by Col. Isaac Trumbo. Significance of Gen. Clarkson's Visit.

"LEND ME A LOCOMOTIVE"

First experiments in the West with oil as a fuel for locomotives were conducted by Union in a borrowed engine. Initial tests were disappointing, but by 1894 oil had been proven practical for railroad use.

Undaunted, Stewart turned the Union Oil mechanics loose on a new burner idea, collaborating with the railroad's mechanics over at the San Bernardino shops. Several burners were tested; eventually one with a flat nozzle that sprayed oil over a wide area was installed forward in the firebox. Came the day, late in 1894, when the little old locomotive powered by oil was hitched to a string of freight cars and pointed up the hill over Cajon Pass, one of the stiffest railway grades in the country. It pulled the train up the grade without any trouble. The railroaders cheered. The Union Oil men cheered. This was the culmination of a dream.

It was a dream that failed to pay off—for Oil Merchant Stewart. The Southern Pacific sent him a bill for $60 for the use of the tracks over which the engine had been moved from San Bernardino to Santa Paula and back. Their mechanical experts had been keeping a watchful eye on the experiment. Taking advantage of Stewart's demonstration, they converted a number of their engines to oil. But they bought their fuel from Union's competitors at cut rates. So did the Santa Fe, which shortly swallowed the little Southern California Railway Company. Then both railroads developed their own oil fields. The Southern Pacific even became a competitor when its executives organized the rival Associated Oil Company. Though Stewart had successfully demonstrated that oil was the fuel for Western locomotives, it brought him no business directly.

But indirectly there was a pay-off. The locomotives drank up oil so ravenously that the supply ran short and prices rose. The oil that Stewart sold to other industries returned a greater profit.

By 1895, the need for a new refinery was desperate. The old stills at Santa Paula were worn out and antiquated. More efficient methods of extracting products from crude had been developed. Stewart still wanted Union's new refinery located near a major market. Even Bard was beginning to see, for the first time, the importance of marketing. He and Stewart were named as a committee to check possible tidewater sites in San Francisco, Ventura, Hueneme, and Los Angeles. After their survey, Stewart reported: "We know now that the San Francisco field is occupied, and this one [Los Angeles] is not. One way to hold this ground is to occupy it. Los Angeles is to be the great city of the future, and if we occupy the ground now we may be able to lead in this business and control a market for such products as we can make right along for years to come."

Although Bard and the other directors sustained him, Union didn't locate in Los Angeles, because the city's leaders opposed a refinery and storage tanks as a great fire hazard. The opposition grew so vociferous that Stewart turned north. For $15,000 he bought, from the California Redwood Company, a sizable parcel of El Rancho Chino, a site that he and Bard had picked out when they visited the San Francisco Bay area the year before. He ordered modern equipment from Pennsylvania and made plans to move the company's refining operations from Santa Paula. Then, to his astonishment, Bard, who had joined him in choosing the site, vehemently objected to moving the refinery from Santa Paula. However, the Union board sustained Stewart, but as a sop to Bard agreed to his demands that the company sell its interests in the California Ink Company. The ink business, which later grew into a substantial industry, was dumped for $16,000, less than Union Oil Company had invested in it.

Bard, who still named five directors on the Union board to Stewart's four, adopted new delaying tactics to frustrate Stewart's spending. He notified the directors, in June 1895, that he would propose at the next board meeting that the company extinguish its debts by assessments on its stockholders. This was a shrewd move. Bard was wealthy, but the Stewarts were still oil-poor. Luckily, before Bard had an opportunity to present his scheme before the board, the company had sold so much oil that it was out of debt—temporarily. Stewart was able to go to his old banker, I. W. Hellman, by this time president of the Nevada Bank in San Francisco, and arrange for new loans for expansion. This time Stewart had more than hopes to offer for security. He told Hellman:.

"As collateral, we propose to give $40,000 worth of stock of the Mission Transfer Company, which is capitalized at $250,000, but which actually has paid in cash capital of $480,000 and has a yearly income of $48,000. The Mission Transfer Company is entirely free from debt, and we believe its stock to be a No. 1 security. The Union Oil Company is also out of debt, but is making additions to its plant which will require more capital than will be available from its current income. It has some 80,000 barrels of oil on hand in its tanks, a daily production of some 600 barrels, and has many thousands of acres of oil lands, which are worth several million dollars from an oilman's standpoint. During the past four years Union has paid $320,000 in cash dividends to its stockholders."

The double duties of president and general manager were proving too arduous for Stewart, whose health was failing. Bard was demanding a general manager apart from the presidency. On August 24, 1895, Stewart resigned as general manager, and F. L. Richardson was chosen for the office at a salary of $3,000 a year. At the same meeting, the number of directors was reduced to five. Inexperienced in the oil business, Richardson organized committees and appointed chairmen, of which Stewart headed the field department; Bard the pipeline and storage and transportation departments; W. L. Stewart, who had been appointed a director, headed the Los Angeles office; D. T. Perkins, the short-term former president, was in charge of refinery operations. Richardson

Torrey Canon Oil Co., by its proxy, Alex. Waldie, 7499 shares, voting No.

Mr Bard stated that he voted in favor of that for the Torrey Canon Oil Co, its power of attorney to him being of record and having been presented.

Mr Fenn objected to such vote being recorded, because no such power of attorney had been accepted by the Committee on Credentials.

Mr Bard called the attention of the stockholders to the proxy and to the fact that he was the only authorized agent of the Torrey Canon Oil Co. to vote at this meeting.

Mr Hardison remarked that he certainly thought Mr Bard was not in order, because the paper was not accepted by the stockholders.

Mr Bard stated that the paper had been presented.

Mr Hardison stated that the paper had been handed to the Committee, who examined the power and that the one held by Mr Waldie had been accepted.

Mr Bard stated that the report of the Committee had not yet been adopted.

Mr Hardison declared that it had been adopted.

Mr Bard called for the result of the motion to adopt the report.

The Chairman declared the motion lost.

Mr Fenn objected to a vote on the question being recorded, as being not before the house.

Mr Bard asserted that a claimant could not be deprived of the right which he has as a representative and of asserting his rights.

Mr Fenn said that he objected merely to the counting of the vote.

Mr Bard insisted upon his claim being recorded.

The Chair ruled that the report of the Committee on Credentials had

Directors' Meeting.

Immediately after the adjournment of the adjourned meeting of Stockholders, held this 29th day of November, 1898, the Directors elect, namely, Lyman Stewart, W. L. Stewart, W. G. Hughes, Thomas R. Bard and R. W. Fenn, came to order at 2:10 p.m. on Tuesday, November 29th, 1898, and held a meeting at the office of the corporation, at Santa Paula, Cal.

Officers of Meeting. On motion, duly seconded, Mr Lyman Stewart was elected to act as Chairman of the meeting.

Mr Bard objected to the other gentlemen undertaking to act as the Board of Directors of the Union Oil Company of California on the ground that none of them were properly qualified to act as such.

On motion, duly seconded, W. A. Carney was elected Secretary of the meeting.

Mr Bard objected and protested against either Mr Stewart acting as Chairman, or Mr Carney acting as Secretary of a meeting of the Board of Directors of the Union Oil Co. of California. For reasons of his protest, he offered in proof that neither Lyman Stewart, W. L. Stewart, W. G. Hughes or R. W. Fenn own shares of the Union Oil Company of California, bona fide, in good faith, and are disqualified to act.

Mr Bard here stated that if the others counted him in as one of the members of this alleged Board, he declined to act with them.

Mr Bard thereupon, to wit, at 2:15 p.m., left the room.

RECORD OF DISCORD

Minutes of the stormy board meetings of 1895–98 bristle with discord, reflecting the conflict between the Bard and Stewart factions.

had hardly taken over his new duties when he died suddenly. The burdensome chores fell again on the shoulders of Lyman Stewart, who was reelected both president and general manager, at a salary of $250 per month.

At the annual meeting on October 14, 1895, the smoldering feud between Stewart and Bard flared anew. Fed up with the sniping of I. H. Warring, Stewart demanded that the secretary be fired. Unable to attend, Bard evidently had some inkling of Stewart's intentions and filed a protest even before Stewart offered his reorganization program for the coming year. The directors backed Stewart, and Warring was out. Bard no longer had his man Friday in the key position.

Bard and Stewart ceased trying to cover up their mutual antagonism. Stewart appointed an all-Stewart staff to run Union Oil. When the Oleum refinery on San Francisco Bay was finished in February, 1896, he placed it under the direction of Frederick L. King, whom he had employed as the new San Francisco manager. Bard moved that the board repudiate Stewart's choice. The board sustained Stewart, who soon wished that it had overruled him. Though the new refinery was the last word in plants for making petroleum products, it failed to show a profit. Stewart moved F. H. Dunham, his veteran refinery man at Santa Paula, to Oleum to straighten things out. Bard was still bitter about the transfer of refining operations from Santa Paula to Oleum. Then on the night of June 29, 1896, fire gutted the Santa Paula plant. Oleum was the only place Union could refine its products. Fortunately, Stewart had contracted for half of the capacity of the tanker *George Loomis*, built by the Pacific Coast Oil Company. The *Loomis* was supplemented by the barge *Enoch Talbot*, which carried crude from Ventura and Los Angeles to Oleum and brought products back to Southern California.

By 1896 Stewart's dream of a pipeline to carry the products to tidewater and tap the markets of the world began to shape up. Union's new wells in the Olinda fields not far from Los Angeles had become important producers. Stewart ordered a 4-inch pipeline laid from Olinda to Los Angeles to compete on better terms in the Los Angeles market. Since the line had greater capacity than the production from Union's wells, he bought crude from other producers and pushed it through the pipeline, showing a nice profit. The following year he extended the line to San Pedro to deliver the oil to ships. As the Los Angeles Basin and Orange County fields poured out their flood of oil, this line grew into a pipeline network.

Other products than fuel oil were becoming important and profitable items. One of these was asphalt, formerly a "black elephant" by-product of the refinery. The heavy California oil left an asphalt residue which made an excellent material for paving roads. While Eastern producers shipped kerosene to the West, selling it cheaper than Western kerosene, Western oil men could beat the Easterners in the asphalt end of the business. In 1896 Stewart consigned an entire shipload of asphalt to the East. A solid trainload of asphalt left California for New York in 1897. The highest grade of asphalt on the market at the time was barreled under Union's Diamond-U brand. Laboratory experiments were

OLEUM REFINERY, 1897— "LARGEST ON THE COAST"

When the Contra Costa News *published this drawing of the two-year-old refinery at Oleum in 1897, it noted that the plant was the largest establishment of its kind on the coast, had cost $150,000 to build, and handled 30,000 to 50,000 barrels of petroleum every month. "There is no industry in the county with a brighter future before it," concluded the paper.*

TWO-HORSEPOWER TANKER

For the first decades after opening of the California refineries, fuel oil and other petroleum products were delivered by horse-drawn tank wagons. Motive power ranged from two horsepower to six mulepower. This tank wagon is tethered at the gate of the Los Angeles refinery.

beginning to pay off in another use, asphalt for roofing. Out of this experiment grew a roofing paper, which in turn gave birth to The Paraffine Companies, Inc., whose Pabco products were a direct offshoot of Union's early research.

By the mid-nineties, the Union brand was on a score of accepted petroleum products. These included a new item, hitherto a volatile drug on the market, gasoline for gas engines, including those that powered gas buggies. Another was naphtha for use in stoves. There was benzene for mixing paint and varnishes, a distillate for cooking and heating stoves, and still other distillates used by city gas companies for enriching gas made from coal. Union was also marketing a dozen different types of lubricating oils and greases, seven kinds of asphalts, kerosene, and of course the No. 1 product, fuel oil.

The glut of oil from the mad Los Angeles scramble to make hole had turned, by 1897, to a shortage, temporarily at least. The Southern Pacific was forced to reconvert locomotives back to coal burning. Union crews were drilling with 12 strings of tools to boost production. Despite his eagerness to find more oil, Lyman Stewart persuaded the directors to resolve "that hereafter no work shall be carried on on Sundays, except in such cases where the field superintendent shall be of the opinion that the cessation of such work shall seriously affect the life of the well or permanently diminish its production."

Union's growth was attracting attention, not only nationally but overseas. Late in 1897, Mrs. S. S. Lightfoot of New York was granted an option for the purchase of Union Oil for $3,500,000. She represented some potential buyers

WIZARDS OF UNION TOOL COMPANY

Union tool-dressers and machinists had built up a reputation as mechanical wizards who could re-design or modify almost any kind of oil-field machinery. Proud workmen in Santa Paula shops of Union Oil built this steam engine in 1896. From this start developed the great Union Tool Company.

in London. Other buyers were in the market for Union Oil, too. In 1896, Standard Oil of New Jersey had offered to buy all of the physical assets of the company. The directors rejected this proposition, but Standard renewed the effort to buy in July, 1898, when it proposed to purchase the entire capital stock of the Union Oil Company of California. This time, Stewart was receptive to the Standard offer, provided he could retain an interest in the company. Standard's president, John D. Archbold, sent word back that it was all or nothing. The negotiations were broken off.

In 1897 the directors employed R. W. Fenn, a civil engineer and a director in Bard's Torrey Canyon Oil Company, to make a survey of Union's operations. Fenn's report was something of a sensation. It proved statistically how tankers could have saved Union much of the $600,000 paid in freight to ship oil to San Francisco during the previous six years. Pipelines would have saved the company's Los Angeles market. A company-owned tool and supply house would have saved Union a small fortune in the purchase of equipment.

Impressed by Fenn's report, the directors authorized Stewart to build a 10,000-barrel tanker. But Bard managed to stymie the appropriation for a pipeline and headed off the efforts to build up a tool company. The latter had an interesting background. Realizing that he had missed out on the Los Angeles City oil fields, Stewart had tried to recoup by opening a branch of Union's Santa Paula tool shops, which could sell tools, pipes, and machinery to the hundreds of Los Angeles wildcatters. Union's tool-dressers and machinists had built up a reputation as mechanical wizards who could redesign or modify almost any kind of oil-field machinery. The Hardison & Stewart Oil Company had also founded the Santa Paula Hardware Company, which served as a supply department as well as a hardware store. But Bard persuaded the directors to sell the hardware company to W. T. McFie, the manager, who opened up in Los Angeles and soon built up a prosperous oil-well supply house.

Biding his time, Stewart sounded out manufacturers on the possibility of buying supplies, not only for Union but for other oil companies. The American Tube Works agreed to sell at factory prices, if Union would establish a separate company to handle its products. The American Tube deal meant a saving of around $23,000 a year. Over the vigorous objections of Bard, the directors authorized Stewart to organize the Union Oil Well Supply Company, a name soon changed to Union Oil Tool Company, and later to Union Tool Company. Taking over Union's machine shops, stocks, and tools, the new company established branches in Los Angeles, Santa Maria, Coalinga, as well as in Santa Paula, and immediately became a prosperous subsidiary.

Lyman Stewart continuously worried about his drillers' sins and prayed for their oil-blackened, unsaved souls. His habit of dropping in unexpectedly on field jobs often jolted his eardrums when they tuned in on the rough oil-field language. One incident finally galvanized him to action. Arriving unannounced at a drilling job in the Torrey Canyon field in 1898, he caught the drillers stretched out in the shade, while a sweating boy pumped a bellows for the furnace. The sweating youngster was obviously tired. Stewart walked over to the lad, glanced at the sleeping men, then said sympathetically: "Well, son, this is pretty heavy work for a fellow your size, isn't it?"

"Mister, she is a — — — and you can tell the whole — — world I said so," the boy replied, adding in sizzling oil-field terms his opinion of the sleepers.

Horrified, Stewart backed out of earshot. At the next meeting of Union's directors, he got authorization to build a chapel in Torrey Canyon and to employ the Reverend Mr. Johnson to conduct services.

Stewart and Bard were drifting farther and farther apart. At the eighth annual meeting of stockholders in November, 1898, the showdown occurred. Bard attempted to jump the gun on Stewart in the election of directors for the Sespe Oil Company. He also counted on control of the Torrey Canyon Company board. This meant control of the Union board. Stewart realized he had been outsmarted. In the office of R. W. Fenn, the engineer employed to survey the Union properties, Stewart covered his face with both hands, saying: "It's all up. I'm a ruined man."

Fenn asked what was the matter. Stewart explained the trick by which Bard had got the jump on him.

"Well, Mr. Bard has forgotten one thing," said Fenn. "He has only two directors on the board of the Torrey Canyon Oil Company. You have two. I am the fifth and deciding man. I will cast my vote for you."

Fenn's vote abruptly changed the balance of power on the Union Oil board as well. When Bard heard that Fenn had swung over to Stewart, he flew into

MAINSTAY OF UNION OIL *Torrey Canyon field as it appeared in 1897 when Union Oil's entire production for the year was around 125,000 barrels, and 56,000 barrels of it came from these few wells.*

FOR THESE MEN, SPIRITUAL SOLACE

Concern for the spiritual welfare of the oilfield workers prompted Lyman Stewart to persuade the board of directors to authorize a chapel at Torrey Canyon for such men as these so they could be encouraged to give up profane habits.

a rage, threatening to wreck the Union Oil Company and accusing Fenn of accepting a bribe to support Stewart in the decisive contest.

From this point, no holds were barred in the battle for control. Bard had one last card up his sleeve. He threatened legal action to force the withdrawal of the Torrey Canyon Oil Company out of the Union orbit, on the grounds that Torrey's articles of incorporation did not authorize the company to hold or vote stock in another corporation. This move would have wrecked Union Oil, because Stewart had done so much drilling on the Torrey Canyon property at the expense of other holdings that the Torrey wells were a "must" in Union's marketing program.

Bard's price for calling off the threatened suit was dissolution of all the holding companies and distribution of Union stock direct to the holders. To avoid a costly lawsuit, which he might lose, Stewart agreed. This dissolution late in 1898 meant that Bard might possibly buy up enough stock to control Union Oil Company entirely. When the new stock was distributed, however, Stewart and the stockholders he regarded as allies owned 50.6 per cent, and Bard and his friends 39.5 per cent. The Hardisons, no longer actively interested in the company, owned 7.4 per cent. Other stockholders held 2.5 per cent of the stock. Lyman Stewart was boss of Union Oil by a margin as thin as a coating of lubricating oil.

But the margin was sufficient to carry out Stewart's proposal that his thirty-year-old son, Will, be promoted to general manager, with a salary of $300 per month; also to carry an appropriation for the building of a temperance rendezvous in Torrey Canyon, Union's largest producing field, and the employment of N. W. Blanchard to run it. The rendezvous was "to contain a temperance bar, library, reading room, gymnasium, etc., for the purpose of giving men and boys a place to spend their evenings and keep them out of saloons."

The board meeting of November 29, 1898, opened in an atmosphere charged with hostility. Bard protested every proposal, including the election of Stewart as president. He lost every round and left in a bitter mood, vowing that it would be Stewart's last meeting as president if any more stock came up for sale. He had the money to buy, the Stewarts didn't.

Before long Bard was aware that the Stewart faction seemed quite sure of themselves for men on the brink of financial disaster. Bard made inquiries. He learned that Stewart had called a secret meeting of friends among Union's stockholders to organize a holding company whose purpose was to keep the "Bard camp" from ever regaining control of Union Oil. The conspirators had organized early in 1899 the United Petroleum Company, headed by Lyman Stewart, with a capital of $1,500,000 consisting of 15,000 shares at $100 par each. Immediately upon incorporation, United Petroleum offered to exchange two shares of its stock for one share of stock in the Hardison & Stewart Oil Company. This offer was accepted by the owners of about two-thirds of the stock. When Hardison & Stewart Oil Company was disincorporated, along with the Torrey Canyon and Sespe Oil companies, the United Petroleum Company became owner of 26,941 shares of Union Oil Company of California stock. This gave United Petroleum control. By means of this financial juggling, Lyman

WILL STEWART TAKES HIS FATHER'S JOB

By 1898 it was apparent that the pressure of double duty as president and general manager was too much for Lyman Stewart. He resigned the managerial post and was replaced by his son Will Stewart, who as secretary of Union knew more about the company's manifold activities than anyone else, including, probably, his father.

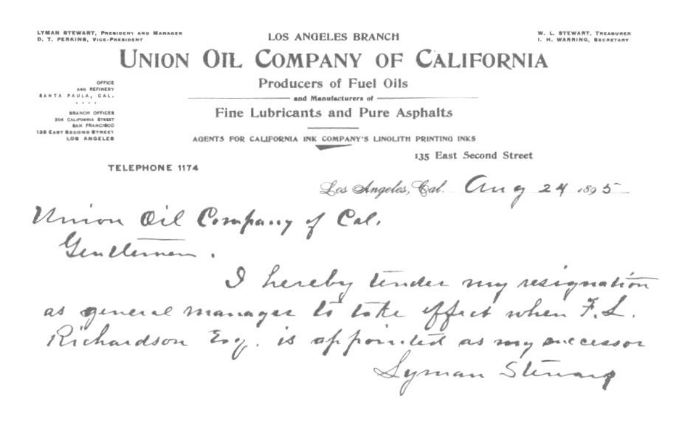

LYMAN STEWART, PRESIDENT AND MANAGER
D. T. PERKINS, VICE-PRESIDENT

LOS ANGELES BRANCH

W. L. STEWART, TREASURER
I. H. WARRING, SECRETARY

UNION OIL COMPANY OF CALIFORNIA

Producers of Fuel Oils
and Manufacturers of
Fine Lubricants and Pure Asphalts

AGENTS FOR CALIFORNIA INK COMPANY'S LINOLITH PRINTING INKS

OFFICE AND REFINERY SANTA PAULA, CAL.

BRANCH OFFICES 204 CALIFORNIA STREET SAN FRANCISCO
135 EAST SECOND STREET LOS ANGELES

135 East Second Street

TELEPHONE 1174

Los Angeles, Cal. Aug 24 1895

Union Oil Company of Cal.
Gentlemen.
I hereby tender my resignation as general manager to take effect when F. L. Richardson Esq. is appointed as my successor
Lyman Stewart

Stewart aimed to thwart Bard permanently. The objective of United Petroleum was revealed in two letters written by Stewart to the Reverend W. J. Chichester of Titusville, an old friend of Stewart and a stockholder in Hardison & Stewart: "With the control thus lodged in a single company where it is subject to the action of the board of directors instead of a single individual," he explained, "there can be not only a safer and more stable policy adopted for Union, but a much more advantageous price can be obtained in case of a sale by being able to sell the control of an established company."

Caught napping by Stewart's tactics, Bard swung into action. In the spring of 1899, about three months after Stewart had launched United Petroleum, Bard called together his friends and associates to organize the United Stockholders' Associates. On the assumption that Stewart didn't yet have control, they went to work to line up more stock than Stewart could control through United Petroleum.

This financial contest occurred in the midst of one of the wildest speculative oil-stock booms in California history. Investors figured that, if both Stewart and Bard wanted Union Oil stocks, they should buy them, too. They bought not only Union but stocks of companies that had no oil wells or oil lands, even under lease.

The showdown came on November 28, 1899, at the annual stockholders' meeting of the Union Oil Company, when United Petroleum Company and United Stockholders' Associates came out in the open for the first time. Tellers began counting the stock controlled by each holding company. United Petroleum, represented by Lyman Stewart, held 26,941 shares of stock. United Stockholders'

Associates, represented by Thomas R. Bard, held 16,685 shares; and there were 6,374 unpledged shares. Bard realized that even if he could buy all of the 6,374 unpledged shares, he would still fall far short of control.

Ignoring Bard completely, the directors elected as officers of the company Lyman Stewart, president; W. L. Stewart, vice-president and general manager; Alexander Waldie, treasurer; W. A. Carney, secretary; R. W. Clark, assistant secretary. Bard remained a director, temporarily. Hundreds of new investors became Union Oil Company shareholders for the first time.

"The state has gone oil mad," reported the Los Angeles *Express*. "A feeling of speculative unrest is abroad. Los Angeles operators just in from Kern County say that a large number of people in that county appear to be actually oil crazed. The county has been staked off by prospectors for miles in all directions from Coalinga, and men, and women too, are up there holding down claims with shotguns. Others have built barbed-wire fences around their possessions, fearing that the land or the precious stuff underground may be carried off."

Having been named United States senator, Bard decided to retire from the oil business. The holding company he had organized, the United Stockholders' Associates, still held a big block of Union stock, roughly one-third of the shares. In Los Angeles, a group of alert young businessmen were looking for op-

NEVER BEFORE WAS THERE SUCH A BOOM IN OIL PROPERTIES

The People of California Seem to Have Gone Oil Crazy—Locations Being Made at a Rapid Rate and Speculation Is Rife.

The state has gone oil mad. A feeling of speculative unrest is abroad, extending from San Francisco down through the San Joaquin valley and the coast counties to Los Angeles and Orange counties.

Oil men in Los Angeles, who have made the pumping of petroleum as fuel a study, say that they have never seen anything like it before, and the conditions do not justify the boom in oil properties, real and on paper, which is just now at its height.

The United States land office in the Potomac block is daily visited by scores of persons seeking information for filing on mineral lands, as oil prospects are termed. The filings are made in the office of the county recorder.

In Los Angeles county the oil belt is now presumed to reach the ocean, touching the Pacific in the vicinity of Santa Monica. Derricks are going up out in that district at an alarming rate, and the country is covered for two miles beyond the Los Angeles military academy.

Los Angeles operators just in from Kern county say that a large number of the people in that county appear to be actually oil crazed. The country has been staked off by prospectors for miles in all directions from Coalinga, and men, and women, too, are up their holding down claims with shotguns, others having built barbed-wire fences around their possessions, fearful that the land or the precious stuff under ground may be carried off.

A crowd of Pennsylvania boomers is said to be in control of the share market in San Francisco, where chamber maids, restaurant girls, clerks, blootblacks and newsboys are stated to be speculating, as was done during the Comstock mining excitement 18 years ago. Some of the shares on the market represent, of course, an investment which can be made good. A large majority of them are, however, known to be merely bubbles, with nothing to keep an equilibrium when the inevitable day of reckoning shall have arrived.

The filings of oil prospects under the mineral act will have aggregated, it is estimated, over 100 for Los Angeles county for November at the end of the month.

OIL FEVER IN THE NEWS

California newspapers ran voluminous coverage of the oil industry during the first decades of its phenomenal growth. Every new development was reported and major events drew headlines and, even, editorial page comment.

portunities to make investments. The group consisted of J. S. Torrance, William R. Staats, Frederick H. Rindge, W. S. Botsford, and John B. Miller. Staats, who was a friend of Lyman Stewart, asked the latter where his group might most profitably invest in an up-and-coming new oil industry. Stewart suggested that Staats try to buy from Bard the holdings of the United Stockholders' Associates. The Staats group secured an option, late in 1900, on the United Stockholders' block of stock. Staats had to raise more money. J. Henry Meyer, of San Francisco, one of the bankers he approached for a loan, checked with Bard to find out why he was selling stock in a company which appeared as promising as did Union Oil. Bard's reply was revealing:

"For some time the Stewarts have been desirous of expanding the business beyond the scope of our original scheme, and for such purpose to borrow or otherwise raise large sums of money," he wrote. "This we might consent to if the management were entrusted to more competent and conservative men, but we oppose the present proposal to increase the capital from 5 million to 10 million dollars.

"The Stewarts are honest and, in the best sense, trustworthy. But they are not competent to carry on the great business of the company and are unwilling to trust it to more capable men. I learn, however, that they have indicated to our option holders that they are disposed to let the new men share in the management. They have come to the realization that the new blood is needed to give the body corporate new health and vigor."

Bard made his final exit from Union on December 18, 1900, when his resignation as director was accepted. The Torrance-Staats syndicate, purchasing the holdings of the United Stockholders' Associates, bought in as an investment and "to furnish new blood and eliminate the friction of the Bard interests," as Torrance later explained. Torrance advocated getting rid of the two holding companies, considering them a menace to Union Oil because they automatically created factions within the company. Lyman Stewart agreed to dissolve United Petroleum Company if United Stockholders' Associates was disbanded. But Torrance didn't push the idea. Later he changed his mind and even favored continuing United Petroleum as a means of stabilizing the direction of Union Oil after United Stockholders Associates dissolved.

"I regarded the service of Lyman Stewart as worth more to Union Oil than all the other directors put together," Torrance said. "His salary was insignificant as compared with the value of his services. He possessed courage that was almost unlimited; he knew every feature of the oil business, the drilling end, the territorial end, the marketing end. But I did not have very much respect for his ability as a financier."

The holding companies were so confusing to the public that it was difficult to make even bank presidents understand the relationship between them and the parent company. In time Lyman Stewart's control of Union Oil became a Frankenstein monster, resulting in the very one-man decisions he feared most from Bard. But it was Lyman Stewart who made these decisions, precipitating Union into two more decades of financial turmoil.

CHAPTER FIVE 1900-1910

Wildcatters' Paradise

THE TURN OF THE CENTURY ushered Union Oil Company of California into a wildcatters' paradise. The last year of the old century had put Lyman Stewart and his son Will firmly at the helm. The hostile Bard minority interest in the company had been replaced by a sympathetic group of Los Angeles financiers who were looking for a long-time investment. J. S. Torrance had replaced Bard as director and as spokesman for the new minority group. The company's capital was doubled to $10,000,000.

More important, the board had authorized Lyman Stewart to staff the company with new blood. He had found and employed young, vigorous men for the key posts. One was his son, Will, who as general manager took over the responsibilities that formerly completely exhausted Lyman Stewart and frequently forced him to take to his bed. Another was John Baker, Jr., an extraordinary salesman who was placed in charge of Union's installations in San Francisco and at Oleum. A third was William W. Orcutt, a young geologist who started as a civil engineer. A fourth was Frank Hill, an inventor and a wizard at solving drilling and production problems. Union started the new century with a winning team.

The time was ripe. California was emerging as the world's leading source of oil. Where the oil hunters formerly had dug for liquid gold only around oil seeps, they now knew, from the holes sunk by adventurous wildcatters, that petroleum might be found almost anywhere under the state's rolling hills and many valleys. The ancient seas under which much of California once had lain had left their deposits of marine life and vegetation, which time and pressure had turned into petroleum. Lyman Stewart's ambition, as he explained later, "was to acquire enough of these lands to control the market."

GUSHER THAT BECAME A LEGEND

World's greatest gusher, Lake View No. 1, hurled a fountain of oil 20 feet in diameter, 200 feet high, spewing out 9 million barrels of high-gravity crude in the 18 months of its activity.

UNION'S VERSATILE "HANDY ANDY"

Frank Hill invented, among many other things, the oil-well cementing process while Union's field superintendent.

In 1900, as this hard-hitting team swung into action, the keyman and quarterback was Will Stewart, a personality the very antithesis of his devout, soft-spoken, precise father. Born in the shadows of the Titusville derricks, Will Stewart literally grew up in oil. He was hale and hearty, a ready mixer either with the boisterous field crews or with his father's dignified financial associates. The early struggles of Hardison and Stewart had taught him to take in stride the heartaches and triumphs of the oil gamble. As a youngster he had written, in boyish hand, many of the letters dictated by his bedridden father during the several life-or-death crises of the partnership.

Despite their differences of personality and outlook, it was Will on whom Lyman Stewart leaned in his dark moments. He confided in his son, saw to it that Will learned the oil business from the drilling rigs up. As a schoolboy in Santa Paula, Will had worked at odd jobs around the shop. Later when the Stewarts moved to Los Angeles, Will spent his summers in the oil fields, working as a roustabout. Lacking enthusiasm for book learning, he had quit the University of California, where he was a football star in 1890, to work full time in the oil fields. He liked the grimy, sweaty labor of the drilling crews. The drillers liked him. Here was one Stewart who could smoke, drink, chew with the best—or worst—of the oil-field rowdies. Will Stewart was one of their kind.

Lyman Stewart's urge to save the souls of his employees was not shared by Will. The father could never reconcile himself to his son's tolerance. These contrasting viewpoints between father and son became more apparent as the years went on. Lyman became more evangelistic as Will grew more tolerant of men's weaknesses. This was illustrated one day when Lyman Stewart urged Will to fire a drilling foreman who had reportedly showed up on the job sober but gradually became inebriated.

"No man who starts work sober but ends up half drunk should be retained on Union's payroll," Lyman Stewart declared.

Will Stewart replied that he knew the man well, that he was a hard-working and dependable employee. Will stated emphatically that any report that the man showed up sober and ended up drunk was false. Pleased to have this assurance from his son, Lyman Stewart relented. Will Stewart afterward explained, but not to his father, that the man was a good driller and "whoever reported him as starting out sober and getting drunk on the job was a liar, because the man never does show up sober. He is always half drunk when he starts to work."

Will Stewart's winning personality had been demonstrated when the directors promoted him to general manager on December 13, 1898, at a salary of $300 per month. The appointment was vehemently opposed by Bard, who became so angry that he resigned his directorship in protest. It was characteristic of Will Stewart's directness that he talked things out with Bard and persuaded him to hold the resignation in abeyance. Before the year was out, Bard proposed to the board of directors "that our general manager's salary be increased to $375, as he is working very hard and spending his whole strength in the interests of the corporation." The directors went even further: they made Will Stewart vice-president as well.

Will Stewart had been instrumental, late in 1899, in persuading the dynamic young salesman, John Baker, Jr., to take over as manager of Union's San Francisco branch with responsibility for seeing that the Oleum refinery ran more efficiently. Oleum had been losing so much money that the directors seriously considered selling or leasing the refinery. Will Stewart and John Baker persuaded them not only to keep it but to double its size. Later its capacity was trebled. Young Stewart and ebullient Johnnie Baker became a winning sales team that sold oil faster than Union's oil hunters could find it.

The oil hunt was in good hands, too. In 1899 Lyman Stewart had hired William W. Orcutt, a former Santa Paula boy who had worked at odd jobs around the Union refinery before entering Stanford University to study engineering and geology. When the Union board of directors approved his employment, the secretary described Orcutt as "a civil engineer, but inexperienced in the oil business, who will look after the company's interests in Fresno and San Benito counties." This was a masterpiece of understatement. A huge, calm man with great self-control, Orcutt had an insatiable curiosity about the earth's formation that soon won him a wide reputation as a petroleum geologist. He attracted and inspired other young geologists, who later became topflight oil finders. Many of his devoted disciples rated Orcutt as the father of modern oil geology.

Orcutt's early geological-survey parties, the last word in their day, consisted of a spring wagon drawn by two horses broken for saddle, in case the going got too tough for wheels. The wagon carried a grub box, blankets, a Brunton compass, picks, kegs, maps, a bale of hay, a sack of grain, a water bucket, a 10-gallon water keg, and a canvas canteen normally filled with water fortified with something stronger. The oil hunters always carried a few extra sides of bacon, because this medium was highly prized by the Basque sheepherders with whom the field geologists sometimes camped at night. The herders usually knew if there were any oil seeps or unusual outcroppings of rocks in the neighborhood.

Their tips led the rock hunters to remote sites which eventually became productive oil fields. After combining this rugged field experience with his book knowledge acquired at Stanford, Bill Orcutt was ready to establish for Union Oil the first petroleum-geology department in the West.

When the board of directors okayed Orcutt's employment, they also authorized the hiring of "a young man of good education and some geological knowledge and experience as a mountaineer, but also experienced as an oil man, to be employed to hunt for oil indications and seepages, and to secure information in regard to the development of oil properties in this state, the understanding being that the latter would work for a very small salary and his expenses."

The young fellow who fitted this description was Frank F. Hill, who in his teens had worked as a helper for Union Oil drilling crews and later had rassled barrels and boxes and machinery, and delivered equipment. A Handy Andy with a genius for invention, Hill was forever coming up with an idea for doing a job better, or faster, or easier. It was the day when Union field crews needed such a problem solver. Drillers were punching holes still deeper, and the old reliable cable and plunging bit no longer did the job. The technique of banging holes into the earth hadn't changed much since the Chinese evolved the spring-pole method for drilling salt wells. Sinking a hole was fast and cheap until the drillers reached depths of around 700 feet, where the spring pole no longer yanked the bit up fast enough. The drillers had rigged up steam engines to turn bull wheels, which in turn rocked the walking beams that lifted heavier bits and dropped them four times as fast as men hopping on and off treadles could do it.

Then the drillers reached the 2,000-foot depth, and the manila ropes developed so much stretch that the walking beams could no longer lift and drop the bits effectively. Steel cable solved the problem until wells hit 5,000 feet; then the steel in the cable became so heavy that huffing steam engines had trouble lifting the weight. It looked as though drillers had gone about as far as they could go. This was where the science of drilling oil wells stood in 1900, when Frank Hill's fertile imagination began turning up a series of inspirations that made Union's new oil fields famous for the "firsts" evolved by its drilling crews.

Now and then, wildcatting new areas turned into a Wild West movie thriller. One Union crew headed by Hill undertook to drill on a lease near Maricopa on the west side of the San Joaquin Valley. When they arrived at the drilling site, they found themselves looking into the barrels of shotguns.

"They told us to get the hell out of there, and get out fast," recalled Hill. "I recognized one of the gunmen as a Los Angeles Superior Court judge. Well, we were drillers and not gun fighters, so we got the hell out, like they said. Later, we went back and drilled, but that was after our land boys had leased the acreage all over again from the crowd that ran us off in the first place."

Oil derricks were springing up all over the upper San Joaquin. On the heels of the Coalinga boom came discovery of the McKittrick field, then the Midway Sunset field. Across the valley, east of Bakersfield, the Kern River field burst into production in 1900. Then came the discoveries in the Santa Maria and Lompoc valleys in Santa Barbara County. With each of these oil strikes, or ahead of them, Lyman Stewart was busily "picking up land," by purchase or by lease.

In 1900, as in previous years, Stewart needed more money for new oil lands than the Union Oil treasury could provide. He achieved a new milestone in money-raising by first borrowing $8,153, and later $16,400, "for necessary corporate uses" from the Protestant Episcopal Church diocese of Los Angeles. More amazing yet, he borrowed from Thomas Bard, whom he had ousted from the company. Apparently Bard, who had been appointed United States senator, held no animosity toward Stewart after the long struggle for control of the company was ended. These loans tided the company over until the sale of newly issued stock yielded much-needed funds for expansion.

By 1901 the reorganization of Union was complete—just in time. Heavy overproduction of crude inspired Will Stewart to launch an ambitious offshore sales program. Baker invaded Hawaii and signed five-year contracts to deliver fuel oil to three sugar plantations on the island of Maui for their cane-grinding mills. Though vessels carrying lumber from the Pacific Northwest to the Antipodes were able to bring back Australian coal as ballast and dump it cheap in Hawaii, the sugar-mill operators found oil so much more efficient that Baker soon lined up more Hawaiian orders than the company had facilities to deliver. To service this profitable new market, Union constructed storage facilities in the Islands and built the barkentine *Fullerton*, with a carrying capacity of 16,000 barrels. Before the year ended, the storage capacity of tanks on three Hawaiian islands totaled 227,000 barrels.

Los Angeles emerged as the hub of Union's operations. The head offices were moved there in 1900. When the Union Oil Tool Company was organized on January 10, 1901, the shops were located in Los Angeles to service not only

EVOLUTION OF DERRICKS

Oilfields around McKittrick, California, went into production at the turn of the century. Heavy wood derricks, right, were replaced by steel, left, and eventually by the modern movable rigs in the background.

"GEOPHYSICAL SURVEY," 1906 VERSION

Union geologists use airplanes, ships, automobiles—and Old Dobbin in rough country. In the earlier years, the bright and eager young geologists fresh out of college were a pain in the neck to the old-time oil hunters who were witching the California hills with willow wands and bailing-wire "doodlebugs."

the company's crews but those of competitors. On one of his trips East, Lyman Stewart had hired another Titusville man, Edward Doble, to design improved drilling bits and other oil-field tools. Doble eventually built the Union Tool Company into one of the industry's outstanding supply companies.

By 1901, when W. W. Orcutt was authorized to organize the first petroleum-geology department set up in the West, his insatiable curiosity had already made him a widely respected geologist. In 1901 Orcutt decided that he had to find out why Lyman Stewart and Dan McFarland in 1888 had found no oil in their wildcat well at Brea tar pits, where heavy tar was oozing out of the ground. While probing the pits, Orcutt spotted on the surface of a pool of asphalt a vast mosaic of white bones, resembling those of no animal he had ever seen. Orcutt had stumbled onto the skeleton of an extinct giant ground sloth, a strange, armored creature that roamed the earth millions of years ago. Further probing revealed more skulls and bones of other prehistoric animals. Orcutt's find electrified the paleontologists quite as much as the world's greatest gusher would have aroused an oil hunter. Subsequently, G. Allan Hancock, owner of the Brea pits, assigned sections of it to a dozen different universities and museums for exploration. In a short time bone hunters, picking up where Oil Hunter Orcutt had left off, assembled complete skeletons of saber-toothed tigers, giant mastodons, prehistoric elephants, horses, wolves, condors, and other ancient life—the richest paleontological bonanza so far found.

That year Lyman Stewart realized another of his ambitions, the Fullerton-Whittier pipeline, which carried oil to tidewater at San Pedro Harbor, where it was pumped aboard the company's barges. This was the beginning of Union's Los Angeles pipeline network. In 1901, the directors approved the policy of shutting in wells when oil was cheap and buying it from other producers. This not only conserved the company's reserves but also established Union Oil as a major outlet for independent producers.

On August 1, 1901, Union's board made a far-reaching decision to remain an independent, when the company was invited to join a syndicate of California fuel oil producers. The minutes of the August 1, 1901, meeting describe the debate of this policy as follows:

"The general manager called attention of the board to the proposed consolidation of fuel oil interests in the state and pointed out in detail the advantages which, in his opinion, would secure to this company if it were to include some of its properties in the proposed combination and he urged the board to take favorable action in regard to the matter. The president also stated his views, which were, in the main, in sympathy with the proposed movement. The affirmative arguments of the Stewarts were controverted by Torrance and Botsford, who advanced the proposition that this company, with its transportation facilities already in operation, and its management second to none, is destined of itself to form the nucleus of a great organization and ought to be free to act independently of any

TANDEM TOW TO HAWAII

Barkentine Fullerton, *16,000-barrel capacity, carried oil to Hawaii at the turn of the century. She was once towed fully loaded to the islands over 2,500 miles of open sea.*

PALEONTOLOGICAL BONANZA
The insatiable curiosity of Bill Orcutt, early geologist for Union Oil, led him to probe into the Brea tar pits west of Los Angeles, where he noticed on the surface of the pool of asphalt a mosaic of white bones, resembling no animal he had ever seen. Orcutt had discovered the skeleton of an extinct giant ground sloth and the skulls and skeletons of other ancient animals. Orcutt's find electrified the scientific world. Sections of the pits were assigned to a dozen different universities and museums. In a short time some 300 complete skeletons were recovered and pieced together—one of the richest of all paleontological finds.

other concern, and that they, as representatives of one-third of the capital stock of the company, could not and would not ratify, in the present state of the organization of said consolidation, the transfer to it of any portion of the properties of this company."

By 1902 Union was expanding over the Southern California oil-field area. Lyman Stewart secured options on 50,000 acres in the Santa Maria and Lompoc area, which geologists decided had all of the features of an American Baku, indicating a potential comparable with that of Russia's great oil-field discovery. The company also acquired valuable holdings in the Kern River and Coalinga areas in the San Joaquin Valley. That year Stewart reported "the company's new acquisitions of oil lands, with the extensions to its plants . . . , have cost approximately $2,031,000, but they have doubtless doubled the value of its capital stock, and possibly quadrupled it."

To handle the San Joaquin Valley production, a new refinery was built at Bakersfield. The barkentine *Fullerton*, carrying 16,000 barrels of oil each trip, was plying steadily between California and Hawaii, where John Baker had lined up B. F. Dillingham's Oahu Railway and Land Company as agent for the sale of oil as fuel throughout the Islands. This deal also gave Union a tidewater terminal in Honolulu Harbor.

One of Union's interesting firsts occurred in 1902 when the steel-hulled steamer *Whittier*, with a carrying capacity of 11,000 barrels, was ordered built in San Francisco. The revolutionary design of the *Whittier* ushered in a new era for oil-carrying tankers. Her engines were set far aft to reduce the fire hazards. The cargo tanks were an integral part of the hull, giving the vessel greater stability in rough weather. In the bow was space for dry cargo. Galley and quarters for engineers and crew likewise aft, with deck officers amidship convenient to the bridge. The ship established a new maritime pattern, and after that nearly every tanker built has followed her basic design. The *Whittier* was built by the Union Iron Works of San Francisco for $198,000.

In spite of the tremendous expansion in new wells drilled, new ships, pipelines, refineries, and storage tanks, Union's board took time, at Lyman Stewart's request, to order that "the Reverend Alex Hardie of Piru be paid $25 for holding religious services in the company's Torrey camp." It also authorized him to borrow up to $100,000, without waiting for the board's approval, to close land deals such as the 60,000 acres he picked up in Santa Barbara County that led to the discovery of the vast Santa Maria field.

In 1903, when the tanker *Whittier* went into service, the wisdom of building a steamer with surplus power in her engines was dramatically demonstrated. Union's marine engineers soon found use for the *Whittier's* extra horsepower. Sawing off the masts of the schooner *Santa Paula*, they converted this ship into a barge which the *Whittier* pulled up and down the coast, almost doubling the delivery capacity of the pioneer steel tanker. When a critical oil shortage developed in Hawaii, the *Whittier* was dispatched to the Islands with not only the *Santa Paula* but the *Fullerton* in tow. No such tandem tow over 2,500 miles of open sea had ever been attempted before, and many mariners thought it was foolhardy. But the *Whittier* left California loaded with 11,000 barrels of oil, followed by the *Santa Paula* with 8,200 barrels and the *Fullerton* with 16,000 barrels, the largest single cargo of oil ever sent to sea up to that time. In ten days she reached Hawaii; on the twenty-eighth day after her departure, the *Whittier* returned to California with the two barges in tow, mission completed.

In 1903, the Standard Oil Company made its third attempt to absorb Union Oil Company. This time Standard proposed to purchase all of Union's refineries, its marketing and transportation facilities, leaving Union Oil in the business of only producing and selling crude oil. During the negotiations Stewart stipulated as one of the conditions of sale that Standard purchase 40,000,000 barrels of Union's crude oil. Standard's negotiators decided this would be too big a purchase, and the deal fell through.

A short time later Edward L. Doheny, who had set off the great Los Angeles oil boom at the end of the nineties, was invited to join Union's board of directors. He accepted. He was permitted to buy 1,000 shares of treasury stock, with a year's option for 1,500 more shares.

Union's board wanted the advice and experience of Doheny to such an extent that they approved his purchase of treasury stock, even though the executive committee had reported shortly before that "in all the history of the oil industry, there probably has never been an oil producing company holding such an advantageous position as Union Oil, with the bulk of its large holdings of oil territory either abutting to or connected by pipelines to tidewater. . . The company's oil properties and other resources are so valuable that the directors

REVOLUTIONARY TANKER

The Whittier *signaled a new era for tankers, for nearly every tanker built since has followed her basic design. Her engines were set aft to reduce the fire hazard. The cargo tanks were an integral part of the hull giving the vessel greater stability in rough weather.*

OIL FOR HAWAII

The Santa Paula, *a full-rigged schooner with a capacity of 8,200 barrels, was the second tank ship operated by Union Oil. She made her maiden voyage to Honolulu in 1900, the first time Union made an offshore delivery in its own ship. Eventually she became a barge.*

have hesitated to dispose of any of the treasury stock, considering it inadvisable to do so, owing to its intrinsic value being so much greater than the market price. . . ."

Rumors of mergers continued to plague Union Oil. One reason for this eagerness to get aboard the Union band-wagon is revealed in the extensive land-acquisition and drilling program for the year. Lyman Stewart added 4,800 more acres in the Santa Maria fields and bought 3,400 acres known as the Sansinena tract in the Rancho la Habra near Whittier, a property that remained a "sleeper" for half a century before becoming one of the company's richest producers. Drillers brought in new wells on the company's Coalinga holdings and made a remarkable discovery in the Lompoc area, where Frank Hill had become the drilling superintendent, at a salary of $175 a month.

The Lompoc-field discovery was a dramatic eleventh-hour race against time. Stewart had rounded up options at grazing-land prices until his holdings in the area totaled 72,000 acres. The options allowed barely enough time to sink exploratory wells. Union's wildcatters drilled frantically. Frank Hill, whose crew brought in the discovery well in the field, has described the battle of men against nature.

"We were drilling Hill No. 1, a wildcat in the Purisima hills near Lompoc. We had to race against time, because the option was a short one. In those days crews worked on twelve hour tours. We landed in Lompoc the night of July 4, 1902, with our steam cable drilling rig. By the next day we had located the drilling site, staked out roads, knocked together a bunkhouse. Then we put up tanks and built the derrick. We located and cleaned out two springs. Seventeen days after we hit the field, we spudded in our first well. We drove ourselves day and night. Shift hours were forgotten in the excitement. Saturday night on most drilling jobs then was pretty much of a let-down time after a week of hard work. The last Saturday night no one left the rig. A little after dark we struck oil. We had won our race by three days."

Hill tried to keep the strike secret. Around midnight he caught a train to Los Angeles, "to report to Uncle Lyman." Frank Garbutt, one of the company's directors, met him the next morning with his brand-new gasoline buggy. They chugged off to Sixth and Lucas Streets, where Lyman Stewart lived. Just as they reached the house, Stewart came out of the door with his Bible under his arm. They knew he never did business on the Sabbath. Seeing Garbutt and Hill, Stewart knew something was up. He shifted from one foot to the other. They did the same. Nobody mentioned oil wells. Stewart wanted to know and they wanted to tell him, but here it was, Sunday, and business was taboo. Finally Stewart asked, guardedly, "What have you got?"

"We've got an oil well."

"What does it look like?"

"Pretty heavy," said Hill, taking a bottle out of his pocket. "Here is a sample."

Stewart stuck his finger in and rubbed the smelly stuff back and forth between a finger and thumb. Finally he said, "We'll take up the options tomorrow. This is Sunday—had you forgotten?"

Not another word was spoken. Stewart continued down the street to church, acting as if he had expected oil all the time but still knew nothing about it.

Stewart's dogmatic insistence that all work be suspended over the Sabbath often interfered seriously with field operations. Oil wells had a way of coming in on Saturday night. Stewart finally relented to the extent of agreeing to a resolution of the board of directors that field superintendents might decide whether halting work arbitrarily would seriously affect the life of the well. After that the field bosses interpreted the new policy quite liberally—without reporting their decisions to headquarters.

In 1903 Frank Hill made oil-well history in the Lompoc field with a new first—the first cementing job completed deep down in a well. Water flowing into oil wells from higher strata slowed down production, even threatening the very life of the field. Drillers had tried shavings, chopped rope, burlap, sacks, and other materials to try to close up the space between the casing and the walls of the hole. These expedients were sometimes effective temporarily, but eventually the water poured back into the hole. At Lompoc, after the drillers had tried everything they could think of to cut off the flow of water as the casings were sunk deeper, Hill designed a bailer that would allow the mud to ooze out through the holes instead of bailing it out. He filled the bailer with cement and lowered it to the bottom of the casing, where the cement was allowed to seep out. It shut off the running water temporarily, but not permanently. But the temporary success inspired Hill to a new idea, a packer at the bottom of the tubing, which allowed the crew to pump cement down into the wells and force it up back of the casing. This experiment quickly evolved into a successful technique for cementing behind casings to shut off the water-bearing sands. Casings were perforated only in strata that yielded oil. Though Hill's "crazy idea" was worth millions of dollars every day in crude delivered to the refineries, Union's inventors were too busy to patent their idea. Later others patented the process, obliging Union to pay royalties on the idea Union crews had originated.

Cementing wells soon became such a common practice that its importance in oil production is often overlooked. Cementing enabled drillers to go down deeper to the big pools. It also doubled the amount of oil recovered from the sands. Without it much of the oil produced in California in succeeding years never would have been recovered. In the Santa Maria and Lompoc fields, the oil producers formed an association, later duplicated in other fields, known as the Producers Cementing Company, which undertook to cement out water for all wells. In time this voluntary agreement was superseded by a law, authorizing the state mineralogist to see that all oil wells were cemented.

Edward L. Doheny, who had bought into Union two years previously and become a director, resigned in 1904. Doheny had his own dreams of an oil empire. Asked why he was made a member of the Union board, Lyman Stewart explained later, "I wanted the benefit of his counsel. There was no personal or private reason for his election. I had no personal influence or power over him. He was not the type of character to be dominated or dictated to."

Asked if he ever attempted to influence Doheny, Stewart replied, "No, except on one occasion. This was when Mr. Doheny offered a resolution increasing the salary of the president of Union Oil to a thousand dollars a month. I refused the offer then and asked that the salary be made $3,000 a year." Nevertheless, the board voted Lyman Stewart the $12,000 salary, the first real "wages" he had received since he founded the company.

Out in the fields Union's sweating drilling crews were punching down some of the most prodigious producers in oil history to that time. Oil wells big and little, whether producers or dusters, are designated in the company's record by field and number, such as Adams No. 28 or Hartnell No. 1. Every now and then a hole in the ground develops a personality, for no particular reason, and the drilling crews honor it with nickname. One such was Hartnell No. 1 in the Santa Maria field, a spectacular well that came in on December 2, 1904. Drillers began calling the well "Old Maud" soon after it was spudded in. Old Maud was a lucky mistake. Had she been located where she was supposed to have been drilled, Old Maud would have been just another number in the oil-well records. Jack Reed, later drilling superintendent for Union Oil, and a member of the crew which brought in Old Maud, tells why:

"We really caught it after we started drilling," he said. "Back in those days, 1904, nobody thought a few feet one way or the other made much difference. Our rigging crew was supposed to put the enginehouse here and the derrick

HE DUG FOR OIL WITH PICK AND SHOVEL

In April, 1893, Edward L. Doheny and his helpers, with picks and shovels, dug a wildcat hole, a shaft 4 by 6 feet, on a lot in downtown Los Angeles. At a depth of 46 feet they dipped up four barrels of oil a day. This unusual well touched off the hectic Los Angeles city oil scramble. Doheny later became a director of Union Oil and a world-wide oil figure.

there. It was a hot day, and when the boiler accidentally fell off the wagon where the derrick should have been, we left it right there and put up the derrick where the enginehouse should have been. The boss was mad, but not quite mad enough to make us tear down a whole day's work and start over again.

"That was our good luck. We spudded in June 22, 1904, and on December 2, when no one was expecting much of a well, Old Maud starts rumbling. Then with a roar, a column of oil and gas shoots up through the rig floor to a height of 150 feet. Oil begins pouring down the gullies and creek beds. We have the biggest producer the world had ever seen. We can't control it, what with 12,000 barrels of oil pouring out every day. We don't even have tanks or pipelines big enough to handle the flow, so we scrape up a series of earth dams. Pools of crude collect for miles below as the flow continues day after day for three months."

"Yes, and by mistake one of the workmen closed a valve," cut in Frank Hill, who was superintendent on the job. "This completely shuts in the well, which is under great gas pressure. This starts the oil flowing through the formations, and for hundreds of yards around every squirrel and gopher hole begins to spout oil. The surrounding fields are full of miniature geysers of oil. We finally get the valve opened and the pressure released. The oil begins spurting through the casing again instead of the squirrel holes."

Petroleum engineers, who came to scoff, excitedly measured the flow in weir boxes, and found the 12,000-barrel-a-day figure to be correct. In the first one-hundred days, Old Maud yielded one million barrels. The well flowed for over

CEMENTING MADE OIL WELL HISTORY *Mixing cement preparatory to plugging Hellman 53, well in Dominguez Field. By using cement behind the casing, water-bearing sands are shut off leaving open only those strata that yield oil.*

two years and yielded nearly three million barrels before it was finally put on the pump.

Even this spectacular strike failed to excite Lyman Stewart outwardly.

"After we had guessed Old Maud's tremendous yield I phoned Frank Garbutt, our treasurer," recalled Frank Hill. "He asked what I figured the well would make. I told him 10,000 barrels a day. He yelled, 'Spell it out; it sounded like you said 10,000 barrels.' So I spelled it out for him."

"Garbutt next called Will Stewart and told him we had a 10,000-barrel producer. Will also asked that the figure be spelled out and commented, 'That's a good story, anyway!' Will phoned his father, who asked, 'Did you say 10,000 barrels?' So for the fourth time that night we 'spelled it out' over the phone. Lyman Stewart said, 'Thank you. I have been expecting something big from up there. Good night.' "

Old Maud continued producing for fourteen years, and even then was good for 250 barrels a day. One day in 1918 the 8-inch casing collapsed. Since it looked like an expensive job to fish the tubing and rods out of the hole, the field men decided to drill a twin well nearby, to be known as Hartnell No. 7. Hartnell No. 7 was located 65 feet away, on the exact spot where they had been told to put the first Hartnell derrick in 1904. Hartnell No. 7 produced only 95 barrels of crude on its best day.

Old Maud, like the proverbial cat, had many lives. In 1943, when the wartime demand for more and more oil became critical, the field superintendent decided to clean out the well and see if Old Maud wouldn't produce again. A crew succeeded in yanking out 1,765 feet of tubing and rods, a working barrel, a joint of anchor, some chain tongs, and pieces of practically everything that was ever fished out of a well. When a new pump was installed, Old Maud yielded 175 barrels a day, once more becoming one of the field's top producers.

Hartnell No. 1 not only proved an important factor in the development of the Santa Maria field but also opened up financial purse strings and established drilling as a "paying and legitimate industry." The gusher launched a boom in oil stocks.

Old Maud also launched a gusher of rumors along Spring Street, Los Angeles' financial row, where it was whispered "on good authority" that Standard Oil already secretly owned Union. Again Stewart issued an emphatic denial, declaring "the policy of Union Oil Company in the future will be, as it has been in the past, that of an independent producer without alliances."

In 1906 Union completed a 6-inch pipeline from Santa Barbara and San Luis Obispo county fields to Port Harford where the company built tanks with a storage capacity of a quarter of a million barrels. From this and from the San Pedro Harbor terminal, Union was ready to supply the world with oil. John Baker, Jr., by now manager of sales, manufacturing, and the marine departments, was marketing all over South America and even in Europe. The company had acquired a tanker fleet to deliver fuel oil to distant markets. Nothing was too big for Johnnie Baker to tackle. When President Theodore Roosevelt launched his drive to complete the Panama Canal, started decades before by the French, Baker hit on the idea of a pipeline across the Isthmus of Panama. On his next Eastern trip, he dropped in at the White House to talk pipelines. T. R. thought the pipeline idea was bully and promised that when it was authorized the Union pipeliners should build it. Later when powerful Eastern interests tried to win the concession, T. R. stood by his word. He issued the permit to the upstart young California company. The line was laid alongside the Panama Railway's right of way and was completed by the end of 1906. Though it proved useful in supplying the canal builders with oil, new fields in South America and Texas made it uneconomical to pump California oil over the Isthmus to the Atlantic. It was a spectacular building feat, but only three tanker loads of oil, about 150,000 barrels, were ever pumped from ocean to ocean.

In one year Baker traveled 50,000 miles, peddling California's liquid black gold in Central and South America, Europe, and along the Atlantic Coast of the United States. Baker not only doubled the sale of Union's asphalt in the New York area but persuaded dealers along the Atlantic Coast to handle Union's other refinery products. He sold so much oil that Union's directors were forced to buy four first-class steamships and to lease two others to handle the offshore orders.

Baker's sales expeditions had their humorous side, too. To get big orders quickly, he entertained lavishly. Union's accountants, accustomed to the trifling expense accounts turned in by Lyman Stewart, scrutinized Johnnie Baker's swindle sheets and gasped. When a clerk showed one of them to Lyman Stewart, he, too, was speechless, particularly when his eyes spotted such items as wine and cigars. Stewart took the matter up with the executive committee, which "disapproved the charges made against the company for wine and cigars and extravagant hostelry expenditures properly belonging only on the personal accounts of employees." It ordered the accounting department to withhold payment on "any unseemly figures not in the interests of the stockholders."

Will Stewart was absent when this resolution was passed. When he heard about it, he voiced his opposition so emphatically that the executive committee, including Lyman Stewart, reversed the order at the next meeting. The board authorized the auditor to "pass items in reasonable amounts" covering "telegrams, telephone, cablegrams, porter tips, waiter tips, bellboy tips, cab hire, baggage transfer, laundry bills, theater and entertainment tickets, dinners (with the names of the parties entertained)."

Baker's sales were so prodigious that he was able to report, in 1905, that the tanker capacity "increases our water transportation fully five times, enabling us to reach out for the markets of the world"; also, that "enlargement of the Oleum refinery has been started and we contemplate an increase of five times its capacity."

That year, 1905, apparently worried about rumors in the stock market, Stewart wrote to stockholders that, "as disquieting rumors emanating from an unreliable but doubtless always the same source are from time to time put into circulation to the effect that your company is owned or allied with the Standard Oil Company, we positively assert that neither the Standard Oil nor any of its allied companies is either directly or indirectly interested in your company. And neither is your company nor any of its subsidiaries interested directly or indirectly in the Standard, or any of its auxiliaries or allied companies."

Nevertheless, the Stewarts were apprehensive lest they lose control of the company. When a group of Los Angeles financiers, including some of Union's directors but not the Stewarts, formed a new company, the Union Stock & Bond Company, for the purpose of buying Union Oil securities, they had reason to

OLD MAUD—GUSHER THAT LAUNCHED A BOOM

Hartnell No. 1, called "Old Maud" by the Union Oil crew that drilled her, came in for 12,000 barrels a day on December 2, 1904, and was world's greatest gusher at the time.

worry. There was a catch in the proposition, which Union's board had to accept in order to get the money. With each $850 bond, the purchaser could buy 14 shares of stock at $60 a share, considerably less than the market value. Luckily Old Maud gushed to the rescue and produced a million barrels of oil in the first hundred days, which was the equivalent of a million and a half dollars. The sale of this oil saved the situation. The public rushed in to buy Union Oil stock.

The new issues of stock in 1905 were snapped up in such quantities that it became doubtful whether the Stewart family could maintain control of the company, even though they voted all of the shares held by United Petroleum, which they controlled, as a block. Since one holding company had saved him in 1899, Stewart decided that another might do the same for him in 1905. He and his family and close associates organized, in June of that year, the Union Provident Company, capitalized at 5 million dollars. The Stewart-

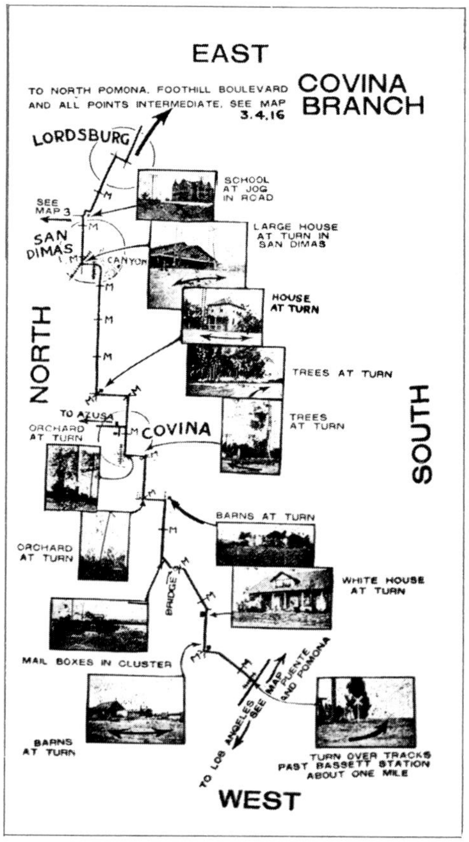

HOW NOT TO GET LOST

First road maps issued by Union Oil in 1910 in booklet form, gave very practical road directions, needed in the absence of highway signs. This map covered a stretch of highway near Covina, a suburb of Los Angeles.

controlled United Petroleum held a controlling interest in this new corporation. The new company's articles of incorporation declared that it was formed "to buy shares of the Union Oil Company to the extent of not more than 50,000 shares," a limitation increased later to 250,000 shares when Union Provident's capitalization was boosted to 25 million dollars.

"Why couldn't United Petroleum Company acquire enough stock to give it a majority, instead of organizing a new holding company?" William Stewart was asked later.

"We simply didn't have the money," he replied.

The performance of Union Provident Company was little short of financial wizardry. From time to time, as treasury stock was offered by Union Oil, the stockholders of United Petroleum and Union Provident were given first chance to purchase the shares, provided they bought a share of Union Provident for each share of Union Oil. With the new capital thus acquired, Union Provident bought more Union Oil shares. By this financial sleight of hand the smaller United Petroleum was able to control the larger Union Provident Company, which in turn controlled the still larger Union Oil Company and its 20 subsidiaries. Thus the Stewarts, with roughly a one-eighth interest, were able to keep an ironclad hold on Union Oil—until a reckoning came at a later date.

Later, in his decision dissolving the Stewart holding companies (October 2, 1916) Judge Louis Myers summarized the corporate strategy of the Stewarts as follows:

"At all times from the organization June 20, 1905, of the Union Provident Company until its dissolution in September 1916, the United Petroleum Company has held slightly more than a majority of the issued and outstanding stock of the Union Provident Company. In this way, since the organization of the Union Provident Company, through devices and instrumentalities of the United Petroleum Company and the Union Provident Company, the Stewart family, while being directly and indirectly the real and beneficial owners of much less than half of the issued and outstanding stock of the Union Oil Company, by controlling the United Petroleum Company, controlled the Union Provident Company, and through Union Provident Company dictated the election of the several boards of directors of the Union Oil Company, and thereby controlled and dictated the management and policies."

The company's need for capital to expand seemed insatiable. Before 1905 ended, Union had a new subsidiary, in cooperation with the Michigan Steamship Company. It was called the Union Steamship Company, capitalized at $5,000,000. Union Steamship bought four tankers. Frank Garbutt, also head of transportation, wanted another half million within six months. John Baker, Jr., of the sales department, budgeted half a million every six months for the offshore sales program. J. S. Torrance, head of finance, sought $2,700,000 to pay for lands purchased and to meet payments on ships, tankers, and the expanding pipeline system. To raise this money, 75,000 shares of treasury stock were sold. In this way Union's capitalization increased by leaps and bounds. Union's stock sold quickly on the open market.

By 1906, a year of disaster, Union needed all of this new money. In April the catastrophic San Francisco earthquake and fire burned Union's storage facilities and records and delayed work on the Oleum expansion program. While the refinery at Oleum was being revamped at considerable expense, the markets were supplied from the refinery at Bakersfield, which was operating at full capacity. In the midst of this trouble, an employee inspected the company's large storage tank at Portsmouth, Oregon, with a lighted lantern. The explosion, resulting in his death, destroyed the storage plant and wharf. Simultaneously, at sea the tanker *Santa Rita* ran into a storm so rough the crew had to jettison much of her cargo to save the badly damaged ship. The newly completed Panama pipeline, instead of proving a money-maker, turned out to be a white elephant. Nevertheless, on May 10, 1906, General Manager W. L. Stewart was authorized to "negotiate a contract for sale and delivery of fuel and refined oil in China, Japan, and other countries of the Orient." This was the beginning of an important expansion across the Pacific.

Despite labor troubles, depressed markets, fires, and earthquakes, President Lyman Stewart reported, at the end of the year: "We are thankful that the past year, in the way of substantial progress in the company's business, has been the most satisfactory of any in its history, notwithstanding disappointment in the amount of net earnings resulting from a depressed market, inadequate transportation facilities, deplorable labor conditions, and so forth following the earthquake and fire. Among the causes for gratitude we have special reasons for thankfulness that the Lord has kept your company from business entanglements and unlawful alliances."

Union swung into 1907 in an atmosphere of optimism. Owing to a dispute over assessments on the franchise tax in the city of Los Angeles, amounting to $80,000 a year, the company had moved its corporate headquarters to the Oleum refinery. John Baker, Jr., reported that "capacity of the Oleum refinery was so increased that during the month of December it refined as much oil as during the year 1905. Our gasoline, benzene, engine distillates, and illumination oil are the best on the market." The company had 207 producing wells, 330 miles of pipelines, storage capacity of 2,204,000 barrels, and a fleet of 10 tankers, not counting barges. In a letter to Lyman Stewart, Baker summed up the picture in 1907: "Our company in the short space of twelve months has risen from local to national prominence, and at the present time occupies a very prominent position in the oil business of the world, for our transportation facilities, together with our Panama line, enable us to reach the markets of the world."

Baker was authorized to spend $200,000 for a refinery site near Philadelphia for the manufacture of asphaltum and distillates for the Eastern markets. Supersalesman Baker wanted to be assured of adequate oil before signing big contracts in South America. Replied Stewart: "If there is any question, even the slightest, about the quantity of oil to meet these contracts, we'll put more tools in the field; if necessary, we'll run thirty, forty, fifty strings of tools in our territory. You get the contracts, we'll get the oil."

All this expansion required still more millions of dollars, and large sales of treasury stock were made, mostly to Union Provident. In 1908 ten new stills were added to the refinery at Oleum to meet the booming demands of the markets. Capitalization of Union Oil was increased from $10,000,000 to $50,000,000, with $24,000,000 in shares issued. The Union Oil Tool Company was merged with the American Engineering Company to form a new $1,200,000 subsidiary, known as the Union Tool Company. Peripatetic John Baker, Jr., was all over the globe. At the August 6 meeting, the board authorized him to investigate the oil situation in the Orient and report back. The following month Baker was authorized to purchase 78 acres at South Chester, Pennsylvania, for a refinery site. But before this could be done, Union's go-getter salesman resigned to go into private business as an asphalt merchant, sometimes in competition with Union. At the end of the most prosperous twelve months in the company's history, Lyman Stewart reported: "In spite of the financial depression, disastrous fires, and disappointing delays in the completing of wells (thereby curtailing its income) the Lord has given your company a more prosperous year than any that has preceded it."

On June 21, 1909, there occurred a small but significant incident which attracted no particular attention at the time. To meet an urgent company need for cash, Lyman Stewart personally underwrote a $375,000 issue of treasury stock offered to investors. As it turned out, the issue was oversubscribed and Stewart did not have to buy any of the stock personally. However, he was entitled to the customary underwriter's commission of 2½ per cent. This he

BOILERS FOR THE DESERT *Hauling boilers across the desert for pumping stations on the Producers' Pipe Line from San Joaquin Valley to the sea was part of race to build the 240 miles of 8-inch line in record time.*

declined to accept. But he did ask Union's treasurer to put the commission's equivalent into a "fund for the purpose of promoting temperance and morality among the men." Always a religious man, Lyman Stewart was becoming a zealot.

By 1909, California had become the leading oil-producing state in the country. The most prodigious production was in the San Joaquin Valley, where 150 small companies had banded together as the Independent Oil Producers Agency, producing a large share of California's 52-million-barrel output in 1909. Neither Standard nor Associated Oil, the two largest bulk buyers, would pay the small producers what they thought they should have for their crude. L. P. St. Clair, spokesman for the independents, long on friendly terms with Union executives, both in the field and in the marketing end of the business, asked the Union management in 1909 to take over as sales agent for the organized smaller independents. A ten-year agreement was reached whereby Union undertook to handle all the output of the Producers Agency, guaranteeing it the same price that Union got for its own products. This vast river of oil, doubling the amount that Union already had to market, was snatched away from Associated Oil Company, owned by the Southern Pacific, and from Standard Oil Company, which had bought up the Pacific Coast Oil Company. Nearly all of this oil came from the San Joaquin Valley fields, where Union had been unable to match the two competitors because of the high cost of rail transportation.

To move this river of oil from the San Joaquin Valley fields to the sea, Union and the Producers Agency jointly organized the Producers Transportation

PIPELAYING THE HARD WAY, 1909

Laying pipe in the early 1900's took large crews of burly workmen. Pipe was laid across arid wastes and mountains. Pipeline enabled the small independent producers in the valley to meet the competition of the giants.

Company, which rushed completion of an 8-inch pipeline from the Valley fields to tidewater at Port Harford in San Luis Obispo County, later known as Avila. At the time this was considered a colossal pipeline project, calling for 240 miles of pipe, 15 pumping stations, field tankage to store 27,000,000 barrels of oil, plus the wharf facilities at Port Harford. It was an expensive project. Before Union and the Agency members had finished it, they had spent $4,500,000—a million more than had been estimated.

"We were in a tremendous hurry," Will Stewart said by way of explaining the great cost. The first pipe was laid on July 29, 1909, and the first oil was delivered at Port Harford in the following March. In one respect the new pipeline exceeded all expectations. It was planned for a 20,000-barrel-a-day capacity, but when the pumps began pushing, they drove more than 30,000 barrels a day over the hills to the sea. When it was built, Union and the Producers Agency were fifty-fifty partners, but as the members of the Producers Transportation Company wished to dispose of holdings, Union picked up shares and eventually owned the line completely.

In 1909 the directors approved the partial financing of the Outer Harbor Dock and Wharf Company to create a terminal at San Pedro Harbor adequate for accommodation of ocean-going steamers—another of Lyman Stewart's big ideas for the future. This brought Union's list of subsidiaries up to 22. They included interests in a dozen oil companies and several pipelines, steamship companies, and a sizable ownership in two oil-well supply companies. Yet that year the board authorized a committee, consisting of Lyman Stewart and W. W. Orcutt, to purchase additional real estate for building stables to house the horses that carried the company's refined products to the customers in the Los Angeles area. Though it was by this time supplying gasoline to early automobile owners, Union was still in the horse-and-buggy days.

On September 16, 1909, Lyman Stewart persuaded the board of directors to employ as the new treasurer of Union Oil, Robert Watchorn, who was destined to become one of the controversial figures in the corporate history. Asked by one director why he wanted Watchorn employed as treasurer, Stewart replied: "He is a very popular man. Every time he appears at a Presbyterian convention, he is greeted with a Chautauqua salute." A religious enthusiast, Watchorn soon became a dubious influence over Lyman Stewart.

By the end of the year, Union held 229,804 acres of oil land, much of it already proven by wildcat wells. W. W. Orcutt, head of the land department, reported that "activity in the oil industry of California during the year has been the greatest in the history of the state." This drilling activity led to a glut of oil on the market—74 million barrels in a single year. R. W. Fenn, head of the manufacturing department, reported a new topping plant at Port Harford, a new acid plant at Oleum, and other new facilities which resulted in great economies of operation. Alex Sclater, the new manager of the sales department, reported hopefully that "population of the Pacific Coast has grown so rapidly, both north and south, that there is no lack of opportunity for us to expand from year to year, and we believe that we are well equipped to take care of the natural increase resulting from this country's expansion. We are quite sanguine."

Union had more than its share of the prodigious California oil wells, among them Hartnell No. 1 (Old Maud), which had produced 2,000,000 barrels in six years; Santa Maria No. 10, which yielded 1,700,073 barrels in three years; Santa Maria No. 5, which yielded 1,662,000 barrels; Folsum No. 2, which was good for 1,635,000 barrels in five years; Columbia No. 1, which produced 887,000 barrels in four years; Hobbs No. 6, which delivered 581,000 barrels in five years; Newlove No. 12, which yielded 255,000 barrels in two years; and, the most prodigious of them all, Lake View No. 1, which spewed out 5,600,000 barrels in its first nine months. Lake View No. 1 is a story in itself. It climaxed a decade that was known as "wildcatters' paradise" in California.

Lake View No. 1 happened to be Union's well because of the policy of Lyman Stewart, who if unable to buy or lease land found other ways to buy or get oil. Frequently he loaned or rented a rig to a struggling independent operator. This made loyal friends for Union Oil among the independents and also gave the crews

PIPELAYING TODAY

Smaller crews are needed today. Every joint in the steel line is welded and tested under pressure to insure against breaks.

drilling on Union's leases something to shoot at, because the independents made hole fast. How fast it was possible to drive a hole into the earth was recalled by Jack Reed, the Union Oil driller whom Stewart once loaned along with a rig to a small neighboring operator.

"That driller knew his stuff," said Reed later. "I was young and hated to see him do more than I did. Besides I felt the prestige of the company was at stake. So we dug 5,000 feet in just 42 days. That was a record. I showed that fellow he couldn't make hole faster than we could. The faster he worked, the faster we worked. We set a record for drillers to shoot at for a good many years to come."

Hitting a gusher is a rare experience. After Adams No. 28 and Hartnell No. 1, Union's drillers never expected to get a still bigger one. Hundreds of drillers made hole all their lives without ever being on hand when a gusher came in. Charles Lewis Woods, one of the early-day Union drillers, had even worse luck—he didn't even hit a producing well of any description for so many years that he earned the distinctive, if unflattering, nickname, Dry Hole Charlie. Year after year, Charlie drilled nothing but dusters. In one year he drilled seven consecutive holes for A. P. Johnson near Newhall and punched down eight more holes for Graham and Loftus near Gilroy without a sign of oil. Woods finally concluded that he was jinxed in California and struck out for other fields. He did no better away from home. He returned and drilled a well 4,500 feet deep for Union Oil at San Juan Capistrano. It was the inevitable duster. Then he was sent to the Summers field at Gardena, where he went down 5,000 feet. Another dry hole. Next he put down bone-dry Francis No. 1 on the Dominguez Rancho.

Woods was a top-flight driller. Where a difficult well had to be wildcatted on a lonely spot on top of the hills miles away from supplies, he was the re-

DRY HOLE CHARLIE'S GRAND SLAM

After an unbroken series of dusters that gained him the name Dry Hole Charlie, drilling superintendent C. L. Woods made up for it all by bringing in the biggest gusher of all time, Lake View No. 1. Reflected in an oily sea of its own making, Lake View gusher roared out of control for 18 months of stupendous production.

sourceful man for the job. The brevity of his reports was impressive. They invariably read: "It was a dry hole."

After drilling dusters in just about every field the company was prospecting, Woods' big moment came early in 1909 on Union's Sage & Webster lease in the San Joaquin Valley. Nearby, seven partners with a big hunch and a little capital held a mining lease alongside the road between Taft and Maricopa. The group called their operation the Lake View Oil Company. They had hard luck from the start. Two of the partners were rig builders. By erecting their own 72-foot derrick, they were able to begin making hole on a shoestring. But soon after they began drilling, their bit wandered off at a bad angle. They had barely enough cash in the treasury to buy one string of tools. When the cable broke and their tools vanished down the hole, they came over to borrow fishing equipment from the Union crew working nearby. After fishing for days, they hooked the lost tools. Then the cable parted again. Everything was lost—tools and fishing equipment as well.

Now strictly up against it, the partners asked Union for more help. The company loaned them C. E. (Barney) Barnhart, one of Union's experienced drillers. He retrieved the lost tools. They began to drill again. At 1,800 feet, the partners ran completely out of dollars. The hole was not deep enough to be conclusive, but far too deep to be abandoned. They asked Union to take over. Already occupied with four wildcatting operations in the area, none of them showing much promise, the company didn't hanker for another. However, to help the luckless wildcatters, Union's management agreed to complete the Lake View well in spare time, if and when drilling crews were idle. Though the partners were willing to sell their entire lease cheap, Union bought only 51 per cent of it, leaving the wildcatters 49 per cent. The Union management figured

LAKE VIEW'S LAST GASP, 1911

The great gusher ceased production as abruptly as it was born. An army of oil-drenched men built sandbag dams around the well and in the mouths of canyons in an attempt to hold the 9-million barrel outflow.

the land could be used later as a site for storage tanks in the pipeline system it was planning to build.

Barnhart continued as superintendent, with Dry Hole Charlie as foreman on the job. No one expected much, but during odd hours the well finally was punched down to 2,200 feet. Union's nearby Sage lease test well had priority. The Sage well sanded up the night of March 14, 1910; so when the midnight tour reported for duty, the men were told to go on over to the Lake View job and make some more hole.

Two hours later they pulled the bailer from the bottom of Lake View's 2,200-foot hole. To their surprise they found it dripping with oil. They hurriedly dropped it again and again, and each time it struck oil at a higher level. Here, in the darkness, was a gusher aborning! By dawn, March 15, water, shale, and sand began burbling and tumbling out of the well. Just as Dry Hole Charlie came on the job at eight the next morning, a column of gas and oil roared hundreds of feet high, drenching the surrounding area.

Hour by hour the roaring increased as the tremendous stream doubled and redoubled in volume. It grew stronger and stronger, blasting out a crater so deep and wide that the derrick and all the drilling equipment disappeared. No one knew how to cap such a terrific geyser of oil. Dams were hurriedly thrown up to catch the torrent of crude, which by this time was a greater flood than oil men anywhere had ever seen, surpassing even Hartnell No. 1. Dry Hole Charlie was dancing like an Indian. "My God, we've cut an artery down there," he yelled.

Calling every man in the area to help, Woods and his crew frantically piled up earth to throw a temporary reservoir around the well. It was filled and overflowing in no time. Woods sent out a desperate call for help. Hundreds of men responded. They worked hour after hour, in clothing drenched with oil, which was raining down over several acres. The gusher roared on. Crews moved down the hill and tossed up a dam, creating a 16-acre reservoir known as the Cornfield. They were just finishing work on this basin when an earthquake shook apart the walls of the sumps they had built earlier—a torrent of oil came cascading down into the Cornfield.

For months the well spouted completely out of control. It was estimated that 125,000 barrels of petroleum was hurled out in the first twenty-four hours. Thirty days after the first gush, the flow was gauged by engineers at 90,000 barrels a day. From the Cornfield a 2-mile-long 4-inch pipeline, leading to eight 55,000-barrel tanks, was installed in only four hours. Never had a line been laid so fast or under such desperate circumstances. These tanks filled while crews were rushing completion of the 8-inch Producers pipeline over the mountains to Avila on the coast.

"What we feared most," said Dry Hole Charlie, "was an early rain. A flash flood could have spread our ocean of oil down over the valley below. To head off this kind of disaster, we recruited an army of 600 men and dammed up the mouths of canyons with earth walls 20 feet high and 50 feet thick. Down below we scooped out storage for 10 million barrels of oil. We had nine million barrels stored up before the gusher calmed down."

Lake View's torrential flood of oil hit the California market with the force of a pile driver. Crude prices were driven down day after day as the gusher kept on roaring, falling to 30 cents a barrel. Preachers conducted excursions to the spot, exhorting people to pray that the oil might not cover the world and bring flaming destruction. That Lake View did not catch fire was a miracle.

On September 9, 1911, after eighteen months of stupendous production, Lake View ceased gushing as abruptly as it was born. The hole caved in. Two years later, when Union redrilled deeper on the site, the resulting well yielded only 35 barrels a day on the pump. Official estimates of Lake View's yield were 9 million barrels of 32-gravity crude. Five million barrels of this were saved; the remainder was lost by evaporation and seepage.

Though Union had struck the most prodigal producer of all times, there were days when the company executives wished that Lake View were somebody else's lucky strike. The oil boiled up from the well in a solid stream 20 feet or more in diameter and spewed 200 feet skyward. The spray covered an area 15 miles away from the well, ruined clothes, covered machinery, vehicles, and buildings, and provoked lawsuits from adjoining property owners. The flood of crude drove the oil prices to an unprofitable low. As for Dry Hole Charlie, he had seen his luck change. He had bossed the drilling of the greatest producer in history. So he went right out and drilled a dozen more wells, nearly all of them bone-dry!

The Lake View Oil Company, a Union subsidiary, pumped 7,536,858 barrels of oil, not including 4,000,000 barrels lost in the great gusher's wild spree, in the four decades that followed and paid $1,293,750 in dividends from the 100 acres in the lucky mineral lease. The subsidiary was dissolved and laid away to rest in 1955, but the Lake View legend lives on, revived whenever old-time wildcatters meet. They allow "there'll never be another gusher like old Lake View."

CHAPTER SIX 1910-1920

Era of High Finance

As the decade 1910-1920 dawned, California's petroleum output leaped to 74 million barrels a year, a 40 per cent increase in a single year as the result of "forced development" to beat the government's new deadline for withdrawing Federal lands from oil exploration. The Union-Independent Producers share, roughly one-fourth of this flood, taxed the company's pipelines and tankers to capacity. Union had more than 300 wells spotted over 229,804 acres of oil land it controlled. Director of Exploration Orcutt estimated that each acre was good for 150,000 barrels. This rosy picture set the stage for a decade of financial juggling unequaled in any other period in the company's history.

As usual, Union was oil-rich and dollar-poor. Appraising the year 1910, Lyman Stewart wrote to the stockholders: "You will doubtless share my opinion that we have abundant cause for being grateful to the Supreme Ruler of all things for the remarkable growth of our business, the profitable development of our properties, and the important service we have been enabled thereby to render the public."

To meet the long-range financial needs, the stockholders, at Stewart's urging, upped the company's potential bonded indebtedness to 20 million dollars. The new treasurer, Robert Watchorn, was authorized to go to New York to raise the first million of this urgently needed money. While he was in the money capital, Watchorn agreed to raise additional cash for Lyman Stewart, who also needed dollars for his current evangelical enthusiasm, the Bible Institute of Los Angeles. Watchorn, like Stewart, was a religious zealot. He mixed his religious activities with his business operations, as did Stewart. This fervor biased the

ACTIVE TO THE LAST

Lyman Stewart at sixty-five had resigned as president and become chairman of the board. He remained active in Union's affairs until the last.

business judgment of both men, causing the Union management great embarrassment for a decade to come. In his later years Stewart wildcatted for lost souls as fervently as he had hunted oil in his youth.

One of his unfortunate decisions, influenced probably by the fact that he was ill and thought his days were numbered and too few, was to commission Watchorn to sell his (Stewart's) interests in Union Oil Company to raise the greatest amount of money possible for immediate use in his favorite charities, the Bible Institute and the support of missionaries in China. This urge to "provide a Bible for every Chinaman" soon became a threat to the stability of the company's management. Stewart's wife was on her deathbed at the time and Stewart himself was a sick man. Watchorn had become his confidant. Thus Watchorn gained far more influence in Union's financial affairs than was originally intended when the directors reluctantly approved his appointment, at Stewart's insistence, as treasurer.

"For the purpose of enabling us to go forward with certain benevolences we gave Mr. Watchorn an option," explained Lyman Stewart. "Word had come that my brother in the East, who was our largest stockholder, was very ill. The message from his bedside stated that there was absolutely no hope for his recovery. The Stewart interests were not organized in any way, and the impending death of my brother threatened to destroy the control. I, however, held the power of attorney from him, and in order to protect the stockholders of the Union Provident and the United Petroleum companies, who, by considerable sacrifice, had made the control possible, I hastened to give an option to Mr. Watchorn at $150 a share."

In New York Watchorn negotiated a deal with Hallgarten & Company to underwrite the first issue of $5,000,000 worth of bonds. The Hallgarten firm extracted its pound of flesh in the form of what was known as the "negative option," which prevented Union from selling more than $1,500,000 worth of new stock, at any time within the next thirty years, without Hallgarten approval. Luckily this option was terminated when the Hallgarten company found itself unable to provide the necessary cash to float the bond issue.

Meantime, to get money for Lyman Stewart personally, Watchorn persuaded Stewart to sign a paper granting him an option on all of Stewart's holdings in the United Petroleum Company and the Union Provident Company and, as it turned out, all of Stewart's Union Oil shares. While still ill and confined to his bed, Stewart signed an option in blank. When Watchorn filled it out, he included Union Oil stocks that Stewart apparently intended to keep in his own name. Later, when Stewart recovered, a violent disagreement occurred between the two men over this part of the option.

The option entitled the holder to buy all of Stewart's holdings at $150 a share. While in New York, Watchorn was able to raise some quick money for Stewart by transferring the option to Eugene de Sabla, president of Esperanza, Consolidated, which later became the General Petroleum Company, for a consideration of $1,000,000. De Sabla paid $500,000 down, the balance due at the rate of $33,000 per month. Out of this down payment Watchorn handed Lyman

INSTITUTE OF BENEVOLENCE *Lyman Stewart founded the Bible Institute of Los Angeles and supported missionaries in China. Stewart's second wife, Lulu M. Crowell, shared his evangelical interests, particularly the Institute.*

Stewart $493,177, which Stewart used to meet personal obligations and to distribute among members of his family. In return, Stewart delivered to Watchorn shares of United Petroleum and Union Provident equivalent to the value of the check. These in turn were delivered by Watchorn to the trustees of the Bible Institute, which Stewart had founded. Subsequent monthly payments made by de Sabla were also turned over to the Bible Institute.

The option quickly became the "million-dollar mystery" in Union Oil affairs. In a sense it meant that anybody holding it could buy control of Union Oil; it cast a gray shadow over the company, particularly after de Sabla had delivered the option to the General Petroleum Company. Unable to exercise the option, General Petroleum assigned it to the Mercantile Trust Company of San Francisco. The trust company assigned it to Andrew Weir and H. Tilden Smith, British financiers and oil men.

Meantime, despite its valuable resources and booming business, Union's financial position was becoming more and more shaky, although, as Lyman

Stewart described operations for 1912, "the company's affairs were never more satisfactory than now," and "its lands are estimated by experts many times more than the company's authorized stock, almost two-fifths of which is unissued. It owns controlling interest in 21 subsidiary corporations; possesses valuable franchises and costly equipment in Chile, Peru, Hawaii, Canada, Panama, Oregon, Washington, California, Arizona, and other places; owns outright and by charter an efficient fleet of steamers, and undivided half-interest in a splendid modern business building, and stock in subsidiary companies the total value of which is greater than the face value of all its outstanding shares." But the company still needed operating capital for its own operation and for several subsidiaries.

One of these was the Outer Harbor Dock and Wharf Company, for which Union had made a $700,000 commitment. This was an ambitious engineer's dream to turn shallow San Pedro Harbor into a deepwater basin capable of handling seagoing vessels. The project was first broached in 1909 by a young Navy engineer, Lieutenant Ralph H. Minor. The Federal government had already completed a breakwater, and Minor proposed to dredge a deep basin behind it, capable of accommodating the largest ships afloat. Stewart agreed to lease some of the water-front acreage Minor would build up by pumping mud out of the basin. To get the harbor work started, Stewart committed Union for one-fifth interest in Outer Harbor Dock and Wharf Company, which Union had organized. When Minor ran into financial difficulties, Union advanced more money to keep the work moving. Eventually Union had to take over the entire project, building sea walls and wharves, creating industrial sites. It was a big bite of geography making for an oil company, already hard-pressed for capital to keep ahead of the increasing flood of oil. Union had just completed two small new refineries at Fullerton (in 1911) and at Santa Paula (in 1912).

By 1913, the company's financial position had become precarious. George H. Burr & Company of New York held two notes, one amounting to a million dollars which fell due in May, and another for a similar amount due in August. Watchorn was unable to raise enough money in New York to meet these payments. At the last minute W. L. Stewart induced a group of Los Angeles financiers to put up a million dollars, which postponed this crisis.

Meantime a new personality John H. Garrigues, who represented George H. Burr & Company in Los Angeles, loomed on the Union scene. Garrigues was the representative who had arranged the loans to Union Oil. When the payments came due, Union's treasurer did not have the money. Garrigues issued a fiat: "If the notes are not paid at maturity, I'll throw you in the hands of a receiver."

But Garrigues had an alternative. If the Union Oil directors would make him treasurer of the company at a salary of $25,000 a year, and if he were given a free hand in Union's financing, he would get the loans extended and would raise another million dollars from Burr & Company immediately. With his back to the wall, Lyman Stewart persuaded the Union directors to employ Garrigues as treasurer, replacing Watchorn, "as insurance—as cheap insurance as we could get."

SAN PEDRO HARBOR *Harbor facilities at San Pedro were developed at great expense by Union Oil Company. Much of the construction was started in the 1890's* (above), *when breakwaters and piers were built. Thirty years later* (below), *Union's installations were already extensive.*

END OF A COLORFUL ERA *Union's first truck put into service in 1910 at Los Angeles marked the beginning of the end for "hayburners" and their rumbling wagons.*

Garrigues proved himself a forceful character with unshakable confidence in himself. He exercised his prerogatives as Union treasurer with a high hand. He demanded and obtained the resignation of the former treasurer, the auditor, the comptroller, the manager of the marine department, the manager of the manufacturing department, and numerous lesser figures from the company. He insisted that a colleague, A. P. Johnson, be elected to the board to represent "minority stockholders." Pointing out that his agreement with Union gave him "a free hand in financing," he ordered dividends suspended and forced Lyman Stewart, on December 8, 1914, to write to the stockholders saying:

"Suspension or reduction of dividends is not due to losses or any falling off in earnings. The situation has been brought about chiefly by too much prosperity. The volume of the company's business has doubled in the past four years with no corresponding increase in capital stock. Growing by leaps and bounds, year after year, from $10 million gross sales on a capital of $30 million, to $20 million on a capital of $32 million, this flow of new business has required each year millions of dollars for fixed investment in oil lands, drilling operations, pipelines, storage equipment, ships, manufacturing facilities, and new stations. At this date the entire outstanding indebtedness and serial note obligations in the hands of the public, including both the direct bonded debt of the Union Oil Company of California and wholly owned and controlled companies guaranteed by it, totals $12,653,000."

HISTORIC SERVICE STATION

Forerunner of thousands of modern Union Oil service stations was this initial unit opened in 1913 at Sixth and Mateo Streets, Los Angeles.

While this financial juggling was going on inside the head office, other developments equally important were taking place in the field and in the markets. One was the increase in the demand for gasoline. Union Oiler Art Roseman, who started work in 1913, recalled at a good-bye dinner when he retired what Union's first customer service looked like. Said Roseman:

"Like Topsy, the gasoline service just grew. I remember when the yard (at Sixth and Santa Fe in Los Angeles) contained a row of 50-gallon gasoline tanks with locked faucets and locked lids. One of our drivers had keys to the lids, and we filled the tanks from time to time. On each tank was painted the name of an automobile owner. When he wanted gasoline, he simply drove around to the yard and filled her up himself.

"Another service pioneered by Union was to open the doors of our garage on Sixth Street so that the motorists could come in and buy a tankful of gasoline at a time, C.O.D. Business got so good that one boy spent most of his time just pumping gasoline. When the line of cars got too long for our garage, we built a little shack east of the Sixth Street office and installed two one-gallon pumps. Customers pulled alongside the curb and we stretched the gasoline hose across the sidewalk to give them a fill.

"Finally when cars got to backing up from our Sixth Street pumps all the way to San Mateo Street, we built the old service station No. 8 down at the corner. It was the super-service station of its day—with two driveways, five standpipes between the drives, and Bowser five-gallon hand-operated pumps

"LATEST MODEL"

This 1914 Alco truck had no cab or headlights, only a rudimentary dashboard, but boasted the latest puncture-proof, hard-rubber tires, chain drive, and a squeeze-bulb horn. It carried 900 gallons of fuel oil.

FRIENDLY SERVICE IS A UNION TRADITION

As the 1920's approached, the Union Oil brands were beginning to appear in service stations throughout California. This friendly quartet is standing in front of a station in Santa Ana.

inside the station building. It did a big business and eventually stayed open all night."

Gasoline was still a side line, and Union's big customer product was fuel oil. In 1913 the company had 30 delivery tankers in Los Angeles alone, powered by 72 "hayburners" bedded down nightly in a huge stable at Santa Fe and Sixth streets. For some deliveries on the muddier streets, four horses were needed, and occasionally, when deliveries were bogged down in a quagmire, a four-mule team was dispatched to get the fuel oil and the kerosene flowing again. The first motorized tankers were a decided improvement because they increased the speed to 8 miles an hour. They were an old Packard car, an old Alco, and several double-decker busses, bought from a defunct transportation company and remodeled into tank trucks in the Union shops.

Juggling finances to meet payments on the company's 12-million-dollar debt kept the Union directors continually on the anxious seat. Early in 1914, when Hallgarten & Company of New York reported that it would be unable to carry out the terms of the Watchorn agreement to market 5 million dollars' worth of Union bonds, the situation suddenly became critical again. The company needed a million dollars immediately. Even high-talking Treasurer Garrigues could not whistle this money up quickly. W. L. Stewart approached a syndicate of Los Angeles financiers, headed by John E. Jardine, manager of the Los Angeles office of William R. Staats & Company. Will Stewart was angling for 2 million dollars, which the syndicate at first appeared disposed to let Union have. However, after Garrigues had injected himself into the negotiations, the financiers whittled the amount to a million dollars, which they agreed to advance on debenture gold notes. They also attached a shocking condition to this offer, namely, that Lyman Stewart resign as president of the Union Oil Company before any of the money would be forthcoming. The syndicate also wanted to name 6 of the 11 directors on the Union Oil board, but this condition was later dropped. Asked why they insisted on the removal of Lyman Stewart, Jardine explained:

"We felt the public laid the blame for the appointment of Robert Watchorn as treasurer of Union Oil Company, and the consequent sale of the de Sabla option, to Lyman Stewart. We also felt that we were taking something of a risk in undertaking to dispose of so large an amount of notes for the company, and if that was the way the public viewed the matter, a change should have a beneficial effect upon the mind of the investing public. On account of the de Sabla option, the investing public had to a certain extent lost confidence in the company. We felt that putting new men on the board, men who were successful in business in this city, would have a beneficial effect."

Later that year William R. Staats, head of the syndicate and a former Union Oil director, agreed to underwrite the entire 5-million-dollar issue on which Hallgarten & Company had defaulted. Staats explained: "It was a pretty panicky time, generally speaking, and the taking of the entire five million dollar issue of gold notes was a big contract. . . . The securities of the company were at a low ebb, and the financial condition was not in good shape. We felt that in case the purchase was carried through, we ought to safeguard against another option being given. That was our purpose. Whether there was a demand for six directors or not I cannot say."

With the company desperate for ready money, Lyman Stewart presented his resignation as president on April 22, 1914. The directors immediately elected William L. Stewart, his son, to succeed him. Lyman Stewart was "pushed upstairs" to be chairman of the board. Thus, for want of a million dollars, Lyman Stewart lost control of a 30-million-dollar oil empire.

However, there may have been some consolation for him in the fact that fifteen years after Wallace Hardison had a tanker named for him, Union got around to honoring him with the *Lyman Stewart*, a 65,000-barrel tanker launched in 1914. This tanker and its sister ship, the *Frank N. Buck*, built for the Associated Oil Company at the same time on adjoining ways, had interesting fates. In 1922, the *Lyman Stewart* collided at the entrance to San Francisco Bay with another ship and sank. Fifteen years later, the *Frank N. Buck* collided with the *President Coolidge* at the identical spot and sank within 50 feet of the *Lyman Stewart*. There the ill-fated sister ships still rest, side by side.

The default by Hallgarten & Company canceled the negative option which had put Union Oil in a financial strait jacket, but before he moved upstairs, Lyman Stewart managed to create a new financial bogey for the company. Almost his last act before he stepped out of office was to sign a contract, approved by the Union Oil board, with two new figures on the Union Oil horizon. They were Andrew Weir and H. Tilden Smith, representing British financial interests. Weir and Smith had just picked up the expired de Sabla option from the Mercantile Trust Company of San Francisco. They proposed to organize a new oil giant, to be known as the British Union Oil Company, which would immediately purchase 150,000 shares of Union Oil treasury stock at par. This deal, providing 15 million dollars in ready cash, looked like the answer to the company's chronic financial ills. Heading the British syndicate, but discreetly in the background, was Earl Gray, former governor-general of Canada. The Britishers wanted Union's oil production primarily to fuel the British fleet. In secret maneuvers, British battleships converted to oil had sailed rings around the attacking coal-burner fleet, and the Admiralty had decided to replace coal with oil on all British men-of-war.

Soon after the contract was signed, the Britishers made their first payment of $2,500,000. Before the second payment became due in August, 1914, World War I had broken out and the British were caught in a life-or-death struggle with Germany. There was no time to convert their battleships. Union's directors extended the deadline for completing the $15,000,000 transaction for one year. Instead of forfeiting the down payment of $2,500,000, as Eugene de Sabla had done on his million-dollar option, Weir and Smith collected Union Oil treasury stock to the value of $2,500,000. The rest of the transaction was called off a year later, because the British were still at war. But the sizable block of Union Oil stock in British hands gave Union Oil Company of California an international status. It also became another question mark in the company's future.

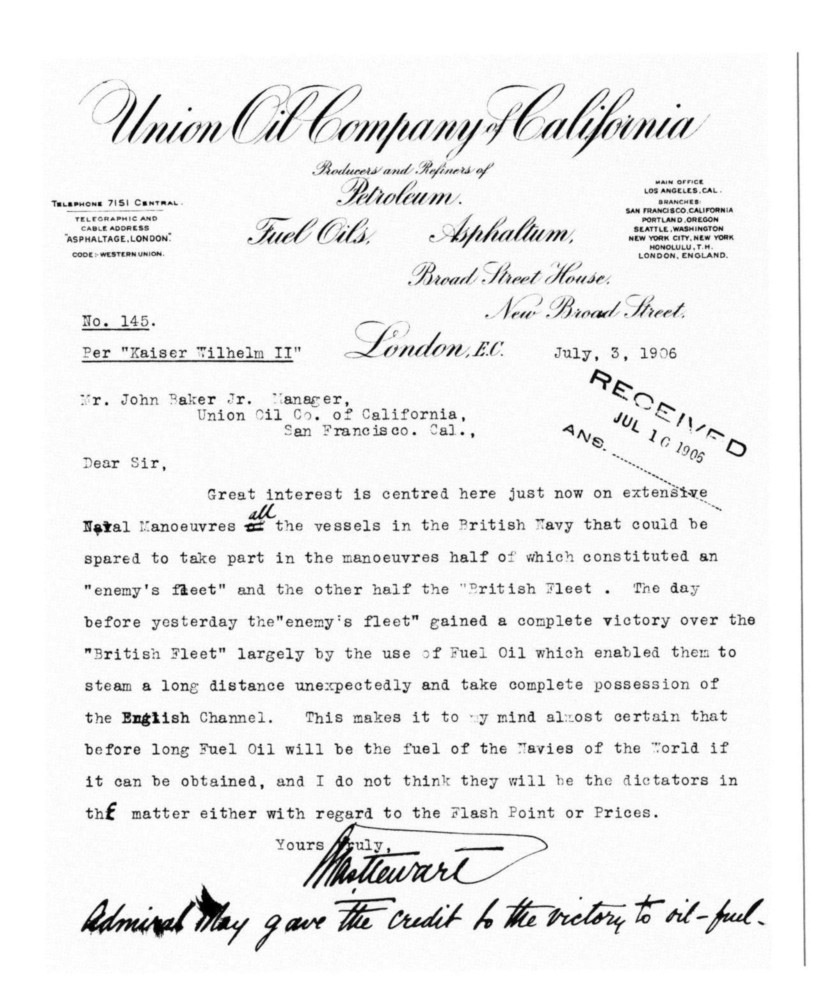

Union Oil Company of California

Producers and Refiners of Petroleum. Fuel Oils, Asphaltum,

TELEPHONE 7151 CENTRAL.
TELEGRAPHIC AND CABLE ADDRESS "ASPHALTAGE, LONDON."
CODE: WESTERN UNION.

MAIN OFFICE LOS ANGELES, CAL.
BRANCHES: SAN FRANCISCO, CALIFORNIA; PORTLAND, OREGON; SEATTLE, WASHINGTON; NEW YORK CITY, NEW YORK; HONOLULU, T.H.; LONDON, ENGLAND.

Broad Street House, New Broad Street, London, E.C.

No. 145.
Per "Kaiser Wilhelm II"

July, 3, 1906

RECEIVED JUL 10 1906 ANS.

Mr. John Baker Jr. Manager,
Union Oil Co. of California,
San Francisco. Cal.,

Dear Sir,

Great interest is centred here just now on extensive Naval Manoeuvres all the vessels in the British Navy that could be spared to take part in the manoeuvres half of which constituted an "enemy's fleet" and the other half the "British Fleet". The day before yesterday the "enemy's fleet" gained a complete victory over the "British Fleet" largely by the use of Fuel Oil which enabled them to steam a long distance unexpectedly and take complete possession of the English Channel. This makes it to my mind almost certain that before long Fuel Oil will be the fuel of the Navies of the World if it can be obtained, and I do not think they will be the dictators in the matter either with regard to the Flash Point or Prices.

Yours truly,
W. Stewart

Admiral May gave the credit to the victory to oil-fuel.

FUEL OIL FOR THE BRITISH FLEET

First-hand reports on first test of fuel oil versus coal conducted by the British Navy just prior to World War I.

the next best thing. Ignoring details, it is enough to say that Sir WILLIAM MAY sallied out from the Irish base, spread out his battleships and cruisers fanwise across the main track of Atlantic navigation, and threatened to sweep British commerce off the seas as if with a huge drag-net. Sir ARTHUR WILSON, with a mighty force, quitted our insular shores, located his antagonist, and bore up in full strength to bring his rival to battle. It was impossible for that wily but most gallant and able foreigner to accept the challenge, and in fact he knew a trick worth two of it. Having lured the ponderous British armada far to the south, he turned in his tracks, with engines throbbing, for a race of life and death, and dashed at the Channel. In spite of the temporary loss of a couple of battleships, the capture of a third, and the breaking down of the furnaces of a fourth, whose ultimate fate is still unknown, the Blue admiral wore down the pursuit inch by inch. Largely by the use of oil-fuel—thus vindicating a theory of which he was himself the pioneer, as our Correspondent has described—he shook off the peril straining hard upon his heels, accomplished an unprecedented feat of long-distance steaming, and reached British waters to find himself undisputed master of the Channel. On Saturday morn-

Other men had dreamed of taking over the oil empire that Lyman Stewart appeared to be vacating. One was Treasurer Garrigues, who undertook in 1914 to assume dictatorial powers in the management of the company. Garrigues went out of his way to be arrogant with the independent producers, who provided Union with much of its crude and who had been loyal friends of the company for years. The independent producers had their own association, headed by T. A. O'Donnell, president of the California Petroleum Company. At a meeting in the fall of 1914, Garrigues laid down the law to the agency and wound up by pounding the table and declaring: "Refuse, and I will not spend another dollar on transportation facilities. I will put a hundred strings of tools to work and get my own production. In the meantime I will take advantage of every technicality in the written agency agreement to transport and sell your oil, and force every member of the agency into bankruptcy."

"You talk as if you were the whole Union Oil Company," replied O'Donnell.

"I am the whole Union Oil Company," shouted Garrigues.

After this flare-up, a peace meeting was arranged with the executive committee of the Independent Oil Producers Agency. S. A. Guiberson, Jr., of San Francisco, an independent oil operator, reported what happened at this meeting:

"He [Garrigues] told us that the oil men of California were a bunch of boobs and that those of us who had made money had done so by luck. He said he was the Moses who had come out to California to lead us out of our troubles. Then he said he had been sent to California to do four things: the first was to acquire control of the lumber industry of the Pacific Coast; second, to acquire control of the oil industry of the Pacific Coast; third, to dominate and control the financial interests of the Pacific Coast; fourth, to change and direct the politics of the Pacific Coast. 'Nothing can prevent me from accomplishing my purpose, not even the Standard Oil, and you can get on my bandwagon and ride through to the goal or you can get in the road and be run over.' "

Guiberson replied: "Mr. Garrigues, you are either a fool or you have been taking dope. You won't have to wait two or three days for my answer. So far as I am concerned, you can go plumb straight to Hell."

At this, the meeting broke up. A little later, Guiberson and Garrigues met in an anteroom. Garrigues stuck out his hand and said: "I like you, Guiberson. I like a man who says what he thinks."

The dream of another oil company colossal enough to compete on even terms with the giants of the industry continued. Hardly had the British given up their option on the 150,000 shares of treasury stock than Edward L. Doheny, formerly a director of Union Oil, made a bid to gain control of the company. Doheny and his associates were forming the Pan-American Oil and Transportation Company, which they hoped would become another Standard Oil or Royal Dutch Shell. Doheny offered to buy 51 per cent of the stock of Union Oil Company at $85 a share and also proposed to buy several other Western oil companies as well. This offer was turned down by the Union directors.

One reason for the turndown was that several key oil men, representing more than 150 independent companies in California, were trying to put together

WRECK OF THE LYMAN STEWART

In 1922 the Lyman Stewart *collided at the entrance of San Francisco Bay with another ship. She lay on the rocks for weeks of merciless pounding by the waves, and eventually sank.*

a 100-million-dollar international oil company, with Union as the nucleus. This proposed merger of the little operators to make another giant got off to a flying start in the summer of 1915 at a conference attended by W. L. Stewart, representing Union Oil Company; T. A. O'Donnell, representing the California Petroleum Corporation; L. P. St. Clair and Mark Requa, representing the Independent Oil Producers Agency; T. J. Currie, representing Andrew Weir and British interests. Requa was the prime mover in the ambitious scheme to build a new oil colossus around Union, already a husky giant.

Requa needed an option on the Union Oil stock controlled by the Stewarts in order to secure financing in New York, where Bernard M. Baruch, Solomon & Company, Hayden Stone & Company, and other financiers had indicated a willingness to put up the necessary capital. The other independents looked to Union to take the lead. The Union management failed to do this, largely because the deal was bitterly opposed by Treasurer John Garrigues. There were other obstacles, too, in Union's complicated ownership. The Stewart family, at the time, held about 4 million dollars' worth of Union Oil stock, but not the majority. However, by means of their holding company, United Petroleum, they were in a position to hand over control of the company to Requa, who offered the stockholders a bonus of $25 a share over the open market price of the stock. Though Garrigues bitterly charged that the Stewarts were proposing to sell the stockholders down the river, the opposite was the case.

Another obstacle was Milton Stewart, who was likewise eager to raise money for religious benefactions. He had already signed the power of attorney for his Union holdings to a Reverend W. E. Blackstone, a former missionary to China who was managing the Stewart philanthropic enterprises. Garrigues soon tangled with the Reverend Mr. Blackstone. Opposing the option, Garrigues told Blackstone that he was guided by occult sources, which informed him that the option was an evil thing. The Reverend Mr. Blackstone, in turn, said he prayed for divine guidance. The missionary's prayers evidently were stronger than Garrigues' occult sources because Requa, with the Reverend Mr. Blackstone's help, eventually secured an option from the entire Stewart family to purchase their holdings at $95 a share. How this option was obtained from Lyman Stewart was described by Requa:

"As I was leaving, thinking that negotiations had been terminated, I said to Mr. Stewart that this was undoubtedly the most momentous thing in the history of the oil industry in the state. I told him he had better sign the option and keep it in his safe, so that if the stockholders ever heard about the matter and criticized him for not embracing such an opportunity, he would have the signed document to show that so far as he, personally, was concerned, he favored the matter.

"This reopened the negotiations, with the result that the option was signed that night. I immediately had it coded and telegraphed to New York, at a cost of $350.

"But as a matter of fact, it was never a completed option. It was given subject to the approval of Andrew Weir, H. Tilden Smith, and the British Union Oil Company. That approval was never forthcoming, and I never had an opportunity to demonstrate that I could raise the money in New York. I returned the cancelled option to the Union Oil Company on January 31, 1916, because it was obviously impossible to obtain approval of the British interests within the life of the document."

As it turned out, the Britishers had other plans for Union Oil, but before these came to light, the company went through another internal spasm provoked by Treasurer Garrigues.

On July 15, 1915, Garrigues persuaded Director Giles Kellogg to offer a resolution increasing Garrigues' salary as treasurer to $50,000 a year. This was

CHARGE AND COUNTER-CHARGE

The dramatic struggles within the corporate structure were matters of public concern. Factions within the board fought their case in the newspapers as well as in the board room.

LYMAN STEWART BARES UNION OIL SECRETS IN AMAZING DOCUMENT

Founder of $50,000,000 Corporation Issues to Stockholders Extraordinary Appeal for Support and Vindication; Bitterly Arraigns Opposition

$14,000,000 IN DIVIDENDS CITED TO DEFEND POLICY

By E. L. Mercado

AN amazing document has just been issued by Lyman Stewart to the stockholders of the Union Oil Company of California, Union Provident Company and United Petroleum Company.

Mr. Stewart, founder of the Union Company, and at present chairman of the board, has, in this letter made perhaps the most extraordinary appeal for support and vindication in the history of Pacific Coast corporations.

Three times within the last few years, Lyman Stewart, now weighted down with years, has endeavored to relieve himself of the additional burden of business responsibilities incidental to the management of a $50,000,000 corporation. He and members of his family control the Union through a holding company arrangement. They actually own only about an eighth of the stock, instead of over half, which would be necessary were it not for the holding companies.

Recent sales of treasury stock to British interests have weakened the Stewart control, although it still serves for all practical purposes.

STRIKING FEATURES OF MR. STEWART'S LETTER

Despite his advanced age and desire for the peace of retirement, Mr. Stewart has become a central figure in the crisis that has appeared in the affairs of the Union Company.

The introduction to his personal letter follows the form that has made his annual statement remarkable. It includes quotations from Scripture and an acknowledgment of the fact that "the Lord has greatly blessed and prospered the business of the Union Oil Company.

Among the more striking features of the letter is a scathing arraignment of the opposition to the Stewarts.

John Garrigues, former treasurer of the Union Oil Company, is prominently identified with the militant Stockholders Protective Association. Mr. Garrigues is accused by Mr. Stew-

bitterly opposed by President W. L. Stewart and Director William R. Staats. Garrigues offered to resign then and there. Although most of the directors wanted to get rid of him, they hesitated to accept his resignation, fearing loss of the financial strength they believed he held. However, after another blowup, on January 13, 1916, when Garrigues again attempted to dictate to the Union board, they summarily removed him from office and named W. L. Stewart to be both president and treasurer, with E. W. Clark, former manager of the Producers pipeline, as general manager.

With Garrigues out, the Stewarts were able to make amends to stockholders for the lean years provoked by the Garrigues-inspired suspension of dividends. At the October 30 meeting, on Lyman Stewart's motion, the board voted an extra dividend of $1.50 per share, a total of $1,535,149. At the same meeting, the board approved the proposal by E.W. Clark to sell 50,000 shares of treasury stock at $100 a share to provide funds for acquiring additional properties and making plant improvements. The oil business was booming, and the company earned the equivalent of 28¼ per cent on the capital stock outstanding. The company purchased a 200-acre site for a new refinery at Los Angeles Harbor. The directors also turned down an offer, made by James Currie on behalf of Weir and Tilden and E. L. Doheny, to purchase the balance of the original 150,000 shares on which their option had expired.

The company's increased prosperity enabled President W. L. Stewart to carry out one of his special enthusiasms, a profit-sharing plan for employees. In addition, Stewart set up an employees' benefit plan to provide medical care and hospitalization at cost. The company took out a 3-million-dollar life insurance policy covering its employees, a policy that was hailed as "the largest amount of life insurance ever negotiated in a single transaction west of the Missouri River."

The ousting of John Garrigues as treasurer precipitated one of the bitterest legal battles in Union's tempestuous history. Garrigues hurriedly organized the Union Oil Company Stockholders' Protective Association. In the name of this group, he filed a suit to dissolve the two holding companies by which the Stewarts controlled the Union Oil Company. Even before the vicious contest reached the court of Judge Louis M. Myers, the fight had been headlined in the newspapers and bitter charges and countercharges were hurled daily. Both Garrigues and the Stewarts used the press as a sounding board. The Los Angeles *Examiner*, in February, 1916, summarized the controversy as follows:

"Out of the Union Oil crisis has come what is perhaps the largest lawsuit in the history of the state courts of Southern California. This litigation involves the total $50 million capitalization of the Union Oil Company. The interests of about 4,500 stockholders are at stake. These stockholders range from the millionaire financier to the investor of modest means.

"The suit is for the purpose of enjoining the members of the Stewart family, certain persons associated with them, and the Union holding companies from voting the stock of the Union Oil Company that is possessed by these holding companies.

"The significance of this purpose is to break down and eliminate forever the device by which the Stewarts hold their dominant position in the management, while their real ownership of Union Oil stock is in the proportion of about one-quarter instead of over one-half of the total issue."

During the long trial, Lyman Stewart attempted to organize a new voting trust, but this effort was abandoned in August when only 163,000 of the necessary 170,000 shares approved his plan. During the trial, the Stewart family voluntarily dissolved the Union Provident Company. Thus, when Judge Myers decided against the Stewarts in a sweeping decision on October 2, 1916, there was only one holding company, United Petroleum, to unscramble. The court's decision was that the system of holding-company control, by which Lyman Stewart and his family could dominate the affairs of the 50-million-dollar corporation, was illegal and must end.

"I never sought to control Union Oil Company for any personal reason," Lyman Stewart explained, following the decision. "I never desired to be kept in office, except on merit. The one idea of having control of the company was to assure stability of management. The Stewarts hold 57,000 shares of stock in the company. They have a selfish interest in making them valuable. In making them valuable, they have made the shares of every other stockholder valuable."

The court's ruling kicked off a hot proxy battle in 1916, during which the Garrigues' faction and the Stewart forces appealed for popular support at the forthcoming annual meeting. When the meeting, twice postponed, was finally called on February 22, 1917, at Oleum (where the corporate office was still maintained as a result of a feud with the Los Angeles City officials over taxes), the Stewarts discovered that they had even more support through popular choice than they had held through the system of holding companies. They won all but 2 of the 11 seats on the board of directors. Garrigues ceased to be a factor in the company's affairs. E. W. Clark was named general manager.

Union Oil was no longer a family-controlled corporation. The Stewarts no longer voted as a family block. Chairman Lyman Stewart and President William L. Stewart were often on opposite sides of propositions placed before the board. Lyman Stewart considered son Will too conservative. Son Will replied that he wouldn't be so conservative if his father didn't want to buy all the oil land in California. The difference in viewpoints between father and son was graphically illustrated when they clashed head-on over a proposal to buy the Pinal-Dome Oil Company for $3,600,000. Lyman Stewart prevailed in this case, but often the decision was the other way around. By this time Lyman Stewart had bounced back from death's door and was in good health. On August 26, 1916, he had married his secretary, Lulu M. Crowell, with whom he had kindred evangelical interests, particularly in the growth of the Bible Institute.

The company was growing in all directions. Union drillers were punching down new holes in a score of oil fields. Among them was a "dry hole" at the western base of Signal Hill. It was abandoned as a duster at 3,449 feet, and Union's bases in the area were quit claimed. A few hundred feet of additional drilling would have tapped the fabulous Signal Hill reservoir, one of California's

FOURTH PRESIDENT:
W. L. STEWART

William Lyman Stewart, fourth president of Union Oil, served from April, 1914, until his sudden death in June, 1930. He worked for thirty-six years in various capacities.

richest discoveries. Acquisition of the Pinal-Dome Oil Company in 1917 brought Union Oil 20 well-established service stations in Los Angeles, Santa Ana, and Anaheim. With the retail selling of gasoline mushrooming, the first units of the Wilmington refinery were rushed to completion to supply the fast-growing Southern California market. Already the company had established more than a hundred bulk marketing stations in key cities of the Pacific Coast, in Hawaii, in the Orient, Latin America, and Alaska. With the Pinal-Dome service stations pushing Union's products, retail sales soared. It was an eye-opener. Union's marketers began adding new service stations as fast as they could be built. Concluding that most of the hastily built retail outlets were unsightly blots on the landscape, the management staged a contest among Western architects for the design of more attractive, functional-type stations suitable for any neighborhood. Out of the hundreds of ideas submitted evolved the attractive, modern Union dealers' service station.

Early in 1917, the board decided to issue more treasury stock to finance the rapid expansion. On April 6, 1917, the stockholders approved the proposition submitted by President W. L. Stewart to increase the capitalization to $100,000,000. United Petroleum was formally disincorporated, and its assets, consisting mainly of stock in the Union Oil Company, were distributed to United stockholders. During the year Union Oil exchanged $2,032,000 worth of its treasury stock for shares in the Producers Transportation Company; the pipeline built jointly with the Independent Producers Agency was now totally owned by Union. At the same time the company acquired the facilities of the terminal at Port Harford.

In August of 1917, Union lost three of its tankers. One was commandeered by the United States government, and two other chartered steamers of British ownership were commandeered by the British government.

World War I brought new demands for oil as fuel. To increase production, Union crews began drilling in Wyoming, Texas, and Mexico, where the Union Oil Company of Mexico was formed to explore a 16,000-acre lease granted by the Mexican government. In the newly discovered Texas fields Union Oil had 31,000 acres under lease. The new Wilmington refinery was processing 10,000 barrels a day. The Bakersfield refinery, destroyed by fire late in 1917, was back in operation by mid-1918.

During the war, Union lost two of its tankers, the *Santa Maria*, torpedoed by a German submarine, and the *Santa Rita*, which foundered on the high seas. These sister ships, each capable of handling 55,000 barrels of oil, had an interesting story behind them, particularly the *Santa Rita*, known as the "ship that ran into itself." Both ships were bought when Union was hard pressed to handle the crude pouring out of the new Producers pipeline at Port San Luis. They were operating on the Great Lakes when Union contracted with the Newport News Shipbuilding Company to convert them into tankers. To get them out of the Lakes, through the locks and down to the sea via the Mississippi, both ships were cut in two amidships, where they were sealed by bulkheads. In the move through the locks, each ship towed its bow. The *Santa Maria* negotiated the locks successfully, but the *Santa Rita* stopped too suddenly one day, and the ship's bow plowed through the stern bulkhead which was ahead. Luckily the *Santa Rita* did not sink herself. Patched up, she reached the ocean and was converted into a tanker. After delivering millions of barrels of oil to Union markets, both tankers were sold by the company at the outset of World War I, only to be lost in the Atlantic.

Union's amazing growth during the war years caught the attention of the important Eastern oil and financial interests. In July, 1919, Henry Lockhart, Jr., wrote to the Union management that he was authorized, on behalf of a group of bankers operating as a syndicate, to offer to buy 20 million dollars' worth of Union's treasury stock. Again needing money badly for expansion, the directors accepted. It developed that the syndicate, known as Commonwealth Petroleum Company, was a partnership composed of Percy Rockefeller, Henry Lockhart, Jr., and Charles H. Sabin, head of the Guaranty Trust Company of New York. Thus Wall Street made its bid for control of the big western independent.

Though the prospective purchasers denied that they wanted control of the company, the public, always suspicious of Wall Street, doubted them. Los Angeles newspapers and financiers, and even President W. L. Stewart, issued statements declaring that the New Yorkers had no intention of grabbing Union and pointing out that the company was owned by upward of 4,000 stockholders, most of them Californians. This allayed apprehensions, and even led the Los Angeles *Times*, on July 7, 1919, to comment:

"Los Angeles bankers yesterday expressed themselves as highly gratified by

Union Oil Latin American Markets of 1920's Saved From Fuel Shortage by Mexican Gushers

UNION OIL
IN LATIN AMERICA

Union's markets in Central and South America were saved by the company's discovery well in Mexico and a sister well that produced 4.6 million barrels of oil in six months. A complex of tankers, oil wells, collecting depots served the company in Latin America for several years before being abandoned during the depression.

the entry of powerful eastern interests into the affairs of Union Oil Company through the purchase of a partnership interest by Henry Lockhart, Jr., Charles Sabin, and Percy Rockefeller. They believe that this move, which is said to involve the purchase of some $20 million worth of Union stock, not only brings financial benefits to the company but foreshadows a new era in the oil development of California, inasmuch as the transaction does not involve control of Union Oil."

Nevertheless, there was an undercurrent of fear among stockholders, which led E. W. Clark, vice-president and general manager of Union Oil, with the approval of W. L. Stewart, to issue on July 20 a circular, sent to all department heads. It read:

"Eastern interests have acquired a substantial holding of stock in this company by purchase on the market and by private purchase from stockholders, but such purchases represent by no means a controlling interest.

"We wish to assure all employees that the control of the company still lies with the stockholders generally and not with any particular interest, and that this, in our opinion, will continue to be so."

Then came word that the New York syndicate had purchased the block of stock held by Andrew Weir and the other Britishers, who had bought into Union before World War I. This put an entirely different light on the Wall Street deal, as did the organization of a new corporation known as Union Oil Company of Delaware, announced in September, 1919. Union of Delaware began picking up other blocks of Union of California stock, and likewise the stock of Columbia Oil Producing Company of California, organized by Wallace Hardison.

A scramble on the market for Union stock eventually sent it zooming up to over $200 a share. Alarmed, the directors decided in December, 1920, to authorize President Stewart and three other members of the board to go to New York and find out what were the intentions of the Eastern financiers. By this time Union of Delaware owned 126,000 shares, approximately one-fourth of the outstanding Union Oil of California stock. In the course of their talks, Will Stewart and his colleagues were able to persuade Percy Rockefeller that, in order to buy another 125,000 shares on the market to gain control of Union, they would have to invest more than the company was worth. The syndicate assured them that Union of Delaware would abandon its attempt to wrest control of Union Oil from the Californians.

While these financial maneuvers were taking place, the *Petroleum Record* declared: "Nineteen-twenty goes down in history as the greatest year in the annals of the Union Oil Company of California. During the year it became a hundred million dollar corporation. During 1920 Union's sales will approximate sixty million dollars, smashing all previous records.

"During the latter part of this year Union Oil stock went on a 12% annual basis. Total dividends paid on Union stock will be brought up to approximately $52,500,000 by 1920 payments.

"This remarkable growth was made possible by the faith and tenacity of one man, who risked his fortune and name when bankers flatly refused to loan money

ne Hundred and Twenty-five Million Gallons of Gasoline Will Arrive in Los Angeles Within the Next Ten Days.

UNION OIL TO THE RESCUE! *The dramatic arrival of a trainload of Union gasoline, brought from Texas to relieve a fuel famine in Los Angeles in 1920, made front-page headlines.*

to finance the oil industry, characterizing oil men as a 'wildcat crowd.' "

While dollars were becoming more plentiful, gasoline was becoming short in California service stations. The state had 500,000 automobiles registered in 1920, compared with 150,000 five years before. The Automobile Age was about to begin. The Union sales department was forced to ration products in the several distant areas it had invaded. Only a fortunate oil strike in Mexico saved Union's South American markets.

By mid-July of 1920, Union service stations, along with those of its competitors, were nearly dry. The Union management hurriedly bought 2 million gallons of Texas gasoline and started special trains of tank cars to rush the gas west at express train speeds. The Los Angeles *Express* reported, on July 27, 1920:

"Union's first trainload of 26 tank cars, bearing a capacity of 202,000 gallons of high test gasoline to relieve the acute shortage in Southern California, arrived from Wichita, Texas, today, after a record run. Its entry into the city was heralded by Mayor Snyder, who rose early and journeyed to the outskirts of the city to hop aboard the locomotive and ride it into the station, where cheers reminiscent of a political rally welcomed the precious fluid."

This "gasoline special" was followed by a dozen others during the next few weeks, until the gas thirst was finally slaked by increased refinery output. To do this, the company was forced to curtail its exports of fuel oil still more. President W. L. Stewart reported: "There developed during the year a great shortage of fuel oil and refined products in the western states, and the company, feeling it to be a public duty and so as to take care of a portion of the requirements of the trade, imported large quantities of crude oil and gasoline; disposing of same in those territories which normally were supplied with California products. Export of refined products ceased, and our Chilean fuel oil trade was supplied almost entirely from Mexico."

MULHOLLAND HIGHWAY

CHAPTER SEVEN 1920-1930

The Automobile Age Arrives

DURING THE TWENTIES, THE UNION MANAGEMENT found itself facing a revolution in the oil industry. The appetites of more than one-half million automobiles registered in California in 1920 seemed insatiable. The open road itself called for enormous quantities of asphalt for pavement. The state gas taxes provided money to build new highways on a scale never before attempted. Gasoline became by far the most important and profitable ingredient in a barrel of oil. Lubricating oils for automobiles and tractors were more important than ever before. To extract still more of these high-priced ingredients and have less fuel-oil residue, oil companies were completely redesigning their refinery facilities.

Union, like the other petroleum producers, needed ever-increasing rivers of oil. The easy oil had already been discovered. Wildcatting for the deep pools was expensive exploration. W. W. Orcutt, director of exploration, had built up Union's geology department into one of the country's finest. His oil hunters could no longer spot new fields by looking for seeps or "smelling for oil in gopher holes," as Lyman Stewart had done. They had to project complicated maps of the earth's structure far beneath the surface to make educated guesses as to where oil might be trapped.

Amazing new tools made possible the mapping of these subterranean structures. One was aerial photography. By 1920 Union's geologists had pieced together over 400 aerial photographs covering 6,250 acres of the Richfield and Santa Fe Springs fields, taken by two former AEF lieutenants, Robert E. Haynes and Ralph M. Like. Another tool was the seismic rig, an evolution of devices developed in World War I to spot enemy artillery. By drilling holes and shooting off charges of dynamite and measuring the bounces of seismic waves on delicate

PORTENT OF THE FUTURE

The ceremony opening Mulholland Drive in Los Angeles in 1924 confirmed that the automobile was here to stay and with it an ever-increasing demand for petroleum products.

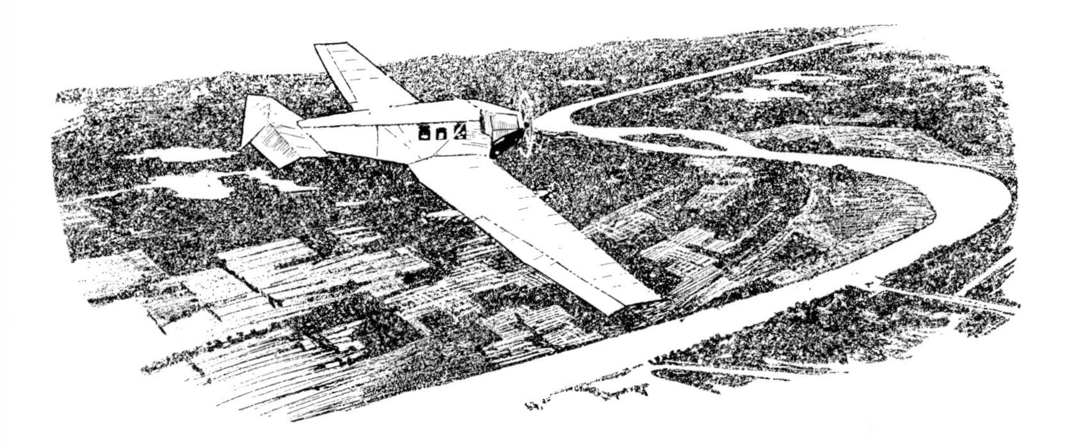

UNION PIONEERS AERIAL SURVEYING

The airplane was first put to work for Union Oil soon after the close of World War I. As a pioneering venture in the new science of aerial surveying, former war aces photographed and mapped oil fields and geologic formations from the sky. Flying the company's own plane, the pilot took pictures from the cockpit with a simple camera.

photographic recording devices, the earth shooters could tell where the hard layers and the soft layers lay. Geologists already knew that the hard layers trapped oil in the softer, more porous formations.

A huge, placid man with great self-control, Orcutt provided the inspiration to fire up younger geologists who later became top-flight oil finders. Big, handsome Bill Orcutt took the discoveries of his geology teams—such as Santa Fe Springs, Dominguez, Richfield, Montebello, and Orcutt fields — as calmly as he had his famous paleontological discovery at the Brea tar pits, or the loss of his arm in an automobile accident, after which he observed, wryly: "Well, I won't need it any more." The handicap did not keep him from becoming Union's vice-president in charge of exploration and production and a key member of the executive committee.

OIL FROM SHALE

R. D. Burnham pioneered one of the strangest oil hunts in history when he was assigned by Union to find shale in Colorado that could be mined and refined economically. Thanks to him and A. S. Crossfield, Union owns enough shale in the Rockies to yield billions of barrels of oil.

By 1920 the company was operating 56 strings of drilling tools in California, Texas, Wyoming, and Mexico, in which areas the company had bought or leased a total of 274,414 acres. As long-range insurance of the future oil supply, Union had embarked on one of the unique oil hunts of history. Geologist R. D. Burnham, accompanied by A. S. Crossfield of the manufacturing department, was assigned to explore in the state of Colorado for shale deposits that could be mined and refined economically for oil.

Burnham and Crossfield connected with Pete Lindauer, colorful Colorado mountaineer, who guided them to shale ledges he had observed high above Parachute Creek in the Rocky Mountains. Some of these averaged 80 feet in depth. When they found a promising deposit, Crossfield ran a test on the spot, cooking a batch of shale in a small portable retort with heat from a plumber's torch. He captured the vapor, ran it through a cool condensing pipe, and measured the oil that condensed. Sample after sample yielded oil in approximately the same amount, 39 gallons of oil per ton of shale. Along with the oil there was combustible gas, which later investigation showed to be about 2,500 cubic feet of gas per ton of shale. The residue was a light black material incapable of producing more oil, but still usable as a low-grade fuel. With the shale oil there was a small amount of water containing ammonia compounds which could be made into fertilizers. Samples of the shale sent to the Oleum laboratory confirmed the findings of Crossfield's "moonshine still." These tests convinced the Union directors that shale might be the company's ace in the hole and led them to purchase in fee simple more than 20 square miles of the shale mountain near Grand Valley, Colorado. Later they bought still more, until Union had enough shale cached in the Rocky Mountains to produce 6 billion barrels of oil, or roughly ten times the company's proved petroleum reserves.

In 1920 Union Oil entered into an agreement to sell its interest in the Union Tool Company to the National Supply Company. In over two decades Union Tool had evolved from a small shop in Santa Paula, staffed by ingenious mechanics who could invent and build almost any kind of mechanism, into one of the West's important oil-well supply houses. However, its ownership by Union Oil handicapped sales to competitors, and the sale to National Supply Company seemed a logical answer to further growth.

Union's fate as an independent oil company still hung in the balance. The assurance by Percy Rockefeller that he and his Wall Street associates would no longer seek control of Union Oil by buying shares on the market was short-lived. In May, 1921, a news bomb exploded in the form of a statement that the British-controlled Royal Dutch Shell interests had captured control of Union Oil of Delaware. This gave them a one-fourth interest in Union Oil of California. Shell brokers were busily buying up Union Oil stock on the open market. Later in the year, they announced that Union Oil Company of Delaware had ratified a plan for merger of the company's oil holdings with those of Royal Dutch Shell Petroleum Company, which had operated on a world-wide scale from headquarters in The Hague, Holland, largely with British capital.

The merger set off international repercussions. In the United States Senate, a resolution was introduced for a Federal investigation of the attempt of foreign interests to take over a big American oil company. The Navy Department expressed concern, fearing the loss of an important Pacific Coast oil source. Stockholders large and small rallied to help stave off the grab, which soon became a no-holds-barred fight for control of the Union Oil Company of California. Newspapers published editorials warning of the dire consequences. Said the San Francisco *Chronicle* on May 27, 1921:

"Enormous possibilities, both in the field of business and stocks, are opened up by news that negotiations are under way in London looking toward the acquisition of control of Union Oil of Delaware by the Royal Dutch Shell interests.

"The all-important question in financing circles is, where will Union Oil of California stand if this deal goes through? For no one imagines that the British would be content to stop with the scattered holdings of the Delaware company in California, Texas, and elsewhere, once they got control of that infant oil giant.

"Union Oil of California with its immense undeveloped holdings in California and Wyoming is the real prize at stake. Whether or not that prize is quite within their reach is another matter—and an important one—in determining whether or not the deal is to go through."

In the headlines, the contest quickly became a battle of the "Americans" to repel the invading "foreigners." Leading the American forces was Isaac Milbank, retired general manager of the Borden Milk Company, who had become a director of Union Oil of California. Milbank formed a stock pool known as Union Oil Associates, organized to defeat the "Shell grab." Thirty-eight hundred Union stockholders, 80 per cent of them residents of Southern California, held some 314,000 shares of the total half-million Union Oil of California shares outstanding. The embattled Californians quickly assumed, and correctly, that the Wall Street interests which had tried to buy into Union Oil in strength were working for foreigners. Warned the San Francisco *Chronicle:*

THEY FOUGHT OFF THE FOREIGN "GRAB" OF UNION

Two leaders in the great battle to save Union Oil from being bought up by foreign investors were directors Henry M. Robinson, head of the powerful First National Bank of Los Angeles, and Isaac Milbank, former general manager of the Borden Milk Company. Joining with the aging Lyman Stewart, they successfully defeated the "Shell grab."

" 'The Street' has suddenly awakened to the possibility that the men who built up Union Oil of California and who have put into it the best years of their lives might have no intention of seeing control pass into Wall Street."

The Los Angeles *Examiner* added:

"Acting on the principle that the Union Oil Company of California is a California corporation and should remain in California, the management of that company has taken steps to avert all danger of its control passing into the hands of the British or other foreign corporations.

"With this view the stockholders have been asked to unite their interest in a holding company that will centralize control to a greater extent and enable them to act as a unit in all matters affecting the corporation. This action by the management is of vast importance to the oil industry of California."

The Union Oil Associates quickly lined up around 200,000 shares in the proxy drive. The British definitely owned 131,000 shares. The big drive was to get enough of the balance into the Union Oil Associates fold before the British could increase their block to more than the Associates held or could obtain. Union Oil shares became the stock-market sensation, jumping up as much as $22 a share during a single day on the Los Angeles and San Francisco exchanges. As the fight for control of the company gained momentum, financial pundits had a field day. Stockholders wrote letters and held mass meetings. Cartoons pictured the menace of foreign control. Door-to-door calls were made, even on shareholders who had only a single share. In Toledo, Ohio, a man who owned only four shares was courted by representatives of both groups on the same afternoon.

As the proxy battle gained momentum, Hiram P. Johnson, Jr., San Francisco attorney representing a group of speculators, organized an independent pool of Union shares, held mainly by Northern Californians. Johnson's group aimed to make a quick killing by offering their 10,000-share block of stock to either the Shell or the Milbank-Stewart interests, depending upon which side would pay the most. Union stock was selling at about $170 a share.

In melodramatic terms, Dennis Donohue of the San Francisco *Examiner* described the line-up for the crucial battle on December 20, 1921, as follows:

"Under the Union Jack, with here and there a Holland ensign, are marshalled the forces of the Royal Dutch Shell combination, a motley aggregation recruited from many races but formidable by reason of their heavy artillery, manned by a regiment of Rothschilds and equipped by a plentiful supply of ammunition from the British treasury. On the left of this vast array is a small group of Americans flying the Stars and Stripes, which, however, bear in the lower corner the blazon of 'Made in London.' The commander of this small body is Percy Rockefeller, nephew of John D. Rockefeller. It will be well to keep an eye on Percy Rockefeller, for he springs from the stock which has never known defeat.

"Across the field, confronting the Royal Dutch-Union of Delaware forces, in solid formation stretch the squadrons of the Union Oil of California, under command of W. L. Stewart and his venerable father, Lyman Stewart. An American flag of the very largest size waves proudly over this array, which is supported by a reserve corps of bankers . . . . The Stewart commanders are endeavoring to organize a household brigade—a sort of Death-Head Hussars, so to speak—but every now and then members of this newly formed corps are seen scurrying to a clump of tall timber on the left of the field. There, flying the Bear Flag—true symbol of independence—one notes a small body of picked men under the generalship of Hiram Johnson, Jr., a testy fighter who long since won his spurs."

Meantime, the Milbank-Stewart forces began to get support from unexpected sources. Banker Henry M. Robinson, head of the powerful First National Bank of Los Angeles, agreed to spearhead the Union Oil Associates. Mark Requa, who had tried to organize the merger of the independents to form another petroleum colossus joined in the battle on the side of the Associates. J. C. O'Donnell, president of the Ohio Oil Company, a potent and substantial unit in the Standard Oil Company, warned that Union Oil stockholders have "everything to gain and nothing to lose by joining the holding company being created to retain American control of Union Oil of California."

The showdown, originally set for a stockholders' meeting on November 17, 1921, was twice postponed. As the proxy fight gained the intensity of the battle of the century, Union's oil hunters were making strikes that made the prize seem even more valuable. Union's drillers made a notable discovery in virgin territory at Santa Fe Springs, where on November 1 they brought in a discovery well 3,788 feet deep, which produced 4,000 barrels a day of high-gravity crude. By this time Union's land men had lined up 1,000 acres in the field. The company's drillers had brought in six wells in Wyoming and a producer in Texas. Production passed 10 million barrels for the year, a new milestone. With the addition of three new tankers, Union's fleet had a capacity, for the first time, of more than 1 million barrels of oil. A new lubricating oil plant was on stream at Oleum, and

SECOND ROUND IN SANTA FE SPRINGS *Union drilled its first unsuccessful hole in what was to become the great Santa Fe Springs field in 1917. It was not until October 1919 that this well, Meyer 3, after 2 years and 7 months drilling time, proved up the prolific area.*

north of the border the new Union Oil Company of Canada, Ltd., a subsidiary, was organized to produce refined oil at a refinery near Port Moody, near Vancouver, to distribute products throughout British Columbia.

As 1922 dawned, the big news was "Who will gain control of Union Oil of California?" The campaign to purchase stock and line up proxies intensified. As the contest approached the deadline, finally set for March 20, 1922, confusion increased as the various groups made conflicting claims about the number of shares they controlled. Newspapers, civic groups, rank-and-file citizens appealed to stockholders to "get aboard the Union Oil Associates' bandwagon." The Los Angeles Chamber of Commerce entered the fray with an urgent appeal, calling attention to "the real danger of foreign domination of this company, which has been heretofore 'of and for' Californians," while the Los Angeles *Express* called upon "all Americans to do 'their' duty," pleading:

"Roughly at midnight, March 20, the wires will flash to the four corners of the world the success or failure of Californians to keep control of one of their largest and most successful institutions. On that night will be decided whether or not large areas of California's richest oil lands are to become the cat's paw for foreign exploitation, or whether they are to proceed in their orderly development for the benefit of all Californians.

"The manner and the very daring of the plan conceived by foreign interests to acquire control of Union Oil of California have never been equalled in the annals of the financial world for its plain audacity. That these foreign magnates could believe that Californians would walk with their eyes open into a trap is

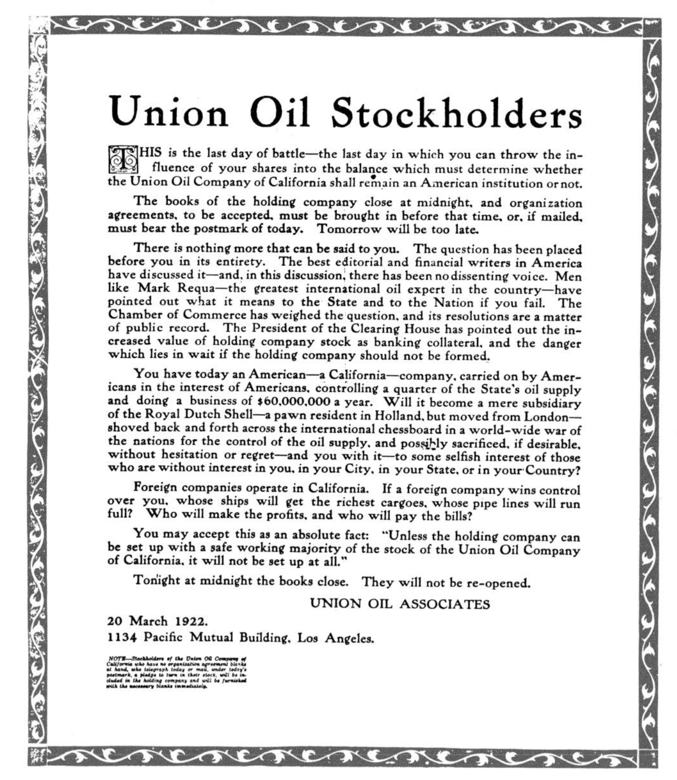

Union Oil Stockholders

THIS is the last day of battle—the last day in which you can throw the influence of your shares into the balance which must determine whether the Union Oil Company of California shall remain an American institution or not.

The books of the holding company close at midnight, and organization agreements, to be accepted, must be brought in before that time, or, if mailed, must bear the postmark of today. Tomorrow will be too late.

There is nothing more that can be said to you. The question has been placed before you in its entirety. The best editorial and financial writers in America have discussed it—and, in this discussion, there has been no dissenting voice. Men like Mark Requa—the greatest international oil expert in the country—have pointed out what it means to the State and to the Nation if you fail. The Chamber of Commerce has weighed the question, and its resolutions are a matter of public record. The President of the Clearing House has pointed out the increased value of holding company stock as banking collateral, and the danger which lies in wait if the holding company should not be formed.

You have today an American—a California—company, carried on by Americans in the interest of Americans, controlling a quarter of the State's oil supply and doing a business of $60,000,000 a year. Will it become a mere subsidiary of the Royal Dutch Shell—a pawn resident in Holland, but moved from London—shoved back and forth across the international chessboard in a world-wide war of the nations for the control of the oil supply, and possibly sacrificed, if desirable, without hesitation or regret—and you with it—to some selfish interest of those who are without interest in you, in your City, in your State, or in your Country?

Foreign companies operate in California. If a foreign company wins control over you, whose ships will get the richest cargoes, whose pipe lines will run full? Who will make the profits, and who will pay the bills?

You may accept this as an absolute fact: "Unless the holding company can be set up with a safe working majority of the stock of the Union Oil Company of California, it will not be set up at all."

Tonight at midnight the books close. They will not be re-opened.

UNION OIL ASSOCIATES

20 March 1922.
1134 Pacific Mutual Building, Los Angeles.

NOTE—Stockholders of the Union Oil Company of California who have no organization agreement blanks at hand, who telegraph today or mail, under today's postmark, a pledge to turn in their stock, will be included in the holding company and will be furnished with the necessary blanks immediately.

BATTLE CALL!

Dramatic, last-day appeal in California papers by Union Oil Associates to "save the company from foreign control."

anything but complimentary to Californians. Every stockholder owes it to his pocketbook, to California, and to his nation to keep the American flag flying over California's oil fields."

On the last day of the battle, March 19, 1922, the Union Oil Associates took a full-page ad in California papers to make this appeal:

"Union Oil Stockholders. This is the last day of battle—the last day in which you can throw the influence of your shares into the balance which must determine whether the Union Oil Company of California shall remain an American institution or not.

"You have today an American—a California—company, carried on by Americans in the interest of Americans, controlling a quarter of the State's oil supply and doing a business of $60,000,000 a year. Will it become a mere subsidiary of the Royal Dutch Shell—a pawn resident in Holland but moved from London—shoved back and forth across the international chessboard in a world-wide war of the nations for the control of the oil supply, and possibly sacrificed, if desirable, without hesitation or regret—and you with it—to some selfish interest of those who are without interest in you, in your City, in your State, in your Country?

"Tonight at midnight the books close. They will not be re-opened."

The excitement reached a near-frenzy state on the crucial midnight before March 20, 1922. When the count of proxies and stockholders was made, the tally showed that Union Oil Associates controlled 275,000 shares, or 25,000 more than were needed. The Johnson group, having waited too long, was holding the sack with a big block of shares not needed in the battle. The fight was a great personal triumph for Isaac Milbank and for Lyman Stewart, both of whom had come out of retirement to work day and night rounding up shares for the

Associates. At dawn on March 21, the Los Angeles *Examiner* banner-lined in 60-point type:

UNION OIL SAVED FROM FOREIGN CONTROL

The Union Oil Associates, victory having been won, lost no time in incorporating a 20-million-dollar holding company, which for the next decade held tightly to 57½ per cent of the outstanding Union Oil Company shares. Despite Judge Myers' previous ruling disbanding the Stewart family holding company, Union Oil Associates was deemed necessary to keep any group, either family, competing company, Wall Street, or foreign interests, from maneuvering control of Union Oil. With the Associates vigilantly on guard, no other serious raids on Union were attempted.

On May 1, 1922, Lee Higginson & Company of Boston announced a 20-million-dollar preferred stock issue for the new Shell-Union Oil Corporation, which took over the 26½ per cent of Union Oil of California owned by the Royal Dutch Shell and Union Oil Company of Delaware. Union of Delaware also held other mid-continent oil interests. (In July, 1924, Shell-Union disposed of its shares in Union Oil of California, selling them to the general public on the open market, and on December 20, 1932, Union Oil Associates was merged with Union Oil Company of California.)

With Union Oil Company of California secure in California hands, President W. L. Stewart moved forward with developments that made 1922 a memorable year in the history of the company. Union's financial position was so strong that the company was able to float a twenty-year issue of 6 per cent gold bonds to provide capital for an important refinery and marketing expansion. A research department to develop new products was organized at the Los Angeles refinery. In November the board of directors celebrated by authorizing the distribution of the unissued shares of capital stock to shareholders, an action which the Los Angeles *Herald* hailed, on December 27, 1922, as:

FORTY MILLION MELON CUT BY UNION

"A forty million melon was cut by Union Oil of California at the board of directors' meeting today in Los Angeles. The directors declared a dividend of eighty per cent, equivalent to $40 million at the par value of $100 per share. Union Oil is quoted at approximately $160 per share."

This generous melon culminated in a decision at the board meeting of December 20 to increase the capitalization to 1,250,000 shares, with a $100 par value. This made Union Oil of California a 125-million-dollar corporation. The company's earnings for the year were 21½ per cent. Santa Fe Springs had become a rich and prodigious field. The oil business was booming, in spite of overproduction which caused the company to shut in 165 wells.

But Union soon found itself with a new fight on its hands, from an unexpected source. The city of Los Angeles, which had become marine-minded, anticipating completion of the Panama Canal, reached out for a harbor, annexing the little municipality of San Pedro, into which for a decade Union Oil had been pouring money to create a deepwater terminal for its tankers. When San Pedro was gerrymandered into Los Angeles by a strip of land 1 mile wide and 20 miles long, known as the Shoestring, the Los Angeles city officials undertook to oust Union Oil from the water-front property controlled by the Outer Harbor Dock & Terminal Company. At the time the Outer Harbor project, which was Lyman Stewart's pet project, was about three-fourths completed.

When they filed their suit for ejectment, the Los Angeles city officials bumped head-on into a wrathy and scrappy old fighter. Rarely given to anger, this move aroused the full ire of Lyman Stewart. He slapped a legal action right back at the city, charging Los Angeles' action was "an unwarranted attempt to confiscate our property—property as justly and lawfully acquired as any property can be," adding that "it is our firm determination to protect our rights at the ultimate latitude given us by the laws of the municipality, the commonwealth, and the nation."

"We have in perfectly good faith invested $1,600,000 in this enterprise," he explained to the city council. "This money is the property of 4,200 stockholders, the larger number of whom are residents and taxpayers of Los Angeles, and it seems inconceivable that the city administration would seek to deprive its own citizens of their justly acquired legal actions."

This vigorous stand stood the city officials back on their heels. To avert a long legal fight, they offered a compromise. Union could hold, under a thirty-year lease agreement, the acreage it had developed and which the city promised to purchase eventually. Stewart agreed to this compromise, which assured Union a harbor terminal for the next thirty years. (When the agreement expired on April 4, 1952, the wharves, piers, channels, and bulkheads became the property of the Los Angeles Board of Harbor Commissioners, while the installations and machinery remained the property of Union Oil Company, which meantime had purchased 260 acres for a refinery site adjoining the harbor. In 1955, Union sold the Outer Harbor Dock & Terminal Company.)

By 1923 the investment of millions for new facilities was paying handsome returns. Union had tanks and reservoirs capable of storing 32,000,000 barrels of oil. They included large bulk distributing stations such as the one erected on the Honolulu water front, to serve Hawaiian plantations, and also a chain of service stations built in the Islands. Union's California storage tanks were fed by 484 miles of trunk pipelines and 351 miles of gathering lines, with a daily capacity of 275,000 barrels. The tanker fleet included 14 steamships and 21 barges. Union's drillers made an important new strike in California with the discovery of the Dominguez field in September. Other drilling crews tapped the Wellington dome near Fort Collins, Colorado, where a well came in as a 75-million-cubic-foot-per-day gasser.

President W. L. Stewart achieved one of his ambitions by establishment of the Provident Fund, adopted by the board of directors on July 1, 1923. This created a retirement fund for Union Oilers, supplementing the employees' benefit fund, which provided medical care and hospitalization, and the profit-sharing

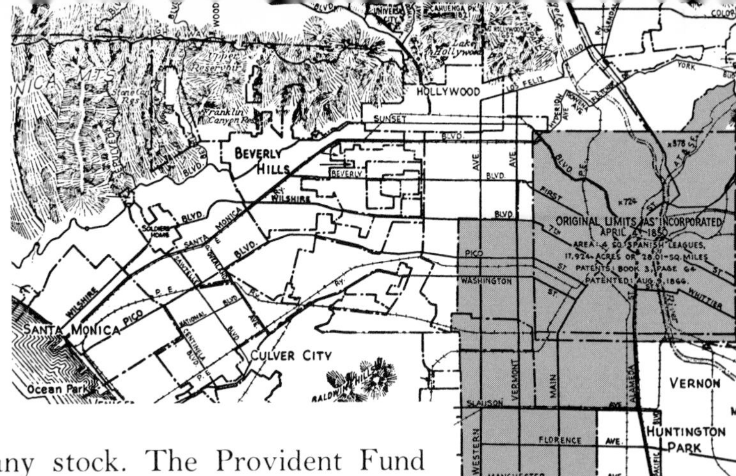

SHOESTRING TO TIDEWATER

Odd shape of Los Angeles boundaries reveals the "shoestring" the city gerrymandered to acquire a port at San Pedro, where Union had spent more than a million on harbor development.

plan, which enabled them to invest in company stock. The Provident Fund rounded out Union's employee welfare program, making it one of the broadest in the West.

In 1923, an eager young newcomer joined W. W. Orcutt's staff of bright young oil hunters. He was a young Kentuckian from Louisville named Albert Chatfield Rubel, better known as "Cy," who had studied mining engineering at the University of Arizona, then served in World War I as a captain in the Corps of Engineers. After spending four years with exploratory crews in New Mexico, Guatemala, and Honduras, Rubel heard in 1923 that Union Oil needed a petroleum engineer. He recommended himself for the job and got it. A scientific oil geologist, Rubel gradually became Orcutt's right-hand man and eventual successor.

On the morning of September 29, 1923, at the age of eighty-three, Lyman Stewart died. His last fight, in association with Isaac Milbank, to save Union the year before from the foreign grab had taxed his strength, as it had that of Milbank, who died five months after the victory. Seven weeks after Lyman Stewart's death, his brother Milton, who had been ill for months, passed away, never knowing that his younger brother had preceded him. Thus the mild-mannered, evangelical, picturesque brothers, who had helped launch the Oil Age on its way sixty years before, and who had pioneered California's oil industry in sleepy Newhall forty years before, passed from the scene, leaving a younger generation of oil men, with a new outlook, at Union's helm.

Appraising Lyman Stewart's role, the editor of the *Petroleum World* wrote, in October, 1923:

"The life of this revered veteran of oil, ended by an attack of acute bronchitis and bronchial pneumonia, was the longest record of oil achievement which can be credited to any American. Sixty-four years he served petroleum, twenty-four in Pennsylvania, forty in California. Eighty-three years old when his gentle soul was called, his name was known wherever oil was spoken of and his three-score years of square dealing in business and kind personal interest in all around him had earned the friendship and respect of thousands. On October 1, when his funeral services were held at the Bible Institute in Los Angeles, for which institution he labored so hard the last fifteen years of his life, thousands of people paid their final respects to his memory . . . . Long recognized as the father of oil in the Pacific Coast region, long given the honored title of 'dean of western oil men,' consulted by the oldest and the wisest and held in respectful awe by the younger element, Lyman Stewart had been the outstanding figure in California oil for forty years."

The editor of the *Union Oil Bulletin* (October, 1923) declared:

"In the history of his life there are many glimpses of the human side of the man. You can visualize his thrifty boyhood when he made his first investment in oil, and just when he was on the threshold of success, came the Civil War. You can imagine the inevitable struggle. On one side were youth and money, the flush of success and the vision of the future. On the other side was duty—often no bright and easy thing. His was the right choice—duty; and the record of it brings more honor to his memory.

"He helped to blaze the trail in unproven California in the early Eighties, when oil production in the state was little more than a dream. He faced difficulties with stoicism and optimism, and played a mighty part in the upbuilding of California's oil industry with which he was constructively identified from its infancy. To his counsel, advice, and leadership, does the Union Oil Company of California largely owe its commanding position in the oil business of the West today."

In 1924, when Shell-Union Corporation unloaded its shares in Union Oil Company of California, the directors decided to split Union's shares four for one. This brought Union's outstanding shares to 5,000,000 at $25 par each. Union's stock was listed on the New York Stock Exchange in November, 1924. By the end of the year, the company was owned by 6,428 stockholders, including the 3,866 shareholders in Union Oil Associates, which still held 57½ per cent of the shares of Union Oil Company of California. The following year, 1925, the board of directors decided to offer 100,000 shares to employees on a time-payment plan.

In 1926 an important new face appeared at the table of the Union board of directors, that of W. L. Stewart, Jr. Like his father, Union's president, Bill Stewart started learning the oil business in the field. Where President Will Stewart had started as a rig builder and roustabout, son Bill started as a pipe-fitter at the Los Angeles refinery. During his college years he went to sea on Union tankers. A graduate of Stanford University and M.I.T., Bill Stewart's interests centered in research and refining. Though proud of his start as a pipefitter, Bill Stewart delighted in recalling the day when Grandfather Lyman Stewart, showing a party of friends through the Wilmington refinery, introduced young Bill, then asked: "How much did this property cost?" Bill didn't know.

"What's the payroll of the refinery?" asked Lyman Stewart. Grandson Stewart didn't know the answer to that one, either.

"What is the refinery going to cost?" When Bill missed the third question, his grandfather led the party away in disgust, convinced that Union's embryo future director and board chairman never would rise above the rank of pipefitter.

The year saw memorable expansions in several directions. Union formed a partnership with Pantepec Oil Company of Venezuela, and committed 3½ million dollars to test a vast concession of 880,000 acres, located in Venezuela, for oil. To carry out this project, a new subsidiary, Union National Petroleum Company was organized under the laws of Delaware.

During the year the company's research and development men employed the

Union Oil Company of California

UNLESS MARKED "COPYRIGHT" ARTICLES IN THIS MAGAZINE MAY BE USED IN ANY OTHER PUBLICATION

ADDRESS ALL COMMUNICATIONS TO THE "BULLETIN" 901 UNION OIL BUILDING LOS ANGELES, CALIF.

W. L. STEWART - - - - *President*

E. W. CLARK, *Executive Vice-President*
W. W. ORCUTT - - - *Vice-President*
L. P. ST. CLAIR - - - *Vice-President*
R. D. MATTHEWS - - - *Comptroller*
JOHN McPEAK - - - - - *Secretary*

R. J. KEOWN - - - - - - - - - - - - - *Treasurer*
PAUL M. GREGG - - - - - - - - *General Counsel*
C. W. BROWN - - *Director, Exploration and Production*
E. I. DYER - - - - - - - - - - *Technical Director*
C. W. RALPH - - - - *Director, Sales and Transportation*

VOLUME 3 | OCTOBER, 1923 | BULLETIN NO. 32

END OF A LONG CAREER

The death of Lyman Stewart at age 83—memorialized in the company magazine—ended a vital 64 years in the oil business. In failing health at the last, he nevertheless managed to wage a vigorous battle to save the company only a year before he died.

gas-lift method for the first time to stimulate production of crude oil and natural gasoline in the company's fields. Another milestone was the marketing of the first ethylene gasoline for higher-compression automobile engines. To produce more high-test gasoline, cracking plants were built at the company's refineries, increasing the capacity to 100,000 barrels a day. Gasoline refining had become a fine art.

The nightmare of Union's transportation men had always been fire at one of the vast tank farms which were necessary in the orderly flow of rivers of oil from the oil fields to the markets. On the morning of April 7, 1926, a storm swept in from the Pacific Ocean, accompanied by dazzling flashes of lightning. At 7:53 a.m., three 1,000,000-barrel reservoirs at San Luis Obispo Tank Farm were ignited simultaneously by bolts of lightning. Fifteen minutes later a bolt hit an adjoining reservoir. The resulting inferno was too huge and hot for men even to approach. After burning out of control for seventeen hours, the emulsified oil in the four reservoirs boiled over, igniting a fifth reservoir and a row of steel tanks. A few minutes later terrific whirlwinds struck the area, generated by the heat and aggravated by 40-mile-an-hour gales. Burning embers spattered the roof of a sixth reservoir, setting afire 1,300,000 barrels of crude. More steel tanks were scorched and warped by the boiling over of the fifth and sixth reservoirs. The flames and smoke billowed skyward like a volcano for days, attracting greater crowds than a circus. Fifteen huge steel tanks crumpled under the terrific heat.

While this inferno blazed at San Luis Obispo, the same capricious storm moved south and east, hovering one day later over Union's great tank farm at Stewart, 1 mile west of the town of Brea in Orange County. At 9 a.m. on April 8, a bolt of lightning ignited two of the Stewart reservoirs simultaneously. When these boiled over, they ignited a third and finally engulfed a small refinery in the lake of flaming oil. An army of 3,000 men, hurriedly recruited from nearby oil fields and refineries, tossed up dikes that held the lake of fire, which finally burned itself out, leaving a tangle of black, hot ruins.

When insurance writers were able to appraise the damage of this double baptism by flame, they branded it the greatest fire loss since the San Francisco fire of 1906. Nearly 8 million barrels of oil were destroyed, plus 21 huge steel tanks. The fires damaged reservoirs, innumerable pipeline fittings, and many pumps, as well as surrounding ranches. After the insurance adjusters finally finished their calculating, Union's treasurer received checks totaling more than $9,000,000.

These great fires led to one of Union's unique operations, the "fire lab," which has specialized ever since in quenching oil fires. The fire lab consists of metal tanks, pits, sheds, towers, vehicles, and other installations which are deliberately set afire, burning various kinds of oils and gases, so that Union's fire fighters may study the habits of blazes and practice putting them out. These fire labs, near the Los Angeles refinery and at Oleum, have made experienced fire fighters of more than 2,000 Union Oilers.

When the first classes, on a hill back of the Los Angeles refinery, began starting fires so that they could be put out again under the direction of Union's fire chief, Jess Marshall, firemen from neighboring towns followed the smoke to see what it was all about. The firemen stayed to learn. Knowing that oil conflagrations are a different breed of fire from ordinary blazes, they asked if they could bring some of their fellow fire fighters to see how Union's team smothered blazes with man-made fogs and dews. Hundreds of Los Angeles and Long Beach firemen have attended Union's fire-fighter demonstrations. When the word got farther afield, visiting firemen from distant cities, including a team

FIRE SCHOOL

Great fires at Union's tank farms led to a unique operation, the Fire Lab, which has taught thousands of Union Oilers as well as naval, military, and civilian fire fighters the latest techniques for halting blazes.

LIGHTNING FIRE AT SAN LUIS OBISPO *One of the most spectacular and costly fires in the history of the petroleum industry was touched off by lightning strikes at the San Luis Obispo tank farm April 7, 1926. As a result of this fire, more effective methods were developed for controlling oil fires.*

WINNER IN UNION-SPONSORED AIR RACE

One of the most attractive entries in the 1929 National Air Races in Los Angeles was Ruth Elder, who finished well up in the heavy plane class. Union contributed $25,000 to help underwrite the race.

from Honolulu, came to study oil fire fighting. Later, when Union dispatched teams over the Western states to train Union Oilers in various depots how to respect and not fear fires, local fire departments assigned more men to take the courses. So did the armed forces. The big pay-off has been the efficiency with which later oil fires at Union installations have been brought under control.

A flurry of merger rumors in 1926 touched off a stock-market boom in both Union Oil and Union Associates stock. On one day 14,656 shares changed hands on the Los Angeles Stock Exchange, while on the San Francisco Exchange 50,000 shares were traded. What started the rumor mill, apparently, was an overseas sales program launched by Union Oil and Atlantic Refining Company jointly to market products in Australia, New Zealand, and other Southern Hemisphere areas. To serve these markets, the two companies formed, on a fifty-fifty basis, a subsidiary known as Atlantic-Union Refining Company. Reaching overseas for outlets for the plethora of oil flowing from California's oil fields, Union's management invested 3 million dollars in this venture. It was an all too brief period when, despite the ravenous thirst of automobiles, California had too much oil, and gasoline dropped in price to 12½ cents. At the time of the merger rumors, both Henry M. Robinson, president of Union Oil Associates, and Union's executive vice-president, E. W. Clark, were in New York. This added plausibility to the reports. Most of California's larger independent oil companies had been absorbed already into larger corporations with headquarters in the East.

On February 23, 1928, President W. L. Stewart found it necessary, as the Los Angeles *Examiner* put it, "to repeat what he has steadily stated during the past two years regarding Union Oil mergers, that there is no truth in the latest revived rumors that Union will be merged with the Atlantic Refining Company or any other large concern. He says there is nothing to it."

Meantime, the Union management was becoming air-minded. It authorized the purchase of four airplanes in 1928 and enthusiastically contributed $25,000 to help underwrite the National Air Races in Los Angeles. It was front-page news when Director Gurney Newlin hopped in a company monoplane at San Francisco at 6 a.m. and arrived in Los Angeles, three hours later, to attend a 10 o'clock board meeting. The board also agreed to pay for the transportation of a Professor Schreiber from Berlin to Los Angeles to lecture at U.S.C. on aviation law.

By the end of the year, the Atlantic-Union Oil Company, moving into the Antipodes with a great sales drive, had 250 sales depots opened in Australia and New Zealand. The subsidiary had spent $4,100,000 developing markets down under. The joint operation with Atlantic Refining unfortunately kept the merger rumors floating. President W. L. Stewart was obliged to continue repeating his denials that Union's directors had any merger plans.

Union Oil had 6,693 stockholders, exclusive of Union Oil Associates, with average holdings of 20 to 44 shares each. Union Oil Associates had 3,853 shareholders, with average holdings of 561 shares each. Union's employees owned 2 million dollars' worth of stock, 5,000 of them having taken advantage of the opportunity to invest through the Provident Fund. The company was in its strongest financial position since its founding. Despite the overproduction in California, Union was buying 67,000 barrels of oil a day. The company could buy "distress" oil cheaper than it could pump crude from some of its own wells. The new fields at Santa Fe Springs, Dominguez, and Rosecrans were providing so much crude that the management rushed additions to refineries, pipelines, and storage facilities and ordered more tankers.

By 1930, the fortieth anniversary of Union's corporate life, financial and

SOUTHERN CROSS FLEW WITH UNION GASOLINE *Union Oil helped to keep the "Southern Cross" aloft on its historic flight from Oakland, California, to Australia in 1928. The plane is shown here being fueled for its over-ocean venture.*

petroleum writers were making eye-opening appraisals of the "big independent" among California's oil producers. The Los Angeles *Times* summarized the company's dividend history by reporting: "When stockholders of Union Oil of California received 50 cents a share in cash and one per cent in stock last Saturday, it marked the 262nd dividend paid by that company. Throughout the history of the company to date, $101,260,373 in cash and stock worth $62,911,272 have been paid out to stockholders. The total of these two items is more than $164,171,000."

The *Petroleum World*, calling Union "the oldest of the existing operating companies on the Pacific Coast," added: "Union's growth, while not spectacular at any stage, borders on the phenomenal. In the past ten years, Union has discovered four of California's major oil fields, Santa Fe Springs, Richfield, Dominguez, and Rosecrans. In the manufacturing of oil, its pioneering has also been in evidence. It was one of the first to develop tubular stills. It has developed a direct fractionation of gasoline and serial fractional condensation. The company was also one of the first to use high pressure cracking on a commercial scale. Major improvements in design for absorption towers and stills for recovering gasoline from natural gas are also credited to the company. The Santa Paula refinery was one of the first built in California; today the company owns seven.

"The company also built the first pipeline for tidewater transportation of oil, and was the first to move oil in bulk by tankers. It pioneered the use of oil for locomotive fuel."

In another article, *Petroleum World* summarized Union's growth by saying: "Its original capitalization, five million dollars, now stands at $125 million, with its assets approximating $400 million. Its annual flow of oil has jumped from 85,000 barrels of oil in 1890 to more than 18,000,000 barrels with several million barrels shut in. Its oil lands have expanded until today the company owns in fee or mineral rights fee more than 600,000 acres in California, Texas, Wyoming, and Colombia, South America. It holds under lease over 100,000 acres in addition to joint interests in 880,000 acres in Venezuela. Its sales have grown from less than $100,000 yearly to approximately $90 million. Since 1900 the company has produced, from its own wells, 226,625,000 barrels of oil, and from controlled wells an additional 18,545,000 barrels."

Eight years free from factional strife had enabled the husky independent to expand and grow into a petroleum producer far beyond the most optimistic dreams of even Founder Lyman Stewart. As he rounded out his fifteenth year as Union's president in 1930, William L. Stewart reported to the 9,626 stockholders: "The company's affairs are in a strong financial position and sound."

This was the bright outlook on paper. Although the 1929 stock market crash had shaken the business world to its foundations, the oil industry was not yet alarmed about the dark clouds on the economic horizon. But these clouds were harbingers of the depression thirties that would test the Union Oil Company more ruthlessly than any period in its history, with the possible exception of the first trying decade, when Lyman Stewart and Wallace Hardison kept it alive by sheer stubbornness and fortitude.

ETHYL ENTERS THE MARKETPLACE

In the twenties, as autos and paved roads became more common, there was a period of great service station expansion. Union stations such as the one above began to appear. The advertisement at the right appeared in April 1927, extolling the first Ethyl gasoline for higher-compression automobile engines.

CHAPTER EIGHT 1930-1940

The Rugged Thirties

UNION OIL WAS SWEPT INTO THE RUGGED DEPRESSION YEARS of the thirties without a Stewart hand at the helm. On June 21, 1930, four months after his cheerful report to the stockholders, President William L. Stewart died suddenly of a heart attack at his summer house at Hermosa Beach. Although he had not been well for some time, Will Stewart had continued to guide the company with a firm hand. During his fifteen years as president, he had welded the conflicting factions in Union together by genial personality plus adroit leadership. He had accomplished by persuasion what Lyman Stewart achieved by corporate power. Will Stewart, who called himself "an old rig builder," knew the oil business from top to bottom, having started as a roustabout thirty-six years before, then working up as a pipeliner, salesman, and production manager. He had a feeling for Union's workers, and one of his outstanding contributions to the company's growth was the industrial-relations program he installed. In his thinking in this field, W. L. Stewart was years ahead of his time, as was pointed out by the *California Oil World:*

"To W. L. Stewart may be attributed a systematic industrial relations activity. He had an intense interest in the problems of the employees. Men instinctively liked him, and he showed the same capacity as his father to enlist in the company's service capable, experienced workmen in all phases of the industry. He was quick to approve worthwhile effort, and believed in giving his lieutenants scope to apply their talents. About his own duties he went quietly and unobtrusively, preferring always to encourage and direct rather than drive. He was amenable to suggestions at all times. Democratic, soft-spoken, kindly, he was nevertheless

REDISCOVERY IN AN OLD FIELD

Lyman Stewart purchased the Santa Maria fields in 1902; but rediscovery of its vast oil reserves was made in 1936. This night shot shows the around-the-clock nature of the oil drilling operation.

a man of decision, and Union Oil enjoyed a remarkable period of progress and prosperity under his leadership."

The loss of Will Stewart at this particular time was a body blow to the company. Suddenly, overnight, the Stewart family, the amalgam that had held the Union Oil Company and its many offshoot subsidiaries together, no longer served that function. True, there were two Stewart sons in the company at that time, thirty-three-year-old W. L., Jr., director of manufacturing, and Arthur C., eight years younger, in the sales department. Both grandsons of the founder of the company had started work at roustabout jobs in the oil fields during summer vacations. Will Stewart had insisted that his sons learn the business from the bottom up, as he had done. So son Bill, after a fine technical training as a chemical and mechanical engineer at Stanford University and M.I.T., had started as a pipefitter at the Wilmington refinery, where he worked up to foreman, then climbed the rungs of the ladder in the manufacturing department. Four years previous to his father's death, the directors elected him to a seat on the Union Oil board of directors. Son Arthur, twenty-five years old in 1930, had graduated from Stanford University as an engineer, then continued his studies at the Harvard School of Business. His book learning did not keep him from shipping as a wiper in the engine room of a Union tanker. Then he started his sales career as a marine-service-station attendant on the fishing docks at San Pedro. Like his father, affable Art Stewart had a flair for making friends and for selling.

Unfortunately, in the emergency brought about by Will Stewart's death, the directors felt that neither of the third-generation Stewarts was sufficiently seasoned as yet to assume the presidency of Union Oil. The Stewart family was no longer a controlling factor in the company's ownership. In 1930 the company was still controlled by Union Oil Associates, headed by Banker Henry M. Robinson, the most influential member of the Union Oil board of directors because he represented more than 6,000 shareholders.

The Union board decided to set up what was regarded at the time as an emergency or interim administration of the company's operations. On July 7, 1930, E. W. Clark, who had retired as executive vice-president the year before but who had remained on the board and on the executive committee, was called back to be chairman of Union's board. L. P. St. Clair, former head of the Independent Oil Producers Agency, who had succeeded Clark as vice-president, was named as president of Union Oil. W. L. Stewart, Jr., who had been director of manufacturing for a year previous, was made a vice-president. Three veteran vice-presidents from the former regime continued at their posts. They were geologist William W. Orcutt, who directed exploration; Robert David Matthews, whose specialty was accounting and finance; and counsel Paul Gregg, a legal authority on California oil laws.

Among these officers, Clark came nearer to filling the shoes of either Lyman or Will Stewart than any of the others. A native of New Hampshire, "E. W.," as he was known to everyone in the oil industry, had come to California in 1897 and had found work on the narrow-gauge Pacific Coast Railway, which ran north and south out of San Luis Obispo, serving Union's oil fields in Santa Barbara

HARD-DRIVING CLARK

During a management crisis, versatile and able E. W. Clark agreed to resume his position as chairman of the board of directors. In earlier years, he had directed operations of the Producers Pipeline (above). *He was well known and liked throughout the industry. He was also noted for his fondness for fast sports cars, which he drove like a racer.*

County. Clark was manager of the little railway when he founded the Pinal-Dome Oil Company, later purchased by Union. When the Independent Producers Agency and Union Oil jointly laid the important pipeline to carry the products from the San Joaquin Valley independents to the sea, Clark became general manager of the Producers Transportation Company, which had since become an important wholly owned subsidiary of Union Oil. Clark became Union's general manager, then executive vice-president, and had served in these capacities since 1921.

A versatile character, Clark frequently turned up in the fields and out-of-the-way pumping stations seldom visited by the "big brass" to talk with men on duty at Union's lonely stations. He was one of the founders of the American Petroleum Institute in 1919 and served two years as president in 1927 and 1928. His hobby was fast sports-model automobiles, which he drove like a racer. A beloved character with friends at all levels of the oil industry, Clark shunned the spotlight so persistently that his role in Union's growth, and that of the oil industry as well, was seldom appreciated. With this background, he would have made an ideal president for the company, but for his age and health.

So the board chose, to pilot Union Oil through the rugged years ahead, another veteran of many oil-field battles as spokesman for the independents, Leonard Pressley St. Clair. A moving spirit in organizing the Independent Producers

Agency, "Press," the agency's head, had jockeyed Standard and Associated Oil into boosting the purchase price of crude, in the San Joaquin Valley fields, from 11½ to 83 cents a barrel. When the big companies refused to pay more, he had leagued up with Will Stewart to make Union the sole marketing outlet for the independents, thus doubling the flood of oil the company had to sell and pushing Union into the world markets. St. Clair became an important factor in the phenomenal growth of the company. For eight years previous to his election as president, he had served as Union Oil Company vice-president.

Born in Dutch Flat in California's Mother Lode, St. Clair was raised in Bakersfield, where as a youngster he helped his father lay out the town's first gas main. After further apprenticeship in San Francisco, St. Clair returned to manage the Bakersfield Gas & Electric Company. When the spectacular Kern River oil strikes were made, he switched to oil and became a producer on his own.

With this background, Press St. Clair looked like the answer to Union's prayers. But, as it turned out, his was not quite the strong hand the directors sought to continue the role of either Lyman or Will Stewart. Where the Stewarts were soft-spoken and persuasive, husky, 6-foot, 220-pound Press St. Clair undertook to dominate committee meetings by out-talking, but not convincing, his colleagues. He was a dominating personality who loved a fight. In place of a meeting of the minds, Union's other executives adopted the practice of letting their vociferous new president talk himself out, after which they ran their departments as they thought best. Each division became a little realm of its own.

It was no enviable task the new president took over. California's oil wells were pouring out an unprecedented flood of crude, 887,000 barrels a day in 1930, for a market that could absorb only 675,000 barrels a day. Never before had there been so much oil in storage. Anything capable of holding oil was running

PRESIDENT PRESS ST. CLAIR

As champion of independent producers, he met crisis after crisis during depression days and managed to hold the company together.

over. Harassed producers dumped oil at prices below production cost. Price wars broke out in 1930. Union cut its drilling rigs from 41 crews to 10, but the crews continued to drill for smaller independents, and they were hitting more prolific oil sands than had yet been tapped. The industry was rapidly slipping into chaos.

To add to the dilemma, hard times were pinching the automobile industry. Factory output of automobiles slipped from a high of 5,350,000 vehicles in 1929 to less than half that figure five years later. Gasoline for motorists had become the industry's most profitable product. In an effort to move gasoline, service stations sold it for less than the cost of production. Early in 1931, a six months' gasoline price war broke out that nearly ruined the Pacific Coast market. As a result of the chaotic marketing conditions, Union's sales toppled from the 89 million dollars high of 1929 to 61 million dollars in the first year of St. Clair's presidency. Sales continued to slip, and fell off another 10 million dollars during the following two years.

Despite the hard times, Union's directors managed to dig deep for $4,000,000 to acquire a one-half interest in the 160-acre King lease in Kettleman Hills, one of the richest oil strikes of the San Joaquin Valley, acquired from the Amerada Petroleum Corporation. They also bought a half interest in the Getty-Armstrong lease comprising 1,260 acres situated on the north dome of Kettleman Hills at an investment of $2,250,000. These purchases, plus acreage already held, made Union one of the top producers in the fabulous Kettleman Hills fields.

Union Oil sustained another blow in 1931, when E. W. Clark died suddenly, while in his doctor's office. The beloved chairman of the board had come nearer being the balance wheel that held together the individualistic Union Oil veterans than anyone else on the scene since Will Stewart's death. The one board member who could have taken over Clark's role was W. W. Orcutt, who by reason of his years of service and reputation in the industry carried much weight when he wished to use it. But Orcutt was a calm, unaggressive man who refused to allow himself to be drawn into controversies whipped up by the outbursts of Union's explosive president. The little empires within the Union Oil empire continued to grow.

In 1931 the Union directors decided it was time to unload some of the company's burdens. As a hedge against the hard times, they liquidated Union's interest in the Pantepec Oil Company, which held 880,000 acres for exploration in Venezuela. Thus they sacrificed the company's share in one of the world's great oil sources. (A small bite of the Venezuela bonanza came back into the Union fold three decades later, in 1965, when Pure Oil Company, which had leased some of the Lake Maracaibo acreage, became a division of Union Oil of California.) They whittled the number of drilling crews in the field down to six, barely enough to maintain Union's lease commitments to landholders. They cut the payroll a million dollars a year by establishing the five-day work week in 1931, thus beating the New Deal to the punch by about three years. To stave off the sales slump, they organized Union Service Station, Inc., a wholly owned subsidiary organized to take over and operate service stations of Union dealers caught in the depression's financial squeeze. These outlets and a small number

AMERADA KING, OF KETTLEMAN HILLS *Union's Amerada King No. 1 well, one of the oil-rich San Joaquin Valley's most famous, produced 20,000 barrels a day. Because of hard times, Union had to dig deep to come up with the necessary $4 million to acquire a one-half interest in these fabulous fields.*

of demonstration service stations built by the company became the nucleus around which Union built one of the outstanding retail service station chains of the country. Union was already strong in bulk depots. The service station chain made the company a big factor in the West Coast retail market.

To free their retail outlets from ruinous price-war competition, the Union refineries gave them a gasoline they could talk about. It was an improved motor fuel of the highest octane, or anti-knock rating that could be made at the time. The marketing department decided that this fine new product should have a distinctive name. After spirited discussions, the advertising meeting seeking an easily remembered name decided upon 76, the suggestion of Robert D. Matthews, the persuasive young Welshman who had been boning up on American history to qualify for his citizenship papers. Matthews was full of the spirit of '76, which by chance coincided with the highest octane rating that Union refineries were then able to achieve in the "finest anti-knock, non-premium gasoline ever offered."

When the new "76" gas was introduced to Union's customers in 1932, the company applied for registration of the name at the United States Patent Office and at the capitals of six states: California, Oregon, Washington, Idaho, Nevada, and Arizona. Six states agreed to register the new trade-mark, but the Patent Office rejected it on the grounds that "76" might be construed as the octane rating of the gasoline and hence could not be the exclusive property of Union Oil. Though Vic Kelly, director of sales, and Union's attorneys pointed out, first to the Patent Office and then to the United States Court of Customs and Patent Appeals, that the "76" referred to the famous spirit of '76 and not to the octane rating, they were turned down. (It was not until fifteen years later, on February 28, 1950, that Patent Office officials certified Union's trade-mark, the blue 76 on an orange background tied with the word "Union.") This was the origin of a famous trade-mark that has become one of Union's most valued, if intangible, assets.

Another milestone occurred on December 20, 1932, when the directors of Union Oil Associates and of Union Oil Company of California decided to merge their holdings. Under the terms of the merger agreement, the outstanding stock of Union Oil Associates was converted into shares of capital stock of Union Oil Company of California, whose capitalization was increased from $125,000,000 to $187,500,000. The merger brought the number of Union stockholders up to 21,274.

Dogged, desk-pounding President St. Clair still believed that the way to weather the depression was to cut expenses to the bone and tighten the company's belt, yet maintain Union's unbroken dividend records. In 1933 he unloaded the company's half interest in Atlantic-Union Refining Company in which Union had invested 3.5 million dollars. Though this relieved Union of further financial commitments, it also meant the loss of an interest in a growing chain of marketing outlets in Australia and New Zealand. The sales volume continued to slide

THE FINEST—IN THE AIR

In 1933 the U.S. Army Air Corps at Phoenix Airport, Arizona, used Union Aviation Gasoline for "speed and power."

downward, partly because competitors captured Union's Navy business by selling oil at less than cost of production, partly because the new NRA code curtailed output. But Union's directors continued the regular dividend.

By 1934 the picture began to look brighter. The marketing division spent $666,000 for new outlets, both for bulk and for retail. In Kern County a Union crew drilled what was the deepest hole in the world at the time, 11,377 feet. It was something to brag about in 1934, when, for the first time, the number of the company's producing wells passed the 1,000 mark. However, many of them were shut in, or beaned back to reduce the flood of oil inundating the market.

More momentous yet, the company spent $2,000,000 to build a lubricating-oil plant at Oleum. Union research people had been working for several years on a refining process to make this 100 per cent paraffin-base lubricating oil from California crude. The need for the oil was critical. The increased horsepower and speeds of automobiles made a "must" of lubricants that would resist oxidation. Pennsylvania crudes had yielded such a lubricant. By 1933 Eastern oils had grabbed almost half of the $80,000,000 West Coast lubricant market. Fortunately, Union's researchers discovered that by use of liquid propane, the asphalt and wax could be removed completely from Western crude oil. The result was a 100 per cent paraffin-base lubricating oil on a par with or better than the Eastern oil. Standard Oil of Indiana and Standard of New Jersey had also been working along these same lines. To avoid a legal contest, Union pooled its propane-solvent patents with those of these two companies. By 1934 the new refinery unit at Oleum was turning out paraffin-base Triton in quantity.

By 1935 a new optimism had spread through the company. Union still held almost 300,000 acres of promising or proven oil lands in California, New Mexico, Colorado, and Texas. The company had 686 producing wells, with 403 more shut in. Union drillers added 95 new wells in one year. The management spent $1,500,000 on new distribution and marketing facilities. To finance expansion, $13,500,000 worth of debentures was issued.

There was good ground for this rosy outlook. The Santa Maria field had been discovered. Deep drilling had paid off at Santa Fe Springs, Richfield, and Dominguez, proving up three more prodigious fields. In fact, the management felt so good about the outlook that they enlarged the employees' benefit plan, providing group disability insurance for employees to compensate them for loss of income during periods of sickness and off-duty accidents. The new executive vice-president, Robert D. Matthews, pointing out that the payroll topped 15.5 million dollars for the 8,928 employees, stated: "The company has for many

TRITON—A UNION OIL ACHIEVEMENT

Introduced in 1934, Triton Motor Oil was the product of years of research and development. Designed to push Eastern oils off the market, it was heavily promoted. Pages at right, from the Union Oil Bulletin *of November 1934, show the start of a 60,000-mile test run at Ascot Speedway and a typical advertisement of the day.*

DEPRESSION-MODEL SERVICE STATION *In the depression-age thirties, only two station designs were introduced. This unit, appearing in 1935, revealed a trend toward rounded corners and a double canopy to offer service to more customers.*

24 UNION OIL BULLETIN *for* NOVEMBER, 1934

and the car was started on its way to run between San Diego and Seattle on a schedule calling for 60,000 miles in 60 days. Earl Cooper, former AAA race track champion and now chief sales engineer of the company, said this schedule was feasible, and selected a crew of nine drivers made up almost entirely of racing pilots. Schedule maintenance required much high speed driving on open roads where such speeds were safe.

The start of the 60,000-mile Ascot speedway runs in which Triton was compared with high grade Western oils. Inset at top shows pit crew draining crankcase of a test car. Below drawing off sample of the crankcase lubricant at end of 500 miles.

years recognized the fact that maintenance of morale and more intimate contact and understanding within its organization is a prime factor in its progress and welfare, and feels that this relationship has been achieved."

By 1937, sales climbed to 83 million dollars, and earnings doubled. President St. Clair reported "both domestic gasoline sales and off-shore shipment of crude were the highest on record." Deep drilling had added millions of barrels to the company's reserves. Union's drillers had discovered the Rio Bravo field in the San Joaquin Valley with another deep well, 11,302 feet, the deepest producing well in the world at the time, yielding 2,600 barrels daily of high-gravity oil. Union was producing in Texas and had launched geophysical survey crews on an extensive earthshooting program to help the company's geologists spot more deep-strata formations under California. Other crews were exploring in Colombia and in Alaska, where Union, with other oil companies, held 135,000 acres under Federal leases. Following up the laboratory work that developed Triton motor oil, Union's researchers perfected a new diesel-engine lubricating oil, known as Diesolife, which proved as efficient in diesel-fuel engines as Triton did in gasoline engines.

Though Union had weathered the depression and both production and sales were on the upswing, the rugged years had changed the company in ways more serious than the scarcity of dollars. As Union rode out the storm, largely by living off its fat, discord developed within the management. All of the directors and many stockholders realized that drastic steps had to be taken to rebuild the company's run-down manufacturing plant and to regain Union's competitive position in both the West Coast and world markets. A start was made in 1937 at Oleum on two new refinery units. One new tank-ship was ordered. But no one was able to spark the entire directorate behind a unanimous plan of action.

President St. Clair, who believed that he had saved the company by cutting expenses to the bone and still maintaining the dividend record, was convinced that time and more belt tightening would eventually solve Union's problem. Recognizing the need for management house cleaning, St. Clair employed an efficiency expert to suggest ways of breaking up the cliques within the Union organization. Unfortunately the expert had ideas for breaking up the little empires, but not for rebuilding a big one.

One important faction was headed by smooth and ambitious executive vice-president Matthews. Born and educated in Wales, Matthews had been appointed comptroller by John Garrigues in the abrupt shake-up of 1913 and shortly thereafter, at the age of twenty-seven, was elected to the executive committee, at which time he was Union's youngest director. Though a Garrigues appointee, he voted a year later to investigate Garrigues' expenditures. After modernizing Union's accounting practices, Matthews was put in charge first of manufacturing operations, then of distribution. After he became executive vice-president in 1936, Matthews developed a flair for high-handed operation, frequently ignoring the president and the executive committee completely. These tactics, resented by his associates, doomed Matthews' dream of sometime becoming Union's president.

HE PROPOSED THE TRADEMARK "76"

Robert D. Matthews was elected to Union's executive committee when only twenty-seven, thus becoming the youngest director. It was while studying for U.S. citizenship that he became imbued with "the spirit of 76" and proposed "76" as a trademark.

Some directors and many stockholders placed their hopes on W. L., Jr., and Arthur C., the up-and-coming third generation of Stewarts, both of whom had worked up during the depression years to positions of importance. Bill Stewart, with his chemical engineering training, believed that Union's future lay in extracting more valuable products from crude petroleum, a program that involved a heavy investment in laboratories and up-to-date refinery equipment. Art Stewart, like his father and grandfather, was a salesman convinced that Union could market at better prices the high-value products that Bill Stewart wanted to recover from Union's flood of crude. Though the Stewart family was in no position to control the company and made no attempt to do so, hundreds of old-time stockholders who had fared well financially for four decades under the Stewart dynasty were for giving the grandsons of Lyman Stewart an opportunity to show what they could do with the oil empire he had founded.

Meantime, in 1937 an event occurred which played an important part in overcoming this impasse. Director Henry M. Robinson, the banker who had headed Union Associates and who had been a stabilizing influence in Union's affairs, died. Bill Stewart proposed, for his vacant seat on the board, the name of a vigorous, six-foot-three, 38-year-old steel man, Reese H. Taylor. Bill Stewart had served on the board of the Consolidated Steel Company, which Taylor headed, and he thought Taylor should sit on Union's board. The other directors agreed and on December 20, 1937, elected Taylor a director. Born in Los Angeles on July 6, 1900, Taylor had studied at Cornell and at the University of California, then joined the Llewellyn Iron Works, which was later merged to become the Consolidated Steel Corp., Ltd. Taylor became president of Consolidated Steel in December, 1933.

The differences between Union's factions came to a head in 1938, when, following a serious automobile accident, President St. Clair announced his retirement. Executive vice-president Matthews was the leading aspirant for

DYNAMIC PRESIDENT REESE H. TAYLOR

The dreams of Lyman Stewart began to come true during the presidency of Reese Taylor who transformed an old family company into one of the nation's lusty half-billion-dollar corporations, while still carrying out the basic policies established by the founders. After 18 years as president, he became chairman of the board in 1956. He died on June 22, 1962.

president but lacked the support of the majority of the directors. The Matthews faction would not settle for another Stewart administration, which several directors and numerous stockholders advocated. While the board was looking for a strong man from outside to pull the discordant Union house together, Director William S. Charnley suddenly had an inspiration. "He is sitting at this table," Charnley told himself. Making an off-the-record inquiry among the other directors, Charnley found that nearly all of them agreed that Reese Taylor was the man they were seeking for Union's president. Charnley put the proposition up to Taylor, who, after much soul searching, indicated his willingness to resign his post with Consolidated Steel to become head of Union Oil. Taylor's one condition was that he be allowed to run the company without interference. The Matthews group vigorously opposed the choice of Taylor when he was mentioned at the October, 1938, board meeting.

Taylor's election took the oil world by surprise. The young mechanical engineer had built a fine reputation as production manager and executive vice-president and finally president of Consolidated Steel, but he had no experience as an oil man. Among steel men, his selling methods during depression years became a legend. When the Metropolitan Aqueduct ordered siphons too huge to be transported by rail from the East, Taylor contracted to fabricate them in Los Angeles and deliver them by truck and trailer, a feat that required clearing all traffic from highways to make room for the big tubes. When Easterners thought they had the fabrication of transmission towers from Hoover Dam to Los Angeles tied up, Taylor turned up with some new engineering wrinkles that won a big slice of this business. Though a steel man at heart and by experience, Taylor was intrigued by oil, he explained, because it was a basic California industry, while steel, at the time, was a Western arm of an Eastern industry. The steel man's impact on Union Oil Company of California was little short of atomic. On the morning of October 24, 1938, when the new president reported for work, "things began to happen fast."

Chief geologist Cy Rubel happened to be in his office early that day, working on a complicated exploration problem. About 7:45 a.m. the intercom buzzed. Assuming that nobody but the janitor would be in the building that early, Rubel ignored the call. In a few minutes the box buzzed again. After the third buzz, Rubel flipped the switch and barked: "Who in the hell is it and what do you want?"

"This is Reese Taylor," a new voice replied. "Where is everybody? I want to talk with somebody who can tell me something about the oil business."

A few minutes later, the lanky ex-steel man strode into Rubel's office to begin learning the oil business from "the top down," as he has described his hurry-up education. Taylor was not so much of an innocent among the oil hunters as he pretended to be. During his year on Union's board he had soaked up facts about oil production and marketing like a sponge. Within an hour, word of Taylor's early arrival at his office had spread from the twelfth floor to the basement of the Union Oil Building in downtown Los Angeles. Everybody sensed that the new Union workday began at 7:45. By the end of the week, Union Oilers had formed the habit of getting to their desks before Taylor reached his, because anybody in the building might be buzzed to help the president with his education.

The executive committee of five, which for years had met once a week to decide on leases, purchases, and other urgent matters, now gathered every morning at ten for a quick run-down of the day's problems. These daily sessions were shots in the arm for the entire organization. Oil hunter Sam Grinsfelder, trying to grab a toe hold for Union in Texas, where he had lost several promising leases to rivals while he waited for an okay from headquarters, suddenly found that he could get decisions faster than his competitors. Superintendents were told to make their own decisions in most cases, because nobody at the head office knew the facts as well as the man in the field.

"We got a team under Reese," said W. L. Stewart, Jr., who took pride that he first proposed Taylor for Union's board and backed him for the presidency. "That was a real revolution in the company."

Taylor took over as Union Oil reached a peculiar and critical period in its history. During the first three decades, the company had grown fabulously, even in the years when its founders were stone-broke. Then, during the depression

UNION OIL HEADQUARTERS FOR THIRTY YEARS

Union Oil Building (under construction) served the company well until it was outgrown by expanding business in 1958. It was located at Seventh and Hope Streets in Los Angeles.

years, it had survived and paid dividends regularly, largely at the expense of replacement of facilities. Of Union's five refineries, only three—at Oleum, Wilmington, and Bakersfield—were turning out products. Several key departments were headed by old-timers who had built their divisions into little realms half independent of the rest of the company. Taylor decreed that these realms had to end. Some department heads took the change of pace in stride; others resisted and were retired.

One top official disapproving the changes was Executive Vice-president Matthews. Heretofore he had successfully by-passed former President St. Clair by taking his ideas straight to the directors. When the board approved them, St. Clair was forced to accept the Matthews program. Matthews tried the same tactics with Taylor, who promptly reminded the directors that he had accepted the Union Oil presidency with the understanding that factions inside the organization would be wiped out. The directors agreed. Then Taylor called Matthews into his office and invited him to retire, which Matthews did early in 1939. Several "Matthews men" also left the payroll at the same time. Factions within the company evaporated. Once more Union's destiny was in the hands of a smooth management team, most of them younger men.

One important change occurred when W. W. Orcutt, who had built up Union's geological department, retired. Orcutt had hired dozens of young geologists fresh out of college, tested them, then built them into top-flight oil-finders. Among them was A. C. Rubel, who had become convinced, while still a field geologist, that the easy oil strikes had been made; to maintain its reserves, Union had to replace rock-hunting and doodle-bugging with teams of geophysical scientists.

When Rubel assumed responsibility for Union's exploration and production, on January 1, 1939, he had the opportunity to put his ideas into effect. Before long, he had geophysical crews shooting the earth, not only in California but in Texas and Louisiana, in the RockyMountain area, and from Alaska to South America. Wherever their subterranean soundings indicated that oil might be trapped, Union's drillers moved in to drill deeper holes than even the six "deepest holes" they had just completed in the Rio Bravo field.

The research and manufacturing division likewise had its quota of eager and ambitious young technicians, graduates of the universities and technical schools. Under the direction of W. L. Stewart, Jr., these researchers unlocked the secrets of making more power-packed gasolines, smoother lubricants, and a remarkable new all-purpose barium-base grease called Unoba, which replaced scores of specialized greases in the automotive and industrial field. What these younger Union Oilers needed were better tools. The research staff was jammed into crowded, inadequate quarters at the Los Angeles refinery and such other nearby space as the company could rent. Sensing that one of the answers to Union's problems was to extract more high-priced products from each barrel of oil, the new president gave the go-ahead for an expanded research and development department.

W. L. STEWART, JR.

Grandson of the founder of Union Oil, W. L., Jr., headed the research group in the 1930's that unlocked the secrets of making more power-packed gasolines, smoother lubricants, and the remarkably versatile Unoba grease. He became chairman of the board in 1962. After serving as chairman one year, he died on August 30, 1963.

Though times were better, the oil industry was again plagued by overproduction, particularly in southern California, where the prodigious Wilmington field had just been discovered. A quick survey by Taylor also revealed that much of Union's plant had to be rebuilt, from the oil fields up. Union had 1,200 producing wells, mostly in California, but nearly half of them were shut down, partly because of overproduction, partly because refining and transportation facilities were inadequate to handle the company's potential output of crude. To produce 7 per cent of the gasoline used on the Pacific Coast, Union had to process 13 per cent of California's crude. A Chase National Bank analysis of 30 petroleum corporations revealed that the average oil company's investment in refinery facilities was 16.6 per cent, while Union's was only 8.3 per cent. Although the belt tightening of the thirties had kept the company solvent and on a dividend-paying basis, Union's position in the industry had deteriorated. Rivals who had built modern new catalytic-cracking refineries had captured much of Union's share of the trade in the more profitable products of the oil industry.

Taylor called on Union's department heads for estimates on the cost of completely rehabilitating the company's facilities, not only to get more out of the front end of the barrel of oil, the high-priced products, but also to recapture Union's traditional 15 per cent of the West Coast market. These estimates added up to a 73-million-dollar building program. This was a lot of money to squeeze out of a company already well squeezed for dividends. The most that Union's treasury could provide, even after cutting dividends and utilizing amortization funds, was 40 million of the 70 million dollars Taylor needed for the immediate building program.

"We will have to go to New York for 30 million," he told the directors. They approved the move. From time to time Union had gone to New York for millions, but never for 30 million in a single transaction. The largest single sum raised in New York was in 1918, $15,000,000 for the new Los Angeles refinery.

LATEST WORD IN 1930's

The use of six wheels in the rear greatly increased the carrying capacity of this early model White truck. Soon to follow was another innovation—enclosed cab for the driver.

UNION OIL COMPANY
CREDIT CARD
PERIOD EFFECTIVE AUGUST, 1925
NAME John L Customer
ADDRESS 13 North Cedar St - Any Town
LICENSE NO 192-519
DISTRICT Spokane
SIGNED C. C. Ireland DISTRICT MANAGER

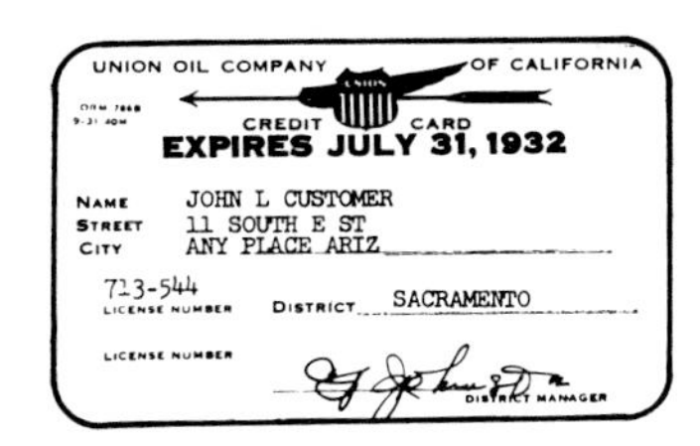
UNION OIL COMPANY OF CALIFORNIA
CREDIT CARD
EXPIRES JULY 31, 1932
NAME JOHN L CUSTOMER
STREET 11 SOUTH E ST
CITY ANY PLACE ARIZ
713-544
LICENSE NUMBER
DISTRICT SACRAMENTO
DISTRICT MANAGER

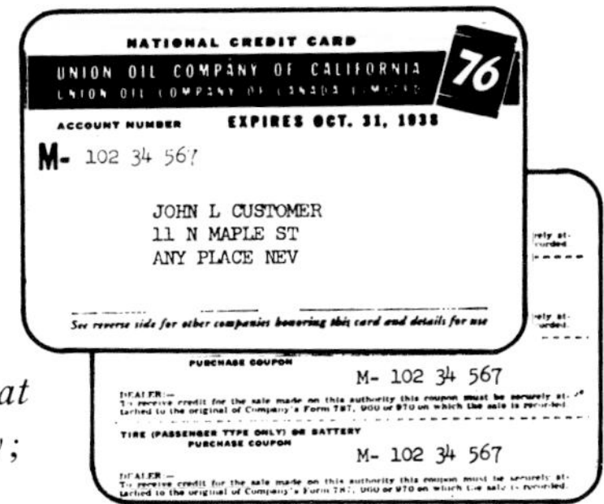
NATIONAL CREDIT CARD
UNION OIL COMPANY OF CALIFORNIA
76
ACCOUNT NUMBER EXPIRES OCT. 31, 1938
M- 102 34 567
JOHN L CUSTOMER
11 N MAPLE ST
ANY PLACE NEV
PURCHASE COUPON M- 102 34 567
TIRE (PASSENGER TYPE ONLY) OR BATTERY
PURCHASE COUPON M- 102 34 567

CREDIT CARDS IN DEPRESSION YEARS

In 1925 (left), *so few cards were distributed that the district manager signed each card personally; in 1932* (center), *the trademark made its first appearance; by 1938* (right), *merchandise could be charged on the card with coupons.*

Early in 1939, Taylor arrived in New York "to wildcat for millions of dollars." He discussed Union's financial predicament with James E. Forrestal, then president of Dillon Read & Company, the investment brokers who had handled some of Union's previous financing. Forrestal called in Frederic H. Brandi, one of his vice-presidents, who later became head of Dillon Read and also a Union Oil director. The trio explored the financial field. Taylor wanted not only "new money" to carry out his ambitious program for modernizing production, refining, transportation, and marketing facilities but also funds to redeem 10 million dollars' worth of debentures and 8 million dollars' worth of bonds, issued prior to his presidency, which would mature early in 1942. Forrestal proposed that Union take advantage of lower interest rates which might be obtained by offering 30 million dollars' worth of 3 per cent debentures.

"The trouble is that the eastern analysts don't know anything about Union Oil and its potentials," Forrestal pointed out. "You will have to tell them."

"All right, get them together and I'll tell them," agreed Taylor.

Forrestal and Brandi set up a series of meetings with 30 analysts and financial counselors. Taylor told the story of Union Oil from its start half a century before, how it had grown to its present position, and what aggressive plans could do for its future. The financial men were delighted with the reception given the enthusiastic Westerner, who had so recently switched from steel to petroleum. Dillon Read set up a syndicate of 25 underwriters, through whom Union's 30-million-dollar debenture offer was snapped up immediately by the investing public. Taylor used 20 million dollars of the new 3 per cent money to wipe out prior obligations which carried higher interest rates. The balance was added to the modernization fund for the refineries and transportation facilities, including a new tank-ship.

The Provident Fund, which W. L. Stewart had launched, was replaced on May 1, 1939, by the Employees' Retirement Fund, operated by an arrangement with the Equitable Life Assurance Company. Under the old Provident Fund plan, the company contributed an amount equal to that contributed by the employees to their retirement. Changed conditions in the late thirties and the enactment of the Federal Social Security Act made a new plan administered by an insurance company more desirable. The assets of the old fund, including 213,350 shares of Union Oil, were distributed to employee members of the Provident Fund.

CHAPTER NINE 1940-1950

The Big Independent

As Union Oil began its second half century in 1940, the company had far exceeded even the most ambitious dreams of its founders. No longer a family company, it belonged to 27,375 shareholders. Annual sales were over $75,000,000. The company's three refineries were processing around 26,000,000 barrels of crude a year. It had 1,221 wells capable of producing, but of these, 506 were shut in, owing to a continued surplus of crude oil on the Pacific Coast and a stringent voluntary curtailment program instituted by the industry. Its crude-oil reserves were augmented by the discovery of vast new oil pools under the bayous and tidelands of Louisiana. Union's researchers had unlocked the secrets of making more power-packed gasolines, smoother lubricants.

The major overhauling of the company's facilities and operations, as outlined by Taylor when he became president, was beginning to be felt. In transportation, a new tanker, the *L. P. St. Clair*, had been put into service, a sister ship, the *Victor H. Kelly*, virtually completed. Two more 100,000-barrel tank-ships were on the drawing board. A reorganizing of marketing, involving a substantial number of new service stations and expansion of the chain into Arizona, Utah, and Idaho, was being carried out. The marketing program was under the direction of Arthur C. Stewart, who was elected vice-president and director, and a member of the executive committee of five, on December 30, 1940.

The rehabilitation was most evident in the manufacturing end of the business, neglected during the long economy program. Here Taylor was exploiting to good advantage the additional working capital obtained through the 30-million-dollar debenture issue of 1939.

Such major refining units as an alkylation plant at Los Angeles and a polymerization plant at Oleum were nearly ready for operation. The alkylation plant

MAJOR PLANT INVESTMENT FOR THE 1950's

Union's Santa Maria Refinery was the first step in a multi-million-dollar plant expansion program begun in the 1950's. Plant, opened in 1955, occupies a 4,260-acre site on the coast west of Santa Maria, California.

50 EXCITING YEARS

OF SERVICE TO THE WEST ★ 1890 ★ 1940

1. 1886...Lyman Stewart and W. L. Hardison discover oil near Santa Paula, California, but transportation costs appear prohibitive. Plan daring solution. Skeptics scoff but they succeed . . . *build the first Western pipeline to tidewater.*

2. 1887...Bad luck... Four dry wells have taken all their capital. Financial ruin threatens. Los Angeles banker finally stakes them to one more loan. They sink it all in one well which *comes in* – a gusher!

3. 1888...With finances assured, Hardison and Stewart turn to other innovations. *Build the first oil tanker on the Pacific Coast,* which runs between Ventura and San Francisco for one year, then is destroyed by fire.

4. 1890...Hardison and Stewart merge with Mission Transfer Co., Sespe Oil Co., and Torrey Canyon Oil Co. – form UNION OIL COMPANY of CALIFORNIA.

5. 1894...Over-production threatens industry. Union Oil men tackle problem independently. Create new market for crude oil by converting old Santa Fe engine into *first successful oil-burning locomotive in U.S.*

6. 1898...Union Oil Company sets up *first geological department in U.S.* Under W. W. Orcutt, department maps and discovers many of California's great oil fields, recovers first fossils from famed La Brea Pits.

7. 1910...Company drilling crew brings in Lakeview No. 1 near Bakersfield – *greatest gusher ever drilled in U.S.* Well flows 80,000 barrels a day.

8. 1913...Anticipating automobile era – Company opens at 6th and Mateo Sts., Los Angeles, one of the first service stations on the Pacific Coast.

9. 1922...Union's independence threatened! Eastern combine quietly buying up stock. Loyal stockholders discover scheme – save situation by uniting their holdings to keep Union Oil independent.

10. 1932...Company engineers startle industry with amazing new gasoline – 76 – *the pioneer, non-premium, anti-knock gasoline in the West.* 76 sales sky-rocket spectacularly, as motorists discover its performance qualities.

11. 1934...Propane-Solvent process for refining Triton Motor Oil discovered. Produces *a 100% pure paraffin-base oil with low carbon-forming qualities.* Enables motors to reduce carbon left by other oils . . . changes PING to PURR.

12. 1940...Union Oil Company celebrates its 50th year of service to the West . . . still independent, still owned and operated *by* Westerners *for* Westerners. Consistent pioneering and a policy of keeping just a "step ahead" have enabled Union to grow from a modest beginning to the leading independent oil company in the West. Look for Union's big orange and blue 76 sign wherever you drive!

UNION OIL COMPANY

1890, INDEPENDENT – 1940, STILL INDEPENDENT

used catalysts to convert refinery still gases and other gases (formerly burned for fuel) derived from natural gasoline into basic material for production of 100-octane aviation gasoline. The polymerization plant likewise produced aviation gasoline from gases formerly burned for fuel. Other modern units were either in the engineering stage or ready for actual construction.

Nor was research neglected. When Taylor pointed out that "only through research can we expect to retain a favorable position in a highly competitive industry" and emphasized that "income appropriated for research is not spent; it is invested,"—Union's directors promptly authorized funds to modernize laboratories and strengthen the research staff. Already the researchers had come up with so many new products and processes that the company established a patent division to capitalize on the results by licensing their use.

Although Union's reserves of crude oil had been increasing steadily over a five-year span and nearly half of its wells were shut in, Taylor encouraged Cy Rubel and his wildcatters to push the hunt for more oil. His encouragement paid off in June, when one of Union's crews made the company's first discovery in Louisiana. This wildcat, Walter White Heirs No. 1, was the beginning of Union's productive Gulf Division.

The modernization program continued through 1941 "with full realization of the seriousness of the world situation and uncertainties confronting the petroleum industry," as Taylor described it. Then came the Japanese attack on Pearl Harbor, December 7, 1941. Overnight, Union, like other oil companies, became a war industry. The demands were tremendous, but not unexpected. In fact, Union's refineries had been stepping up since early in the year the output of 100-octane aviation gasoline to fuel the armada of war planes which President Roosevelt had called upon the aircraft builders to turn out faster than planes had ever been built before.

"There are two great jobs confronting us," Taylor told Union Oilers. "First, to meet the acid test of all-out war production to fulfill all of the demands being placed upon us. The second, to do such a good job in this respect that the American system of free enterprise will never again be threatened.

"The fact that mechanized warfare is dependent upon petroleum places great responsibility upon the oil industry. The government has asked us to quadruple production of 100-octane aviation gasoline during the next year. Vast quantities of petroleum fuels, lubricants, and technical products of all kinds are required by the armed forces and war industries. Union Oil is doing its utmost to aid the war effort and to carry its allotted share of the staggering task laid upon the nation."

Fortunately, the refinery units already under construction could be completed, in spite of a shortage of material. To give further aid, a small refinery, shut down for many years, was returned to production.

GOLDEN ANNIVERSARY PROMOTION

Union did not let 1940 go by without forcefully reminding Californians that the company was celebrating its 50th progressive year. This capsule history appeared in color in all major Sunday supplements.

UNION'S FIRST DISCOVERY WELL IN LOUISIANA

Walter White Heirs I, first well drilled by Union Oil in Louisiana, struck oil in East White Lake at 10,658 feet July 19, 1940, and led to development of the company's valuable Gulf and West Texas Divisions.

"We recognize the prior claim of the government upon all the petroleum products the company is capable of producing," Taylor told Union Oilers. "So long as the war lasts, supplying government needs must be the company's first responsibility."

Early in 1942, Taylor reverted temporarily from an oil man to a steel man, when he was called to Washington to head the Iron and Steel Division of the War Production Board. This duty lasted only six months, but later in the war he was called back to Washington again to help set up a Fuels and Lubricants Section for the Army. When he returned to his desk in 1942, Taylor was wrathy over the difficulties encountered by private industry in trying to mesh efforts with those of the government.

"Businessmen have so much trouble in Washington primarily because the government people don't understand what makes business function," he declared, concluding that Union could do a job not only for itself but for business generally by explaining this relationship. Taylor assigned a big chunk of the company's advertising budget for the job of telling the public how one business, Union Oil Company of California and its satellites, the smaller businesses that prospered because Union thrived, functioned in the free-enterprise scheme. Each advertisement told the story of one employee and what he did, or one dealer or one contractor, and what his functions were, in the highly competitive American free-enterprise system.

Spending Union's hard-earned dollars to talk about the free-enterprise system in an institutional way encountered considerable resistance at first among Union's marketers, who thought that the purpose of advertising was to sell products. The first ad of the now famous free-enterprise series was worked up by Margaret Corrie (Mrs. Reese H. Taylor after 1944), who was advertising manager at the time. Launched early in 1943, this opener explained in six simple paragraphs and seven sketches how Union's 1942 net profit of $5,473,329 actually meant $147.94 for each shareholder, with $27.52 from each stockholders' share left to build up Union's future business.

Each month a new story, bearing always on the slogan "America's Fifth Freedom Is Free Enterprise," followed, to give the public an insight into how a lot of individuals and their dollars teamed up to make a big corporation. One explained "How to Drill an Oil Well for $2.08," each shareholder's part of a new Union Oil hole. Another, picturing an oil-field workman, told how "It Cost $35,000 to Get This Man a Job." Intended only as a wartime measure, the free-enterprise series caught the public's imagination. So many people wanted copies of the series of advertisements that Union had to publish them in a book, *How and Why American Business Functions*, which ran through a dozen editions. To the great surprise of the marketing department, talking about the men and women of Union Oil Company proved a product seller as well as an idea seller.

By the end of 1942 Union's refineries were able to double the production of aviation gasoline. But, with demand for products constantly rising, other new plants had to be built. The company was producing more crude oil than ever before in its history, and refineries were working at abnormally high levels.

To pay for this emergency expansion, Taylor had gone to New York in January, 1942, for another 15 million dollars' worth of 3 per cent debentures. These were sold quickly by the same 25 underwriters who had handled the 1939 issue. As it turned out, this was only the start of a 58-million-dollar wartime refinery expansion program which enabled Union to boost its aviation gasoline output to sevenfold what it was when the war started.

PROSPERITY UNDER FREE ENTERPRISE

A stint in Washington during the war convinced Reese Taylor that the workings of the free-enterprise system were neither well understood nor fully appreciated by the public. In an effort to overcome this lack of understanding, he launched a series of advertisements to explain free enterprise and Union's part in making it succeed. The series was widely acclaimed.

Union Oilers were not long in discovering that they were at war. Within two weeks after Pearl Harbor, the tanker *Montebello* was at the bottom of the Pacific. Under the command of Captain Arnold Edstrom, the tanker had loaded at Avila with a cargo bound for Vancouver. She headed out to sea December 21, 1941, without escort. Two hours later, barely out of sight of land, a lurking Japanese submarine, which had started its journey to the Pacific Coast well before the war had been declared, sent a torpedo crashing into the port side of the tanker. Surfacing, the submarine's batteries poured shells into the wallowing, smoking ship as the tanker crew took to lifeboats. While the *Montebello* slid beneath the waves, her crew pulled for shore under a rain of Japanese bullets, which miraculously failed to wound a single crewman.

By this time Union's tanker fleet had been taken over by the United States War Shipping Administration, which reassigned the tankers, together with a score of government oil carriers, back to Union for operation. Five Union tankers were already in the war at the time of the Pearl Harbor attack. Two were carrying British oil between the Dutch West Indies and the Atlantic Coast; three more were delivering petroleum products to Vladivostok and to American outposts in the far Pacific. Two new 100,000-barrel tankers, the *Paul M. Gregg* and the *A. C. Rubel*, launched early in 1942, helped beef up Union's wartime fleet.

As the demands for oil mounted, Union was able to increase its crude-oil production 17 per cent by the end of 1942 by operating 1,566 wells. The newly discovered Vinton and Fresh Water Bayou fields in Louisiana added to the reserves. At one period field-development work was cut in half because of severe priority controls over critical materials, such as oil-well casing and pipe. As fast as new oil came out of the earth, it was rushed to the refineries and to depots

"WELL DONE!" SAID THE NAVY

Union's tankers, drafted to serve in World War II, earned special commendation from the Assistant Secretary of the Navy for their outstanding contribution to the war effort.

UNION TANKER TORPEDOED OFF CALIFORNIA

One of the first tanker casualties of the war with Japan was the Montebello, *torpedoed and sunk off the California coast two weeks after Pearl Harbor. She had just left Avila and was enroute to Vancouver. The presence of a Japanese submarine so close to the coast gave Californians a bad case of the jitters.*

that supplied the war fleet. Never before had Union Oilers handled such quantities of petroleum.

The modernization program was paying off in an accelerated flow of military products, but the war effort demanded still greater production. To increase output of aviation gasoline, additional units were built and put into operation at all refineries. At Los Angeles ground was broken for a giant "cat cracker," which utilized new refining methods to increase gasoline yields.

Union's tankers were fueling American ships around the world. In 1943 the tanker *Gurney E. Newlin*, commanded by Captain Herman Dahlhof, was torpedoed without warning in mid-Atlantic. Only seven of the tanker's crew of 41 Union Oilers were saved. The tankers were part of the vast river of oil flowing across the oceans, so important that Admiral Chester W. Nimitz called it "one of our greatest secret weapons" when he sent a personal citation to Union's tanker *La Placentia* for outstanding service at Majuro Atoll in the direct fueling of combat ships. Tankers bearing the big U on their stacks filled Navy bunkers from Australia to Guam to Saipan to Manila and Okinawa, Iwo Jima, and finally Tokyo.

It was only after the war ended that the Japanese learned how this man-made river of oil had kept their attacking forces continually off balance. The Japanese naval strategy was based on the idea that warships had to return to bases for fuel, as they had always done previously, after each battle. The Nipponese were completely confounded when the American ships fought one battle and kept on striking before the Japanese admirals were ready for the next fight. The oil-company tankers were floating supply bases, pumping fuel into high-speed Navy tankers, which in turn refueled the combat ships on the move.

ROCKY MOUNTAIN REFINERY *Even a blizzard approaching Cut Bank, Montana, fails to slow operations of refinery purchased in 1944, and sold in December 1970. The refinery is located east of the Continental Divide, near the Canadian border.*

The tankers also kept the river of oil flowing ashore at the islands on which the Air Force based fighters and bombers. They fed the tanks and trucks and the bulldozers of the Army, the Air Force, and the Marines. One of Union's effective weapons was Operation Roll-Out-the-Barrels. Beginning early in the war, Union Oilers filled and secretly shipped 4,000 drums of gasoline a day from a special plant at Pittsburg on San Francisco Bay. Altogether they filled 862,000 barrels with 46,000,000 gallons of gasoline for the spectacular landings at Hollandia, Saipan, Guam, Leyte, Luzon, Iwo Jima, and Okinawa.

To provide its share of this river of fuel, Union stepped up its crude oil production rate to an all-time peak. The yield from the newly found fields in Louisiana increased nearly fivefold in a single year. In August, 1943, the company's wildcatters completed their first discovery well in Texas, the forerunner of what has since become the valuable West Texas Division.

By mid-1944 Union's new catalytic-cracking plant and other units at the Los Angeles refinery were in operation, and the output of urgently needed aviation gasoline was increased fivefold over what it had been two years previously. This lofty cat cracker, whose tower rose 268 feet, as high as a 20-story building, was at that time the last word in efficient extraction of petroleum products from a barrel of crude oil. In it a steady stream of catalytic pellets, about the size of peas and made of special clay, fell in a steady round-the-clock rain as the hot petroleum vapors rose. As they rained down, the millions of pellets encouraged the rising vapors to crack apart and reform themselves into smaller molecules. The changing vapors continued to rise and flow out the top of the tower into another unit, where they were condensed into various components, one of which became a base product for further refining into high-octane aviation gasoline. In the meantime, the catalytic pellets dropped to the floor of the tower and were returned to the top to begin their work anew. The pellets, being porous, were practically all surface. The 2,200,000 pounds of pellets that made seven round trips a day in the new cat cracker had a fantastic surface area equal to that of the entire state of California!

The combined capacities of the older plants and newer units completed in 1944 made it possible for Union to boost output further. Under a special arrangement with the Navy, half of the crude oil produced from the Naval Reserve at Elk Hills was dispatched via a hurriedly built pipeline to Union's refineries for processing. As pressure for more and more oil mounted, Union's directors decided to increase the company's sources in a hurry. In 1944 they bought the Glacier Production Company of Montana, which held 90,000 acres of oil-and-gas-producing properties in what was then the most productive oil field in Montana. With this purchase came a new refinery and natural gasoline plant at Cut Bank, Montana, as well as a distributing system. The timely investment gave Union an additional 2,700 barrels of crude oil a day from 172 wells and increased the company's potential reserves by 20,000,000 barrels. To swing the deal, and to secure additional funds for general use, Taylor negotiated a $12,000,000 long-term loan from several banks.

Union was looking even further afield for new sources of crude oil. Lengthy negotiations within the Republic of Paraguay culminated in 1944 in rights to explore for oil in the 5,000,000-acre Chaco concession, an area half the size of California. Wildcatting this vast concession proved a challenging adventure for Union's crews, who were obliged to operate largely by airplane from abandoned and overgrown air strips that were relics of the Paraguay-Bolivia War. Unfortunately, Union's explorers found no oil in commercial quantities in Paraguay.

At home, researchers were experimenting with new means of secondary recovery of crude left in the ground after the pumps ceased to bring up oil. Geologists estimated that only about one-fourth of the total volume of petroleum trapped in the sands of an average California field was being recovered by routine methods. Secondary recovery looked like the answer to finding more oil near to markets. Union's engineers tried water flooding in five fields, gas injection in three fields to release more of this trapped oil. Wherever possible, the company joined other producers in unit operations using pressure maintenance. These experiments paid off in the recovery of additional oil.

By the close of 1945, when Union's 330 servicemen and women returned from the armed forces, the Union team was primed for the most spectacular growth period in the company's history. The Union management found itself at the marketing end of the greatest migration tide in history, a population movement that provided, for the next decade, what Taylor describes as "Union's built-in growth factor." The company's immediate problem was to find enough crude oil and products to satisfy 15 per cent of this fabulous and fast-expanding market.

Just as the war closed, Union's drillers made a most remarkable discovery in the company's own back yard, only a few miles from the Los Angeles refinery. This was a "sleeper" oil field which Lyman Stewart had picked up in 1903, known as the "Sansinena fee" property, which lay east of Whittier at the edge of the prodigious Los Angeles Basin. Tramping over this rugged and hilly area half a century before, Stewart had smelled oil and also spotted it seeping out of the hillsides and into several canyons. As usual, the insatiable oil hunter bought the mineral rights on about 3,400 acres of the La Habra Rancho, known as the Sansinena tract, and then told his directors about it later. Union was so hard pressed for funds at the time that the exploration department was able to drill only one well, abandoned after a series of accidents. Over the years subdividers had sold off the surface rights for small farm homes. Before long the potential oil field was completely hidden by homes and avocado orchards.

URBAN DRILLING IS HARD TO FIND *As part of its community-relations program, Union camouflages production facilities and landscapes well sites* (above) *to make them nearly invisible, and* (right) *shrouds drilling rigs in fire-resistant fabric padded with glass wool to soundproof the operations.*

When Union's exploration department wanted to drill a wildcat well to test the area in the early forties, the homeowners rose up in wrath and zoned out oil derricks. Though the company still had legal title to the mineral rights, a long-drawn-out legal battle in the courts loomed to determine whose interests were paramount, those of the oil hunters or those of the homeowners. Several of Union's geologists were not too sure there was any great quantity of oil under the Sansinena hills, anyway, and some favored abandoning the field entirely. Others, including Cy Rubel, director of exploration, wanted to drill. When the proposition was finally put up to Reese Taylor in 1945, he said: "Let's drill or get out." The decision was to drill.

Before the drillers moved in, Union's land men preceded them, signing up the landowners to whom the company agreed to pay royalties on any oil produced in the area, even though Union still owned the mineral rights in fee simple. The exploration department also promised to drill only from selected "islands" hidden deep in canyons and agreed to sheathe the drilling rigs so that they would be virtually noiseless. As a result of this good-neighbor policy, the homeowners withdrew their objections to drilling.

The first hole completed early in 1945 was a duster. So were the second and the third. It looked as though history were repeating itself and that latter-day oil hunters could guess as wrong at Sansinena as Lyman Stewart and Wallace

Hardison had done seven decades before in Pico Canyon. But the fourth Sansinena hole tapped a reservoir of oil a mile beneath the surface. So did the next 30 wells. Sansinena became one of Union's finest fields, yielding for a time one-tenth of the company's California production. Driving through this area of homes and avocado orchards, the casual visitor never suspected that he was in an oil field, unless by chance he stumbled onto a camouflaged "island" from which a dozen to 20 holes were whipstocked out under the orchards. Cy Rubel once drove a party of club-women, who were protesting that oil fields ruined the landscape, through the Sansinena field and offered to buy a new bonnet for any lady who could point out an oil well. Rubel didn't buy a single hat.

By this time whipstocking, or slant drilling, had become one of the oil hunter's effective techniques. Holes were seldom pushed straight down any more, the way skilled drillers once were proud of driving them. Instead, the crews slanted the holes out at angles, often spudding in six to a dozen wells from one island, to be bottomed anywhere within a radius of half a mile of the starting point. Ingenious instruments checked the slanting so accurately that the drillers "bottomed" their holes within a few feet of the spot pinpointed on the geologists' subsurface map. These islands, incidentally, were sometimes actual man-made islands, like those in Long Beach Harbor; or they might be platforms on pilings driven into a lake bottom, such as Union's East White Lake field in Louisiana, or into the ocean; or they could be levels bulldozed out of the mountain. Wherever these man-made drilling sites were located, they were, in the lingo of oil men, "islands."

In other ways, too, oil wells were a whole lot more than they used to be. To most people an oil well is just a hole in the ground. That is what it once was when holes were a few hundred feet deep and relatively cheap. If holes were drilled with the haphazard abandon of the pioneer days, most wells would come in as gushers, spewing oil and gas all over the countryside, as the Lake View gusher did in 1910. The deep wells of the forties came in with tremendous pressures, up to 6,000 pounds in California and double that in some Louisiana wells. The last thing the modern oil drillers wanted was another Lake View, which wasted 4,000,000 barrels of oil and countless cubic feet of gas. Modern scientific drilling eliminated this danger of bringing in a gusher. Oil wells were brought in under such fine control that "you can walk around with your Sunday clothes on," as one driller put it.

At one time Union owned and operated more than 40 "strings of tools," as drilling rigs were known during the early days. But during the war and after, Union's drilling, whether in California, Texas, Louisiana, Canada, or elsewhere, was done by independent contractors, who were often paid thousands of dollars a day for the use of their expensive rigs and the services of their crews. They were worth it, because the cost of some of the huge drilling rigs and essential accessories range from a half a million to 5 or 6 million dollars. Some of these scientifically drilled holes cost a million or more, too. It called for some highly scientific guessing to decide where to drill these expensive holes without going broke.

LAST OF THE STEWART DYNASTY

Arthur C. Stewart, youngest member of the Stewart family to play a major role in Union Oil, served as a senior vice-president until his retirement in 1965. He continued as a director.

While drilling was under way in the Sansinena area, Taylor again took stock of Union's position. The refinery-modernization program begun in 1939 had proved its worth by enabling the company to keep pace with wartime demands and with improved processing of better products. The $58,000,000 expended to accomplish this had been obtained, in part, through sale of debentures and bank loans. Under the then existing debt structure, heavy annual cash interest payments were required. A refunding plan proposed by Taylor was approved by the shareowners. On June 25, 1945, the refunding plan was effected through the issuance and sale of 250,000 of $3.75 preferred shares and $25,000,000 of 2¾ per cent twenty-five year debentures. The bank loans made in 1944 and the outstanding balance of 3 per cent debentures issued in 1939 were retired. Long-term debt was reduced by $13,700,000 and cash resources increased by $10,000,000.

During the war the company's operations had all been geared to meet the requirements of the armed forces; now the company lost no time in converting to peacetime commercial operations and development of its civilian market. Union had greater crude-oil reserves than when the war began; its pipeline systems were strategically located; its tanker fleet had been returned; its refineries were able quickly to shift emphasis to civilian needs. Only one department—marketing—had of necessity been neglected during the war years.

Responsibility for bringing this important department up to the effective standard of the others rested upon A. C. (Art) Stewart. Appointed vice-president for marketing on December 30, 1940, he had held his marketing operation together during the war years, but had little opportunity to expand or improve its functions. Soon after the war ended, Stewart launched an aggressive sales and service program which increased Union's annual sales fivefold in the decade that followed.

"Believing that an independent businessman, operating his own station, would have a more personal interest in the business and produce excellent sales results,

POST-DEPRESSION SERVICE STATION *After a period of depression-induced inactivity, architects turned to their drawing boards in the 1940's, coming up with ten new designs. Typical of the Union stations in that period was this 1947 unit with wide canopies that covered both gasoline service islands.*

we leased out the majority of the company's service stations," explained Stewart. "We retained only a few for personnel training and to test merchandising and operating procedures. Then we backed these independent operators with aggressive advertising and the finest of products."

Among the "finest of products" the Union Oil merchant had to sell the motorist were a better Triton motor oil, a line of Unoba greases, and an improved new aviation-type gasoline. New Union service stations dotted the western states to meet the demands of motorists who, flush with wartime savings, were taking again to the open road. The "76" stations were offering a new product, Royal Triton, a remarkable purple-hued motor oil to which a detergent had been added, which successfully counteracted rust, corrosion, and oxidation. Royal Triton also had greater lasting qualities. The new lubricant put Union's retail products selling on a national scale. Salesmen from the field were given a two weeks' course at the refineries under supervision of research technicians. Graduates of leading universities were selected for intensive training in the research and refining departments before joining the sales department. Stewart was building for the long pull.

The entire company was driving ahead fast. The new refining facilities were hard pressed to keep up with the demand. Anticipating the need for additional expansion, President Taylor accepted a 15-million-dollar loan offered in 1947 by the New York Life Insurance Company at 2.8 per cent. Part of this new money went into a new plant at the Oleum refinery to increase production of Triton-type motor oils by 140 per cent. Some went into further modernization of pipeline facilities to effect economies and speed operations. More millions, spent for exploration, brought quick returns in important discoveries in California, Louisiana, Texas, Canada, and elsewhere.

As the civilian market boomed, the "76 Union" trade-mark was becoming famous over a wider and wider area. In 1947 a survey of motorists in Los Angeles, San Francisco, Portland, and Seattle revealed that 82 out of every 100 gasoline buyers readily identified the 76 as Union's symbol, more by far than were able to identify any other oil company's trade-mark. Armed with this evidence the company's attorneys again presented the 76 Union trade-mark before the United States Patent Office for registration. This time the patent officials were convinced, although it took them almost three years formally to certify registration of the now famous trade-mark.

By 1948 Union was producing more crude oil than ever before in its history—more even than at the wartime peak. Despite this record withdrawal, Rubel's crews were so successful in their search for oil that they were able each year to increase the company's reserves by millions of barrels. Union seismic crews were shooting the earth for possible indications of oil traps along the Gulf of Mexico, in west Texas, in New Mexico, Oklahoma, Kansas, Montana, and North Dakota. More important, they were covering California with their man-made miniature earthquakes to make as sure as it was possible to do, without drilling, that they were overlooking no major sleepers near to the company's markets. Colleagues were always asking Cy Rubel, director of exploration, why his men persisted in discovering new fields in the most outlandish and inconvenient spots on the globe. Why couldn't they make their oil strikes closer to Union's big refineries? Rubel's reply always was: "If it was easy, the Chinese would be doing it." In 1948, Union, with two other oil companies, launched a seismic survey of the earth beneath the Pacific Ocean along the Santa Barbara and Los Angeles coast.

Union's wildcatters had been amazingly successful in finding oil where it was most needed. Their drilling bits probing into the earth's subterranean folds invariably left the company with more proven oil reserves each succeeding year than it had the year previous, in spite of the tremendous production of the company's wells. Nearly all of Union's finds were in the United States. The bulk of Union's reserves were in California, under lands bought or leased by Union's intuitive pioneers without the help of modern scientific exploration facilities. Nearly 40 per cent of the company's production was still from lands that Lyman Stewart had bought in fee simple.

Even with these new finds, the company needed more high-gravity crude oil than it was finding. The opportunity came in 1949, when the Los Nietos Company, owned by the five grandchildren of Edward L. Doheny, was offered to Union for $22,400,000 cash and 600,000 common shares in Union Oil. The Los Nietos Company held valuable producing acreage in California, Texas, and Canada with a daily production of 7,500 barrels of high-gravity crude and reserves estimated to be in excess of 46,000,000 barrels. To finance this huge purchase, Taylor arranged a twenty-five-year $40,000,000 loan at 2¾ per cent from a group of eight institutional investors. The $40,000,000 not only provided the cash for the Los Nietos purchase but also enabled him to retire $14,800,000 in outstanding 3 per cent debentures and put more money into the company's general fund.

Simultaneously, Union was able to add still further to its supply of high-gravity crude oil by entering into a long-term contract for the purchase of the entire production of several leases held by Mrs. Carrie Estelle Doheny in California, largely in the Coalinga Nose, Pleasant Valley, and Guijarral Hills fields. This deal provided the company's refineries with 6,000 barrels a day of high-gravity oil.

Up in North Dakota at the southern end of the Williston Basin, Union staged in 1949 the biggest land play in its history, in conjunction with two other oil companies. Prodded by Union's exploration department, which was convinced that the rich Williston Basin strikes in Canada extended south of the border into the United States, 22 land men hustled over the area, signing 13,000 leases aggregating 4 million acres. The leases committed the three companies to 12-million dollars in rentals. Unfortunately, the drilling on the huge acreage did not produce a commercial discovery, and most of the land was later sub-leased to other companies drilling in the area.

During 1949 a major problem arose. Once more, the old bugaboo, glut of heavy fuel oil, the major product obtained from California's low-gravity crude, developed on the Pacific Coast. Union's engineers intensified their study of methods which might possibly enable the company to increase the percentage yields of gasoline and other light products and reduce the output of fuel oil. As a long-range answer to the problem, plans for a great new research center were expedited.

Meanwhile, a new 12-million-dollar plant for making increased quantities of Triton and Royal Triton motor oils was nearing completion at the Oleum refinery. This enabled Art Stewart's marketing department to make one of its most aggressive sales drives. Years before when Eastern motor oils had captured nearly 80 per cent of the Western lubricant market, Union's researchers had developed a process which enabled the company to make a Western motor oil superior to those made from Pennsylvania crude oils. So Union's marketers decided to push the sale of Western motor oils—its Triton and Royal Triton—in Eastern markets. By 1950 Stewart was able to report Royal Triton and other Union products were being sold in every state in the nation, Canada, Cuba, and elsewhere.

OLEUM HELPS LAUNCH TRITON

Expansion of the Oleum Refinery in the 1940's helped Union capture a bigger share of the motor oil market with its new Triton line.

The free-enterprise principle launched by Reese Taylor in 1942 had become a basic feature in the company's operation. Wherever a Union Oiler could set himself up as an independent operator to perform a segment of the company's business, the company handed him a contract, often helping to finance him through the lean and struggling years. The story of how one big business was good for many little businesses, and vice versa, made good reading in the series of pen and sketch portraits of typical Union Oil capitalists run in the company's advertisements.

Not all of these free enterprisers were in the marketing end, by any means. The Oleum refinery alone had 65 contracts for services formerly performed by people on the Union payroll. The Wilmington refinery had 69 contractors. The transportation department entered into contracts with more than 400 commercial truckers. The field department used 270 contractors for drilling, construction, well pulling, and other operations. How these Union contracts, plus financial backing in many cases, helped more than 5,000 men and women to establish themselves in their own businesses became a convincing demonstration that "free enterprise, America's fifth freedom," was a theory that works out in actual practice.

Joe Robinson and his Santa Fe Drilling Company were a shining example. Robinson and 62 former employees of the Union Oil Company drilling department incorporated the Santa Fe Drilling Company, with Robinson as president, late in 1946. When Robinson came to vice-president Rubel, proposing that he and his 62 colleagues organize a million-dollar company to take over the firm's drilling equipment and put 10 crews in the field making hole for the company, the Union management accepted the offer. Robinson and associates made the business pay from the start. In three years they were out of debt, their assets had doubled, and they had 20 drilling crews scattered from Canada to Italy and owned the largest independent drilling company in California.

Just before the war, an enterprising chauffeur entered a Union service station competition for a better paint cleaner and preserver. George Sevelle's product was better than any of the dozen others submitted. Since he had concocted the stuff primarily to wash and polish cars, Sevelle was astonished when the contest manager asked if it would do to wash service stations. Out of the talk grew a deal whereby Sevelle agreed to wash 5 Union service stations on a regular schedule. By the end of the year the contract had been increased to 150 stations. Then it was jumped to 1,100 stations, and finally to 4,000, which Sevelle scrubbed with the aid of 35 men, 14 big trucks, and 5 house trailers, in which his crews lived in comfort while on the road.

George Sevelle built service station washing into a sizable business in itself. Born in San Jose, an honorary Boy Scout commissioner and a community leader, Sevelle styled himself "one of the oldest native sons of Negro parentage in California." His paternal grandfather came from Key West, Florida, and settled in Grass Valley to become the first Negro owner of a gold mine in the state. His maternal grandfather, who hailed from Philadelphia, came West to be a chef for the Palace Hotel, San Francisco's gay bonanza inn of the luxury-loving eighties and nineties. Before his better cleaner led to his contract with Union, Sevelle tried a lot of callings—door-boy, window dresser, pantryman, waiter, candymaker, serviceman for electric automobiles, mechanic for famous racing drivers.

"When Union asked me to wash service stations, it was all right with me, so long as I sold my product," said Sevelle. "There was one drawback. I didn't have a truck to get my equipment from station to station, and I didn't have any money. It looked like no money, no truck, no contract. That's when Union came to the rescue, setting me up in business. It supplied the truck, charging me $1 a year. Union treated me the way I like to be treated and in turn I've treated my men that way. That's why I have no help turnover. I still have that first little old truck Union gave me. I've retired it from service, but I keep it polished and it sits alongside my fleet of big new trucks and trailers as a reminder that in this country the big fellow is willing to help the little fellow succeed if he wants to try it on his own."

Darrell T. Stuart, who painted his first Union Oil service station in Santa Barbara, eventually needed 92 trucks and 200 people to fulfill his contracts to keep 3,700 stations throughout the Southwest freshly painted.

"I gave them their money's worth with no cheating or skimping," said Stuart. "Union liked it and gave me some more jobs around town. I got an idea this might be a business to specialize in about the time the company suggested I

Or how to paint your way up the ladder

'You hear a lot of talk these days about the danger of big companies getting still bigger.

"What people overlook is that every big company creates opportunity for small ones to start and grow strong. I'm a good example.

"I quit school at 15 and went to work as an apprentice painter. When I was 22 I started a little decorating business in Santa Barbara, California.

DARRELL STUART, DECORATING, 1919

"In 1930—when I was 33—I had an idea I could do better by specializing. So I bid on painting a Union Oil service station. I got the contract, gave my decorating business to my superintendent, and started to specialize.

"I had a truck, a hired hand, and $1000 I'd borrowed from the bank. I did a better paint job on that first station than Union had ever been able to get for the money—and still made $40. As a result, I kept getting more contracts—and borrowing more money. Profits I put back into the business for equipment.

"Today, Darrell Stuart Inc. gets most of the paint work for Union Oil's marketing department, and a sizeable amount from other departments, too. We still bid competitively on every job—and still do a better one than Union itself can do any other way.

DARRELL STUART: "BIG BUSINESS IS THE BEST FRIEND SMALL BUSINESS HAS."

"We employ over 200 people, work 92 trucks and own our own building, mortgage-free. Last year we grossed over a million dollars.

"But the point is: if Union Oil hadn't given me the chance, I'd never have had the incentive to come this far. In my book, big business is the best friend—and customer—small business has!"

* * *

Last year our customers paid us a record $368,760,900. That's big business.

But when you take a closer look, you find we spent 72% of that $368,760,900 with more than fifteen thousand other companies and individuals with whom we do business.

Many of these companies—like Stuart's—have grown with us. As long as we continue to do a better job, there's a good chance some of those small companies will be the big ones of tomorrow.

ONE OF DARRELL STUART'S JOBS: THE UNION OIL STORAGE-TANK PUMPKIN.

YOUR COMMENTS ARE INVITED. *Write: The Chairman of the Board, Union Oil Co., Union Oil Bldg., Los Angeles 17, Calif.*

MANUFACTURERS OF ROYAL TRITON, THE AMAZING PURPLE MOTOR OIL

September 1956

1. George Sevelle, at 26, had been a waiter, window dresser, candymaker and race driver's mechanic. In spare moments, he dabbled in home chemistry. Through this hobby he developed a paint cleaner and preserver. In 1939, he brought his product to Union Oil.

2. Sevelle demonstrated how it could be used to "launder" our service stations with better results and for less money than we had been spending. Naturally we were interested in improving station appearance at less cost. So Sevelle took on the job of cleaning several Union Oil stations on a regular schedule. He was in business for himself.

3. The sole drawback was that Sevelle had no truck to haul his equipment from station to station. His capital consisted of a single dollar. So Union Oil agreed to lease him one truck. He did such a good job that his contract was soon expanded to cover 150 stations.

4. Today Sevelle is almost an institution. He contracts for the cleaning of all Union Oil stations in 7 western states. He operates a fleet of trucks and several house trailers where his crews live in comfort. On top of running a $100,000-a-year business, he's a Southern California community leader, an active member of five local organizations.

5. This story is important, we think, for several reasons. First, it's a real rebuttal to the defeatists who say there's no opportunity left in the U. S. A. for a go-getter who'd like to be his own boss. We say (and Sevelle seconds us) that there's ample room for the ambitious to spread their wings.

6. Sevelle's success also points up something many people don't realize—the relationship between big and small business in every field of industry is healthy and helpful. Each is dependent on the other. So as Union Oil grows, it helps other enterprises grow, too. After all, any company keeps on growing only as long as it pleases people.

UNION OIL COMPANY
OF CALIFORNIA

INCORPORATED IN CALIFORNIA, OCTOBER 17, 1890

This series, sponsored by the people of Union Oil Company, is dedicated to a discussion of how and why American business functions. We hope you'll feel free to send in any suggestions or criticisms you have to offer. Write: The President, Union Oil Company, Union Oil Bldg., Los Angeles 17, California.

Manufacturers of Royal Triton, the amazing purple motor oil

August 1953

THE FIFTH FREEDOM IN ACTION *When Union Oilers could become independent operators to perform segments of the company's business, Union sometimes handed them contracts and helped finance them through the lean beginning years. These ads described two of the success stories launched under this enlightened system.*

contract to do all their service station painting in the county. My assets at the time were a single beat-up truck and about $600. I couldn't swing the deal without more money, but with the prospects of a contract with Union and with the company's encouragement, I was able to borrow. Union, you might say, set me up in business on my own."

Before long Stuart's crews were spread out over California, Utah, Arizona, and Nevada painting stations for several other companies as well as Union's.

"Sure, it was a tough struggle," says Stuart, "but when things looked the blackest the boys at Union would give me a helping hand and a pat on the back. To me, Union epitomizes capitalism in action by giving the smaller fellow a 'break.' I try to spread the gospel in turn through my employees."

The experiences of Union's little business people, some of them no longer small, followed a lively pattern—an idea, an opportunity, a boost, a lot of sweat and toil and initiative, and a new business that flourished. Union's affiliated small businessmen prospered so remarkably during the postwar years that their aggregate profits equaled those of the Union Oil Company itself, which goes to show that big business can be good for little business, and vice versa.

CHAPTER TEN 1950-1960

The Explosive Fifties

UNION'S MANAGEMENT PLUNGED INTO THE FABULOUS FIFTIES with a quick look back and a long look forward. The quick look back took the shape of the California Oil Museum, founded by the company in 1950 at the suggestion of Clarence Froome, then superintendent of the Ventura exploration and production division. Appropriately, the museum was located in the old brick building in Santa Paula erected six decades earlier by Thomas R. Bard to house the Mission Transfer Company. In 1890, it became the first corporate home of the fledgling Union Oil Company of California. In this historic spot Froome assembled from old California oil fields the crude tools that recalled the struggles of the plucky pioneers who launched the Western petroleum industry. The display included a primitive drilling rig, handmade tools and bits, historic documents, maps and photographs, all dramatizing the oil bonanza from its beginnings in the surrounding hills and canyons. The museum quickly became a showplace attracting thousands of visitors.

The long look forward was a "must" to get on top of the booming new decade. The population explosion in the Western states, Union's major marketing area, meant a million new potential customers each year for "76" products. The explosion was caused in part by natural increase of a young and vigorous population, partly by the never-ending migration west. The statistical crystal ball revealed that within the decade California would overtake the population of New York. Other Western states were growing proportionately.

For Union's planners this burgeoning of customers presented some knotty problems. One was to find more petroleum and find it fast. The oil wells that had caused a glut a decade back were now unable to meet the ravenous appetites of automobiles, airplanes, tractors, trucks, and diesel engines. But as the demand

MEASURING THE SECOND ROUND

Fields once thought to have yielded their last drop of oil are brought back to life with modern methods of secondary recovery. Here, the potential success of recovery operations are measured with a scale model of a field.

MEMORABILIA OF A LUSTY PAST

Working models and relics from pioneer days in the oil fields draw 10,000 visitors a year to Union's California Oil Museum in Santa Paula, first opened in 1950. The museum occupies the ground floor in the building where Union started its corporate life 60 years earlier.

for gasolines skyrocketed, the use of fuel oil tapered off. Industrial plants were converting to natural gas, some piped in from as far as Texas; railroads had switched to diesels; the Navy cut down purchases. With storage tanks overflowing, Union shut in more than 20,000 barrels a day of crude at the wells and resumed shipment of fuel oil to East Coast markets. Competitors followed suit. In 1950, President Taylor assured the company's 35,653 stockholders that "the current situation of over-supply is not new or unique" and that "in the long pull these situations tend to be self-corrective." He proved to be a prophet; within weeks the Korean War had flared and the Navy was clamoring for more fuel oil for ships.

CENTER FOR PETROLEUM RESEARCH

Union's multi-million-dollar Brea Research Center, opened in 1951, is dedicated to increasing production, developing processing techniques, and improving product quality. It has evolved from the 1891 appropriation of $2,500 for a single scientist and the West's first petroleum laboratory.

Looking back over the company's fabulous six decades of growth, neither Taylor nor the Union directors were satisfied to wait for these periodic conditions of feast or famine to correct themselves in the future. Basically, they were faced with the same problem that led Lyman Stewart sixty years earlier to wheedle $2,500 of the company's meager capital for the West's first petroleum laboratory. The dilemma still was how to get more products from a barrel of crude. In 1950 the Union management upped this original research appropriation some three-thousand-fold to build a new $8 million center at Brea, California, in the heart of an area of productive company oil fields. The original "research" lab at Santa Paula had consisted of a small one-room building back of the Santa Paula home office. Its equipment included a counter, some glass bottles and tubes, a burner, and a microscope. By contrast, the new Research Center at Brea, fifteen miles southeast of Los Angeles, was a complex of a dozen compact, single-story, connected buildings housing laboratories, shops, offices, a library, and ample space for duplicating in miniature almost any working problem faced by Union Oilers from the frozen muskeg of the arctic to the tropical bayous of Louisiana.

The research staff of 300 men and women moved from crowded quarters at the Los Angeles refinery to their new petroleum products workshop on September 1, 1951. Their chief was founder Lyman Stewart's grandson, executive vice-president William Lyman Stewart, Jr. The Research Center had been Bill Stewart's dream almost from the day he started work in 1914 as a pipefitter at the Los Angeles refinery. It was unique in several ways. One was that the researchers themselves had designed it. The center was laid out so that the company's scientists and technicians could team up handily with groups of Union Oilers from the fields, from pipeline stations, from refineries, or marketing outlets to wrestle with specific and practical day-to-day problems. While one team in one area worked on a better drilling mud, another in a different lab sought ways to coax more oil out of depleted sands, or to rearrange hydrocarbon atoms into more valuable products. In a way, the Research Center was the Union Oil empire on a Lilliputian scale. As exploration vice-president Cy Rubel observed, "Union gets more from researchers than does any other company because our projects are all on the practical side. Each project is guided by a sponsoring group from the field or from refineries."

MAN-MADE EARTHQUAKES SEEK OUT HIDDEN OIL

Seismic blasts such as this directed sound waves into the earth to enable scientists to draw a "picture" of the subsurface as a guide to possible undiscovered oil-bearing areas. Newer energy sources which are more environmentally compatible are used today to create shock waves. The digital computers which process the readings are a real breakthrough in seismic technology.

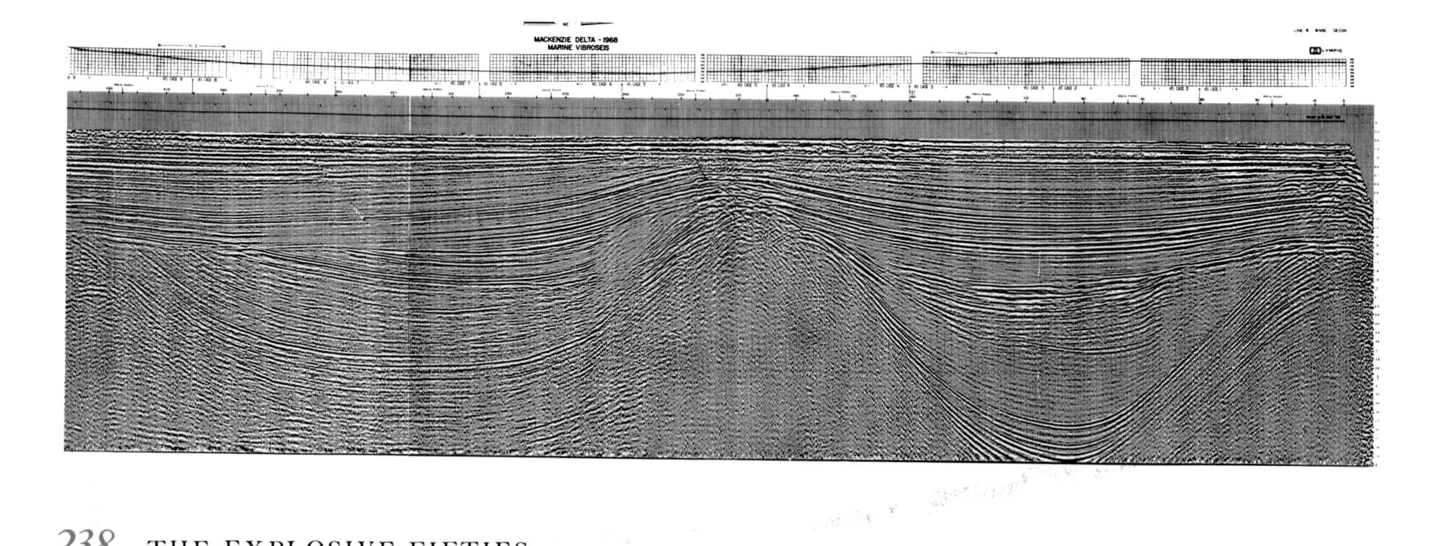

In a remarkably short time the new Research Center was paying off, not only in more efficient petroleum production and refining of products, but in royalties collected from other companies on processes developed and patented by the center's scientists and engineers. By 1955, forty oil companies and chemical manufacturers were paying royalties to Union.

While the researchers were exploring for better ways to use petroleum, Union's oil hunters were wildcatting equally energetically for more millions of barrels of crude and more billions of cubic feet of natural gas. To keep the company healthy, the oil hunters had to find more new oil each year than Union's customers consumed. Rubel and his staff were convinced that, except for offshore discoveries, the possibility of finding a major oil field under California's worked-over surface was negligible. Small oil strikes brought in new reserves each year and many older fields still had more petroleum trapped in their sands than the pumps had been able to pull out. To further complicate exploration near the major markets, offshore wildcatting was fouled up by a tangle of local, state, and federal red tape. So Union's oil hunters scouted the wide world for new petroleum finds. The hunt led them to Texas, Louisiana, Canada, Argentina, Central America, Africa's Sahara Desert, Alaska—to mention a few of the areas where drillers were about to make hole in the greatest oil search in Union's history.

To help the geologists and the wildcatters in their hunt, the company bought the United Geophysical Company of Pasadena in 1950, acquired for 40,000 shares of Union Oil stock. United Geophysical had been built by Herbert Hoover, Jr., who joined Union's board of directors, continuing to direct seismic crews that were shooting the earth from Borneo to Saudi Arabia. Thus Union operated its own seismic survey operations until 1954, when Hoover resigned to become Undersecretary of State for the Eisenhower administration. At that date the geophysical survey subsidiary was purchased by its own officers, but crews continued to earth-shoot for Union's geologists. An unexpected bonus to Union from the United Geophysical purchase was a huge body of copper ore in Pima County, Arizona, discovered by geophysicists with methods used in the search for oil. Union sold a majority interest in this copper strike to the Cyprus Mines Corporation and Utah Construction Company, thereby becoming a copper producer in a modest way.

The energetic wide-world oil hunt yielded discoveries that maintained Union's crude oil reserves at more than 600,000,000 barrels, despite increased production each year, and piled up 3.5 trillion cubic feet of natural gas reserves. Some of these finds were dramatic episodes in Union's history. They more than justified the huge capital expenditures earmarked for exploration, ranging from $62,500,000 in 1951 to over $68,000,000 in 1959. The most spectacular discoveries were along the Gulf of Mexico where drillers pushed holes more than two miles deep beneath the swamps or drilled from costly steel platforms rising out of the waters of the Gulf itself. Many of the new wells turned out to be gassers, which were shut in, awaiting construction of pipelines for delivery to markets. After the great pipelines were built to send the natural gas whooshing a thousand miles to the Eastern seaboard cities, gas wells were prizes more valuable than oil producers.

One spectacular strike was the discovery in 1951 of the East Lake Palourde field in the Louisiana bayou country, which made Union one of the major producers in the Gulf area. The strike demonstrated anew the old axiom that "oil is where you find it." Vice-president of operations Dudley Tower recounted how "Union first drilled a 12,000-foot dry hole in Lake Palourde in 1942. We had the whole area leased, but we dropped it. Then Shell came in, leased it up, and drilled two holes. Sun Oil and Humble followed. They were all dry holes, but they narrowed down the area. One Sun hole looked like it was on the edge of something, so Union's landmen went back and leased up all the acreage that was available. We drilled and got a well, proving that we just didn't go deep enough the first time. Only five hundred more feet of drilling would have put us in the oil zone with that first dry hole."

Forty miles northwest at Big Bayou Pigeon in the Atchafalaya Swamp Jungle, Union's wildcatters pushed in another drilling barge and sank a 13,000-foot well. It was a dry hole, but geologists after studying core data recommended another quarter million dollar try. This one came in with 600 barrels a day of 45-gravity oil. So did five more holes. A profitable new oil field was added to Union's reserves. It was the same at West White Lake, Vermilion Parish, Tigre Lagoon, Fresh Water Bayou, East Timbalier Bay, where drillers drove their bits to 17,395 feet—over three miles down—for Union's deepest well. It was still more exciting hunting oil under the waters of the Gulf of Mexico, where Union's earthshooters turned watershooters and found evidence of formations that might have trapped oil two miles beneath the sea. Union bid expensively and successfully on blocks of watery waste, then reared steel islands, each a drilling base for up to a dozen wells. These brought in the Caillou Island Field, the Vermilion Block, the Block 26, and a dozen other rich fields. It seemed like Union's drillers couldn't miss down there in the swamps, the bayous, and out in the Gulf's waters. The oil finders themselves were a new breed of Union Oilers, mostly natives of the marsh and swamp country, men happily acclimated to spending half of their days and nights on islands or barges as long as pots of strong, black coffee brewed on the stove. By the end of the decade, Union's 497 Gulf Coast wells were delivering a daily output of 16,000 barrels of crude and over 200,000,000 cubic feet of natural gas.

Two thousand miles to the north other teams of Union Oilers were making oil-field lore under vastly different conditions. These were Union's wildcatters in the jelly-like muskeg of northern Canada. This was rugged oil hunting. The millions of acres of swamp in northern Canada were accessible only in the cold, dark winter months when the muskeg was frozen deep and solid enough to support trucks, tractors, and drilling rigs. Parka-clad crews made hole 'round the clock, working under artificial lights. For weeks the sun barely peeked over the horizon. Their first oil strike, in 1953, was at Fairydell, west of Redwater in Alberta Province. In the spring of 1956 the Exploration Department decided to attempt summer drilling to round out the potential field.

THE WELL THAT TRIGGERED A LAND BOOM *Union's northernmost discovery, wildcat Red Earth 12-17, came in with 1,000 barrels a day of high-gravity crude and started the greatest land rush in Canadian history in 1956.*

By heroic efforts bulldozers pushed a primitive all-weather road through the swamp and forest before the muskeg thawed. Trucks, power wagons, and cars started hopefully over the road but were caught by an unexpected deluge. Equipment mired down hub-deep as men sweated like oxen trying to winch the vehicles loose from the mud. Then Canada's busy beavers got into the act, blocking culverts under the road to make dams. The crews managed to fight their way out on foot, leaving their vehicles to be recovered after the next fall freeze turned the earth solid again. Bush pilots rescued families stranded at Red Earth Camp. The next winter, Exploration drilled more wells and rounded out the field, on nature's terms in the harsh northland. When the wells were finished and tested, they were capped until the Peace River Pipe Line was completed in November of 1964.

In other far places, the Union oil hunters found better drilling conditions, but less oil. Seismic crews "shot" three million acres in Costa Rica, half a million

FANTASTIC TORREY CANYON

The hilly, oil-rich property is one of Union's early producing areas. Crowded on this hilltop are producing wells, a pipeline station, oil treating plant and at far right, a compressor plant.

SENTINEL ON THE MOUNTAIN

High above the Santa Clara Valley and Santa Paula is the silhouette of an early rocker arm pump, a sentinel standing on Torrey mountain. Farther down the hill, the modern pipeline pumping station sends crude oil on its way to the Los Angeles Refinery.

more in Peru. In the Argentine, they teamed up with the government petroleum agency to explore four million acres in the Comodoro Rivadavia Basin. After the wildcatters found oil, a new Argentine government canceled the concession. In the Spanish Sahara, Union and a Spanish partner signed up to explore 1,750,000 acres of African desert. The first seismic crew to start shooting the area was captured by bandits and held for ransom. In Australia, Union, with Kern County Land Company and the Australian Oil and Gas Corporation, joined in an oil hunt on a 40,000,000-acre concession. In Alaska, with Ohio Oil Company as a partner, Union's crews drilled for oil on the Kenai Peninsula near Cook Inlet. The first test well drilled into a vast reservoir of natural gas at 4,232 feet. But the gamble soon paid returns. The new gas field was only seventy-five miles from Alaska's largest city, Anchorage, whose residents eagerly awaited the delivery of natural gas for heating and cooking.

These distant strikes were gratifying, but what Union needed was more oil in California, where the Los Angeles and Oleum refineries could turn it into gasoline for the 76-Union service station pumps. Union's geologists knew there was more oil in the company's pumped-out old fields. If ways could be found to release it from the hard-packed sands it might be the equivalent of making a million-barrel new oil strike next door to the refineries. Water flooding had successfully flushed sluggish crude out of the old Richfield area wells. Gas injection had revived production in the old Dominguez Field. Union's researchers had other brainstorms for making the sands give up their oil. One fantastic idea was a blowtorch operation at the bottom of an old hole which expanded underground air, thereby forcing more oil out of adjoining wells.

Union's most unbelievable strike was at Torrey Canyon Field, a producer since Union Oil Company was born in 1890. Water flooding had boosted the flow of oil from what was then considered the lower zone. Superintendent Clarence Froome and chief geologist John Sloat had a gnawing hunch that "there's another oil zone down below." Torrey Canyon had fifty-nine shallow wells, which cost $3,400 apiece to drill in 1889, still yielding oil, their ancient pumps with nodding rocker arms and wooden sucker rods actuated by a spiderweb of jack lines powered by wheezing central gas engines. Scattered among these oldtimers, in production since 1889, were a score of still productive 1,600-foot medium-depth wells drilled around 1910. In 1950 Froome and Sloat were given the go-ahead to drill a deep well. They lost no time making hole. At the two-mile depth, Torrey No. 83 came in on April 30, 1952, for 526 barrels a day of oil and half a million cubic feet of gas. Subsequent deep wells, costing up to $750,000 apiece, were even better producers. Torrey Canyon again became one of Union's top fields, right where the oil was needed for the ravenous Southern California market.

To the oil hunter, Torrey Canyon is the story of oil compressed into one compact paragraph. There are seeps still trickling heavy oil and tar as Professor Benjamin Silliman reported seeing them back in 1864. There are the shallow, wooden-sucker-rod pumpers of 1890 vintage; next come the second-zone wells bottomed at 1,600 feet in 1910 when it was thought this was about as far as drillers could make hole. Two miles down the whipstocked wells slanted out in all directions tapping the third zone reservoirs. This type drilling was necessary in these rugged coastal mountains so that multiple wells could be drilled and later serviced from one accessible central location.

"We have everything in this field from the beginning of the industry," boasted Froome, whose hunches were still working overtime. When the drilling rigs finished the deep-zone Torrey Field, Froome moved them over to nearby Oakridge two miles to the east. Here drillers found another rich oil field beneath another oldtimer, this time only 3,000 feet down, but deeper than wildcatters could drill holes when the original Oakridge Field was discovered. By the end of the decade, Union's geologists, aided by seismic surveys, were taking a second look at every old field owned or leased by the company. Secondary recovery projects under thirty-five fields added 70-million barrels to Union's reserves in oil-hungry California.

Union's geologists were sure there was one other untapped source of oil close to market. That was the continental shelf off the California coast. "When you are hunting for oil you have to shake loose from the idea that there is any particular significance to a shoreline, geologically speaking," insisted Cy Rubel. The rich Louisiana offshore strikes had proved this. But drilling in the comparatively quiet and shallow waters off Louisiana was easy compared to battling the tides and currents of the Pacific on a shelf that fell off fast to great depths. A few companies had erected costly rock and steel islands, others slanted wells out from the California shore. To drill in the rough ocean waters, Union joined a four-company group—Continental, Union, Shell, and Superior—which in 1953 converted a huge surplus Navy freight barge into a floating platform, complete with derrick, drilling rig, and crew's quarters. The monster, known as CUSS I, the initials of the owners, was anchored over the watery drilling sites determined by seismic survey. CUSS I, under the direction of Union Oiler Bob Bauer, made 300,000 feet of exploratory hole off the coast of California. In the summer of 1957 it pushed down six holes in 54 days. Some of the holes were under 1,000 feet of ocean current. CUSS I proved that the oil hunters could wildcat successfully under the ocean waves. But they couldn't drill through the oceans of red tape in which the state and federal governments had tangled the California offshore leasing program. When the other partners became disheartened, the joint venture was dissolved. Union bought them out, becoming temporarily an 80 per cent owner of Global Marine Exploration Company, which built and operated several of the mobile and self-sufficient platforms that drilled holes in Davy Jones' Locker off Alaska, Peru, Surinam, Jamaica, Libya, Australia, the Gulf of Mexico, the North Sea, and in the Great Lakes. One customer, the Project Mohole Group, wasn't interested in finding oil but wanted some holes drilled through the earth's crust to find out what was inside our global eggshell.

In 1955, Union's directors voted to invest $5,000,000 as a starter in proving up the company's potentially most colossal oil reserve. This was the shale oil deposit in Colorado's Mahogany Ledge, which geologists estimated to hold 6-

OIL FROM ROCKY MOUNTAIN SHALE *Union's ingenious engineers designed a retort to extract oil from shale carved from this Colorado cliff.*

billion barrels of crude oil—if and when anybody could figure out how to extract the oil from the solid rock. At Union's Research Center, under the direction of Fred L. Hartley, the staff had successfully built a miniature retort that worked. So the company ordered a full-scale model, still experimental, in a Rocky Mountain canyon below a cliff from which the shale could be dropped down by conveyor to the retort. The pilot plant was something Rube Goldberg might have dreamed up. A powerful "rock pump" at its base rammed the shattered shale upward through the four-story steel hopper. As the rock was pushed upward, hot gases were pulled downward by blowers. They released the raw shale oil in the form of gases, which were drawn off at the bottom of the weird contraption. The spent shale rock flowed upward and spilled out of the retort at the top. Amazingly, the whole process worked without using a drop of water, a rare commodity at the site of the shale beds, and a major necessity of most oil refineries. In test runs during the next three years, the retort cooked up to a thousand tons of shale per day and extracted a barrel of oil from each two tons of rock. The shale oil was evil-smelling and full of sulphur and ammonia. But a new refining process developed by Union researchers extricated these bad agents and turned them into marketable by-products. The one unsolved problem was how to produce the shale oil as inexpensively as petroleum could be pumped from underground pools.

"PIPELINER, SAVE MY TREE!"

There is a bend in Union's 225-mile pipeline from the San Joaquin Valley to the Oleum Refinery where the line passes a cherished oak tree. When the 87-year-old landowner granted right-of-way for the pipe, she requested that the ditch miss the tree under which she had played as a child, and Union's crews made a respectful detour.

Another ace-in-the-hole was a small mountain of tar sands in Santa Barbara, likewise owned in fee simple. Geologists described these sands as a fossil surface oil reservoir which had been uncovered in past ages, allowing the volatile gas and light oils to escape. The residual tar, trapped in the sand, can be scooped up by pit mining methods used in coal mines. Experiments at the Brea Research Lab demonstrated that the heavy oil could be extricated from the sands but the cost of processing in an environmentally acceptable way is presently not economic. When that day comes, Union will have some 50-million barrels of tar-sand oil handy to the market place.

During the fifties the oil man's old axiom, "oil is where you find it," changed to "oil is where you deliver it." Decades before, the company had pioneered both tankers and pipelines to carry Southern California's oil to market. Now it needed pipelines and tankers to bring oil to California's thirsty refineries. Lyman Stewart, who pushed the company's first pipeline from Santa Paula to tidewater at Ventura, had envisioned a network that would send rivers of oil flowing from the oil fields to the state's population centers. It was not until 1955 that his vision came true in the form of the 65-mile Torrey Canyon pipeline, which connected the prolific new deep-zone producers of the Torrey Canyon, Oakridge, and Tapo Fields with the refinery at Los Angeles Harbor. The pipeline would have sparked a gleam in the founder's eye. Stewart was thwarted because the company lacked funds to build the pipeline. President Reese Taylor built it without tying up any of Union's capital. The line was laid over the Simi Hills in a hurry and was paid for by the Santa Clara Pipeline Company, which leased it to Union for twenty years, after which ownership reverts to Union Oil Company.

The following year, the same pipeline company had another important river of oil flowing through the 225-mile Oleum line from the southern San Joaquin Valley oil fields to Union's refinery on San Francisco Bay. It had been possible to push oil through a hook-up of pipelines owned by various companies from the San Joaquin to Oleum, but most of the crude had gone via the San Joaquin-Avila line, laid in 1909 by W. L. Stewart, thence by tanker to San Francisco Bay. It was now possible via the new Oleum line for Union's dispatchers to push a few buttons to move an 80,000-barrel-per-day river of oil (with a 110,000-barrel-per-day future potential) directly to the northern refinery. Before long, practically the entire system could be operated by a single dispatcher located in Los Angeles using microwaves beamed to various pumping stations.

These amazing rivers of oil were fast becoming one of the marvels of the age, as well as a necessity to modern civilization. Without them oil wells in remote areas were virtually useless, as was demonstrated by Union's early capped wells brought in by drillers in northern Canada. Some crude as it flows out of the wells, particularly in California, is heavy, thick, and sluggish fluid. So the pipeliners' rivers of oil must often be heated every few score miles to make the stuff flow. The pressure from powerful pumps moves the oil along roughly about as fast as a man walks. Since nearly every field yields a different kind of crude, the oil is shoved along in batches, known as "tenders." Some finished products pipelines from refineries handle a dozen or more different products daily, ranging from light aviation gas to heavy fuel oil. These tenders of products chase one after another through the pipelines like trains on a railroad without getting scrambled. Keeping them moving and pulling them out of the pipeline into the right tank is the skill of the pipeline dispatcher. He watches the map of his pipeline system on the wall, marking the progress of each tender with little pegs. He can open or close valves along the line with push buttons or now by microwave. To mark the end of one tender and the start of another the pipeliners inject slugs of radioactive oil or dye, or sometimes a "go-devil," an ingenious round plug that scrapes rust and wax from the inside of the pipeline and polishes it to reduce friction.

Dials warn the dispatcher of stoppages or breaks in the line. In the early days of the industry, inspectors had to walk the pipelines checking for breaks. Not any more. The inspectors have taken to air in slow-flying planes or helicopters, covering as many miles in a minute as the old-time inspector made in a day. Because the aerial inspection is so effective it continues to be widely used on Union's field pipelines. To check on this aerial inspection, a superintendent once dumped five gallons of crude over the pipeline at a remote point. Within an hour the watchdog called in to report the break, then added, "By the way, you left your oil can under the sagebrush on the west side of the line."

The Torrey Canyon and Oleum pipelines brought Union's California network up to nearly a thousand miles of major lines, fed by 500 miles of smaller gathering lines bringing the crude from the wells to mainline tanks. One network, short in length but big in importance, fed crude from the Los Angeles Basin fields to the Los Angeles Refinery. Another carried crude west over the hills from the

San Joaquin fields to Avila, Union's big tanker terminal near San Luis Obispo. Still another carried oil to Avila from the Santa Maria field. A Kern County network gathered crude for the Bakersfield refinery. Through these lines dispatchers pushed round-the-clock rivers of oil aggregating more than 100,000,000 barrels a year in volume.

Almost from the beginning, Union's tankers have played a key role in delivering the company's products to refineries and distant markets in Hawaii, Japan, South America, Alaska, and the Atlantic Seaboard. Each decade these tankers have grown in size .The expanding fifties were no exception. In December, 1953, the tanker fleet was augmented by the *Santa Maria*, with a capacity of 143,000 barrels of crude and products carried in 34 separate compartments. The next year she was joined by the still larger *Sansinena*. The *Torrey Canyon* and the *Lake Palourde* were on the ways. These 470,000-barrel super-tankers were the behemoths of the Union fleet. Their launching marked a turning point in the flow of crude. They reversed the flow of the rivers of oil. Up to this time, the company operated tankers primarily to carry California oil to refineries or to markets. Now the tankers assumed a new role, bringing crude from the prodigious Near East oil fields to feed the ravenous California refineries.

Super-tankers make money only when they are moving oil or products, and lose it fast when they are waiting to be loaded or unloaded. So with the advent of the super-tankers, Union embarked on a super-terminal building program. This included longer wharves and more storage tanks both at Los Angeles Harbor and at Oleum. Before the super-terminal program was completed, Union had re-built tank farms at Los Angeles, Oleum, Seattle, Anchorage, and in Hawaii. Facilities for delivering the oil to market were becoming almost as expensive as finding it.

The fifties decade opened with Union, like other Western oil companies, facing a famine of high-value gasolines and a glut of low-value fuel oils. President Taylor set about to correct this imbalance—at the refineries where the low-priced crude could be converted into high-priced products. In 1950 ground was broken for a new $9-million catalytic-cracking plant at the Los Angeles refinery. The massive new cracker, capable of processing 28,850 barrels a day, gave Union the largest catalytic-cracking capacity on the Pacific Coast, when it went "on stream" in 1952, just in time to meet the mushrooming demands of the

GROWTH OF UNION OIL'S TANKERS

FULLERTON	SANTA RITA	MONTEBELLO	L.P. ST. CLAIR	LOMPOC
235′	430′	457′	442′	504′
———	9 knots	10 knots	12 knots	14.5 knots
16,000 barrels	55,000 barrels	80,000 barrels	101,000 barrels	140,000 barrels
1902	1906	1920	1939	1945

Korean War. Half of the fuel for planes, tanks, and other vehicles used in the war was supplied by California refineries. Union's new refinery, abetted by a $6,000,000 new topping and distillation plant, increased both the quantity and the quality of gasolines. A new process removed the problem ingredients of the crude and turned them into tons of marketable sulphur and agricultural ammonia sulfate. Other plants at the Los Angeles and Oleum refineries and a new one at Edmonds, Washington, converted the residue from the barrel of crude into asphalt for paving and roofing.

In the mid-fifties, Union's researchers perfected and patented a remarkable new step in refining that solved a baffling problem confronting the oil industry. Crude from many productive oil fields was high in sulphur and nitrogen content. These ingredients were readily burned in fuel oil, a fast declining market, but were bad actors in gasoline, diesel and aviation fuel, the fast growing market. Union's refiners, like others in the industry, wanted more gasoline and less fuel oil per barrel of crude. The new process cleaned up the crude and turned it from a "sour" feedstock to a "sweet" feedstock.

"Unifining" was Union's name for the process known more technically as catalytic hydrodesulfurization. The key to the process was the use of beds of cobalt molybdate particles impregnated in alumina pellets to remove the impurities from a variety of petroleum distillates. The catalysts could be used over and over for long periods. Their cost was less than one cent per barrel of oil processed. At Oleum, the engineering staff, unwilling to wait for a second Unifiner, adapted existing equipment and converted their one unifiner into two.

Other companies were quick to see the advantage of Unifining, as Union arranged with Universal Oil Products Company to license competitors to use the process on a royalty basis. Fred L. Hartley, manager of commercial development when Unifining was perfected, also took to the road to market the process. More than a hundred refining plants of various kinds took out licenses to utilize the Unifining process, which not only helped to boost the quality of Union's gasoline to a new high, but earned the company substantial royalties. The impact of Unifining on the petroleum industry was stupendous.

FLAG
1888-1965

FLAG
1965-

SANTA MARIA
551′
15 knots
146,000 barrels

1952

SANSINENA
810′
17.2 knots
470,000 barrels

1958

LAKE PALOURDE
975′
16.2 knots
870,000 barrels

1965

UNION'S UNIFINER THAT SOLVED A BAFFLING PROBLEM *In the mid-fifties, Union introduced the Unifiner, which solved certain refining problems so successfully that it was adopted throughout the industry.*

The researchers were providing Union with so many saleable new items from petroleum and natural gas that in 1952 Brea Chemicals, Inc., a wholly owned subsidiary, was set up to manufacture and market by-products. By 1957, the subsidiary had become an important producer of petrochemicals. Sales of ammonia pellets and liquid aqua ammonia for fertilizer boomed. Union had bought a major interest in another thriving petroleum by-products concern, the R. T. Collier Corporation of San Jose. Hard-driving Bob Collier had built up a unique business by utilizing surplus petroleum coke from Union's Oleum and Santa Maria refineries to manufacture briquets for fireplaces and calcined carbon for electrodes used in aluminum refining and other electrochemical processing. In July, 1957, Brea Chemicals, Inc. and R. T. Collier Corporation merged into a new carbon petrochemical subsidiary, Collier Carbon and Chemical Company, owned by Union, with Collier as director of the $20-million a year by-product business.

But there were some set-backs in the fifties, notably the big fires, the most spectacular since 1926, the year of the lightning-ignited blazes that destroyed Union's tank farms at San Luis Obispo and near Brea in simultaneous infernos. A gasoline tank at the Los Angeles refinery exploded on July 12, 1951, a conflagration traced to static electricity. As the roof from the exploded tank crashed, it smashed pipelines and fittings, releasing fiery jets of gasoline from six other 80,000-barrel tanks. Firefighters from other companies and from cities, all of whom had learned the tactics of containing blazing oil from Union's fire Lab, joined Union's crew to give battle. The blaze raged three days and nights, destroying $1,685,000 worth of fuel and tanks, but miraculously there were no serious injuries or deaths. Probably no fire was ever "seen" by so many people. Daring cameramen followed firemen right up to the flames to shoot live broadcasts for thousands of TV watchers.

The next fire the following year was at Oleum refinery on San Francisco Bay. It destroyed one tanker, damaged another, engulfed the docks—but proved a blessing in disguise. The transportation department immediately designed a longer wharf, 1,250 feet in length. The new wharf was connected to the refinery by a causeway which carried two dozen pipelines. Built of fireproof concrete, the new wharf accommodated two super-tankers and five oil barges simultaneously.

The epic oil fire fight of the decade was with "The Wild Tiger of the Gulf." The Tiger was a wildcat hole drilled 6 miles off the Vermilion Parish shore in Gulf of Mexico waters 26 feet deep when the battle started but 125 feet deep when it ended. On June 6, 1957, drilling crews encountered abnormally high pressures 2 miles beneath the waves. These increased steadily from 1,500 to 3,800 pounds per square inch. Then a lower flange on a blow-out valve gave way. Gases hissed up through the break, whipping out sand so fast that the blast cut through metal. The hiss mounted to a roar. By June 8 the well was blowing wild. Workmen were ordered off the platform, just in time. The drilling tender slipped anchor, backed off.

An emergency call to Houston, Texas, brought Myron Kinley, famous fighter of oil-well fires and blowouts. Arriving with Union's Gulf Division chiefs, Basil

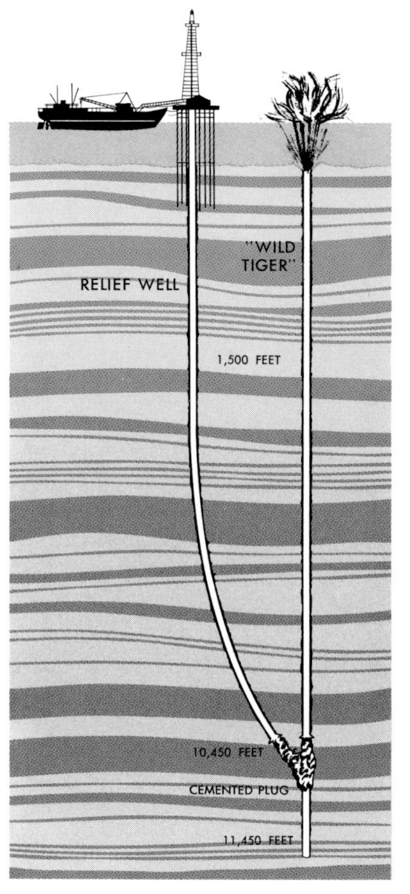

WILD TIGER OF THE GULF — *An inferno of flames spewed out of the sea after a well drilled in the Gulf in 1957 went wild. The flames raged unchecked for 162 days before a relief well* (right) *sealed off the flow of gas. Once tamed, the well became a prolific producer.*

Kantzer and Ed Sands, Kinley admitted that he had met his match, just as the leaning derrick and platform toppled and were swallowed up by the gas-dug crater on the Gulf bottom. To prevent the volcano of gas from creating havoc, Navy aviators were called in to air-drop a tank of gasoline, which they ignited with tracer bullets. The Wild Tiger became an inferno of flames spewing out of the sea. Sea gulls, gliding in to investigate the wonder, were whipped skyward to the private cloud hovering above the flames. Curious fish crowded around the fiery waters. At a respectful distance, in a circling launch, a humbled but undefeated team of oil men planned a new and fantastic attack to put the cork back into Nature's deep-down gas bottle.

Under the drive of Kantzer and Sands, contractors erected a new drilling platform and derrick a third of a mile from the burning waters. Drillers started making hole, fast. This was no ordinary hole. It had to be drilled at an angle to hit a target no larger than a lamp post, 2 miles deep and ⅓ mile off center. Taking no chances, the crews tested every length of casing to stand pressures up to 11,000 pounds. The well was cemented at a depth of 10,482 feet. When, by engineer's calculations, the bottom of the hole was 100 feet from the unseen target, a flotilla of pumping and cementing rigs was called to stand by. After

200 additional feet of hole, the drilling mud ceased to circulate back to the surface in the casing. The drillers knew they were at grips with The Tiger.

Thirteen pumps went into action, pushing 1,800 barrels of mud down the hole in one hour and a quarter. Then, for thirty-six hours, sea water was forced down. Next 3,500 barrels of mud were shoved in the hole, followed by more sea water, then 4,600 barrels of mud and 3,700 sacks of cement. When the cement had plugged up the hole, the drillers turned to their bits again. As they hit 10,800 feet, the angry flames on the water flickered out. After a few burps of gas, a wonderful quiet settled over the waves. The private cloud, the seagulls, and the fish drifted away. The 162-day battle was won.

Pausing to rest for the first time, the fire fighters realized that they had found an oil field. After dragging the crater, hollowed out of the Gulf floor by the wild gasser, and finding no trace of their lost rig or platform, they completed the relief hole for a new producing well, then a dozen more whipstocked holes from the same platform for a dozen more producers. The Wild Tiger had become another legend in the hunt for oil.

Back in California, the home ground, other Union Oilers were locked in a different kind of battle—for independence. Some major oil companies were sponsoring, on the November election ballot, a confusing 30,000-word initiative measure known as "Proposition 4." If enacted into law, it would put all petroleum production in the state under control of a politically appointed commission empowered to "unitize" the pumping of oil from the state's many fields. Ballyhooed as a conservation measure, it would have virtually confiscated properties of the small independents, which the Union Oil Company had championed for four decades. Again Union became the champion of the small independents in one of the most bitter election campaigns in California history. When the ballots were counted, Proposition 4 was snowed under four to one.

The lusty growth made by Union in the fifties called for new capital in large chunks. Reese H. Taylor proved to be the president who could wildcat for dollars and find them. The $40-million loan he had arranged in 1949 got Union off to a healthy financial start in 1950, but by 1952 Taylor had to prospect in New York for more millions for capital expenditures. This time he negotiated the sale of $35 million in convertible debentures by 95 underwriters who sold out the issue the first day it was offered to investors. This helped pay for new refineries and terminals. By 1955 the company needed still more capital for expansion. Dillon Read & Company headed a group of underwriters of a $60-million issue of 3 per cent convertible debentures that sold at a premium price. By this time nearly all of the earlier issue of debentures had been exchanged for common stock, thus reducing Union's debt. With $60 million of new money, Taylor was able to retire loans, obligations, and preferred stock totaling $39-million, further simplifying and stabilizing the company's financial structure, but still providing $21 million for new capital outlays. The stockholders had already approved doubling the number of common shares to 15 million.

By now Union's resourceful chief had discovered that money, like oil, is where you find it. To free still more millions for exploration, Taylor was able to sell

PETROCHEMICALS ON COW ISLAND

The great transmission pipelines from the Gulf funnel through this Union co-owned plant at Cow Island, Louisiana. The plant "dries" the gas, removing valuable hydrocarbon liquids that become chemical building blocks.

Union's tanker fleet, six modern vessels, at a fine profit and charter them back into Union's service. Union's fleet of 630 tank cars had already been sold under a similar leasing arrangement. These sales added $20 million to the reserves for exploration, refining, and marketing. Union's 47,000 shareholders still had a $354-million equity in 1955, which was the company's sixty-fifth anniversary. The book value of Union's assets was over one-half billion dollars and many oil experts estimated the company's actual worth at nearer one billion dollars.

Looking back at Union's growth on October 17, 1955, the company's sixty-fifth birthday, Taylor observed, "We are not ambitious to be the biggest oil company in the business, but we do like to be thought of as the best oil company. We are still in our infancy in the uses of petroleum. In the next six decades we will accomplish far more than in the past six, provided we do not tax out of existence the economic climate that enabled Union Oil to grow and thrive."

Among contemporaries who considered Union's future bright was W. K. Whiteford, president of Gulf Oil Company, who had become a close friend of Reese Taylor. Gulf had an outstanding record of oil discovery, particularly in Venezuela and in oil-rich Kuwait on the Persian Gulf. Gulf also had a surplus of crude and likewise of cash. Taylor told Whiteford early in 1956 that Union Oil needed both crude and cash. Since Gulf and Union were noncompetitive, Taylor suggested that Union dispatch tankers on regular schedules across the Pacific and Indian Oceans to pick up some of Gulf's surplus petroleum for Union's refineries. He proposed also that Gulf might put some of its surplus cash to work by lending it to Union Oil Company for further expansion.

The upshot of the Taylor-Whiteford discussions was the sale to Gulf in April, 1955, of $120 million in 25-year debentures which Gulf might convert at a later date, if it elected to do so, into Union Oil common shares, at prices ranging from $70 to $80 per share. Union's shares at the time were selling for around $50. In the event Gulf's shares were converted to common stock, Gulf agreed to pay premiums ranging from $48 million to $72 million, depending on the date of conversion. The somewhat complicated deal meant that Gulf might eventually own up to 2,400,000 shares of Union's common stock, becoming Union's largest shareholder. But it was clearly understood between the two presidents that the financing was not a contemplated merger. Gulf was just selling its oil and putting its spare capital to work.

This big injection of capital came at a propitious time. In 1956, the company's sales topped the $400-million mark for the first time. Union's 4,330 wells were yielding only 70 per cent of the crude needed by Union's refineries. Three super-tankers, each with a 470,000-barrel capacity, were assigned to the Trans-Pacific-Trans-Indian-Ocean run to bring Gulf crude from Kuwait to California. To handle the new river of oil, huge new storage tanks and blending plants were added to the Los Angeles and Oleum terminals. The new bankroll enabled Taylor to retire the previous $60-million issue of debentures. Two-thirds of the holders took cash, the rest converted to Union common shares.

On August 1, 1956, Union Oilers came to work to find a new man in the president's chair. Their new boss was Albert Chatfield Rubel, whom the board of directors had promoted the day before from vice-president for exploration

A. C. RUBEL, UNION'S TWO-TERM PRESIDENT

Chosen to be Union's seventh president in 1956, A. C. Rubel capped a long and successful career with the company with an outstanding term as its head. He retired in 1960, after 38 years of service, but was called back in 1962 to serve as the company's ninth president. He retired for the second time in 1965.

and production. "Cy" Rubel had worked steadily up the ladder in thirty-three years since he had signed on as a young University of Arizona geologist fresh back from four years of oil hunting in the jungles of Central and South America. Reese Taylor moved upstairs, as chairman of the board and chief executive officer, to devote all of his energies to the company's accelerating growth problems. At this time a new vice-president joined Union's officer group. He was Fred L. Hartley, who had started as a trainee at the Oleum Refinery in 1939 and moved up through several departments to general manager, and then to vice-president of research.

The ample financing and reorganization sparked a new spell for Union in the late fifties. The surge swept through two recession years without a slow-down. The centennial of "Drake's Folly," the 69-foot hole that launched the petroleum industry on August 27, 1859, found Union Oil one of the few pioneers that had grown steadfastly with the phenomenal industry. As Chairman Taylor pointed out in his letter to Union Oilers commemorating the 100th anniversary of the discovery of oil, the industry had burgeoned from 2,000 barrels a year in 1859 to 2,461,000,000 barrels in 1959, and like Union Oil Company, it was still in its youth.

By this auspicious date the 1200 men and women of Union's head office staff had comfortably shaken down in their impressive new business home, the glistening Union Oil Center, dominating the downtown Los Angeles skyline from a bluff overlooking the Harbor Freeway. The $25-million complex of buildings and parks was a far cry from Union's first old brick home office in Santa Paula, now housing the California Oil Museum. Taylor had arranged with an investment company to finance the spectacular center, lease it to Union for fifty years, then turn it over for outright Union ownership without further cost. The center was Union's seventh home office.

The 1200 Union Oilers who moved into it on March 31, 1958, from offices scattered in half a dozen Los Angeles buildings, found themselves riding up escalators for the first seven of the central building's thirteen floors. Downstairs they had a 1500-car garage, a restaurant, a bank off the reception lobby. The offices were spacious, quiet, efficient. Over the weekend movers had brought in 4-million pounds of records and equipment. At night the soft lights of the new center shone as a symbol of free enterprise. As Reese Taylor put it, "This is the building that freedom built." As a daily reminder, the Union Oilers had in the lobby a handsome bronze plaque bearing the greetings of Herbert Hoover, former President of the United States, who said on the day the center was dedicated:

"The American way of life is based on representative government and personal liberty. The Union Oil Company of California is a magnificent demonstration of the product of this system. But there are many enemies of this system and many encroachments upon it in our midst. No one can say that when the documents of this cornerstone are opened, sometime in the distant future, that this system will still prevail. But if it does, it will be because of the determination of men like those who head the Union Oil Company to maintain our system of free enterprise and the American way of life."

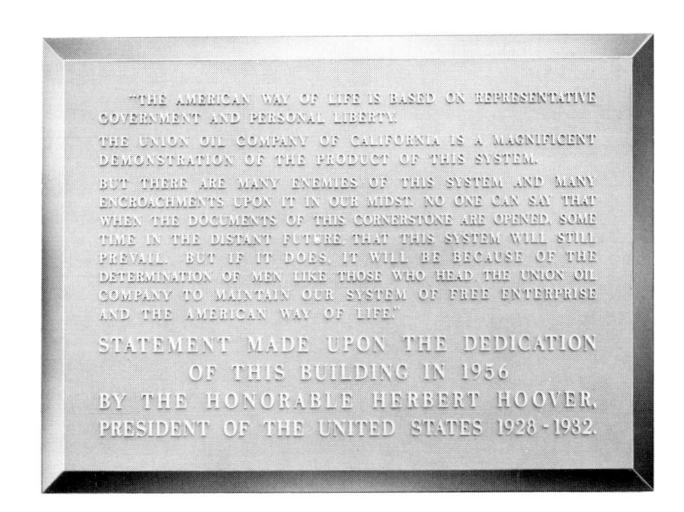

CHAPTER ELEVEN 1960-1965

Gearing for Growth

UNION OIL COMPANY MOVED INTO THE CHALLENGING SIXTIES DECADE making headlines on many fronts. The company's insatiable oil hunters were proving up new sources of oil and gas in Australia, along the Gulf of Mexico, in Canada and Alaska, even under metropolitan Los Angeles. Population in the Union marketing empire was burgeoning at the rate of a million a year. The company's research scientists were on the verge of a breakthrough that miraculously made almost two barrels of gasoline possible where one had been the end product of refineries in the previous decade. Union Oil had outgrown the role of "the big independent;" it ranked as one of the country's top petroleum and natural gas producers.

President Rubel reached the retirement age of 65 on April 26, 1960, after 38 years as a Union Oiler and the company's Number 1 oil hunter, shortly after receiving the notable Anthony Lucas medal for outstanding contributions to the petroleum industry. Though Rubel continued as a company director and a member of the executive committee, he looked forward to pursuing his hobbies and public activities. No one was ever more mistaken about what the future had in store for him. Temporarily, Board Chairman Taylor took over presidential responsibilities. By October, the directors had found the man for Union's eighth president. He was Dudley Tower, a rugged University of California trained engineer who had joined the Union family as a pipeline roustabout at Dominguez Field in 1935. Tower had climbed the ladder through exploration, as district engineer for Texas operations, manager of the Gulf Division, vice-president of field operations, then executive vice-president.

WHIRLYBIRD APPROACH

Union Oil drilling rig in Gulf looks like this as you come for helicopter landing. Crew, materials are ferried to offshore wells in fast boats, hoisted aboard rig in cage-like elevators.

Discovery of Moonie Oil Field in Queensland, Australia, was one of the headlines of the early sixties, although Union's strikes in Louisiana, Canada, and even California yielded far more oil and gas. For Australians, Moonie was a turning point in history. Over the years, oil hunters for scores of companies had spent millions drilling more than 600 dry holes in the vast island continent down-under in a desperate search for home-produced petroleum. Australians were great oil users and every drop of the 250,000 barrels they used daily had to be imported. In 1960, in a deal negotiated by vice-president of exploration Sam Grinsfelder, Union, in partnership with Kern County Land Company and the Australian Oil and Gas Corporation, undertook exploration of 40-million acres of grazing land and desert in Queensland and New South Wales. Union as operator provided the seismic and drilling crews and ran the play. Union and Kern each had a 40 per cent interest in the venture, AO & G had 20 per cent. Union-Kern put up all of the money but under a subsidy plan the Australian government refunded a part of the exploration cost.

The great Australian oil hunt got off to an encouraging but inauspicious start. The first hole drilled by Union's crews, Cabawin Number 1, hit a gas and oil pocket at 12,000 feet that yielded 65 barrels a day. This was hardly commercial production, but it proved there was petroleum under Australia. The second hole was a duster. Then, directed by Doyle T. Graves, Union's resident manager, the drillers moved twenty miles south and spudded a new hole, Moonie Number 1. This was the hole that made history for Australia. On December 17, 1961, at the 5,800-foot depth, Moonie Number 1 came in for 2,196 barrels per day of high-gravity crude. The exuberant Australians celebrated the discovery as a national Christmas present. Within a year the Union drillers had rounded out the Moonie Field with a dozen holes, all but one good producers. Encouraged by this discovery, Union assigned two more strings of drilling tools to make hole fast in other areas of the vast concession, as large as the state of Oklahoma. At sites that looked good on the seismic survey maps they drilled twenty-five holes, one dry hole after another. Then luck changed. In the Alton area of the Surat Valley north of Moonie, drillers brought in a well that flowed on test at the rate of 480 barrels per day of high-gravity crude. The next Alton wells were equally promising. Still farther north, another crew of drillers tapped a third potential reservoir of petroleum, known as the Conloi Field.

The excited Australians made a gala occasion of the momentous strike on March 6, 1963, when Queen Elizabeth II and her consort, Prince Philip, Duke of Edinburgh, journeyed to Brisbane to dedicate a monument commemorating the discovery of oil under their continent. Her Majesty commended oil finders Cy Rubel and Bill Stewart and their colleagues in KCL and AO&G in person for their role in the great Australian oil hunt. But oil in the well wasn't gasoline in the auto tank. Moonie was 200 miles from the nearest seacoast city, Brisbane, and Australian refineries were an additional 500 miles down the coast at Sydney. The Union-KCL-AO&G partnership wiped out this gap by laying a 190-mile ten-inch pipeline to Brisbane where the crude could be fed into tankers. After the first 300,000 barrels of Moonie Field crude had filled the pipeline, the

UNION'S EIGHTH PRESIDENT

On the retirement of A. C. Rubel in 1960, the board of directors named Dudley Tower, then executive vice-president, Union's eighth president.

Australians' dream came true. Oil was flowing from Australian soil into tanks that fed it into tankers that delivered to refineries supplying the Australian market. The first step had been taken toward plugging an annual $250-million drain on Australia's foreign exchange.

Union's most prodigious play in the early sixties was along the Louisiana Gulf shore where the company's drillers were hitting high pressure "gassers" with amazing precision. By 1961 they had punched thirty-one holes two miles deep beneath the Gulf's waters. Twenty-nine of them were producers, an almost unbelievable record. Even the costly hurry-up platform tossed up in 1957 to whipstock the hole that quenched the burning Wild Tiger turned into a bonanza. From it, drillers whipstocked fifteen more holes, every one a producer. The high pressure pool that had blown out the Wild Tiger became the Gulf Division's most prolific gas field. Day after day it pushed up 162-million cubic feet of natural gas.

The demand for natural gas had boomed to a peak where Union's explorers actually preferred a "gasser" to an oil well any day, at least along the Gulf Coast. A "gasser" had become a sort of nature-built service station that "pumped gas" around the clock. Union's "gassers" were pumping millions of dollars annually into the company's bank account by the early sixties. But finding them ran into big money, too. In one year, Union paid over $14 million for the right to drill on blocks of federal or state lands that were only tiny rectangular spots on the map of the Gulf of Mexico. Each well, ten to seventeen-thousand feet deep, was $500,000 or more down the hole. Drilling from the swampy bayous was almost as costly as from the huge steel platforms erected in the Gulf. When Union drillers hit their first "gasser" at Fresh Water Bayou in the early fifties, it had been anything but a welcomed strike. But a decade later, after the drillers' bits had discovered two dozen new gas pools, it was another story. The gas fields were great and profitable new resources. Crews were mobilizing to drill farther and farther out into the Gulf in waters up to 200 feet deep. By 1965, Union had 447 productive oil and natural gas wells in the Gulf area.

Over the ages, nature has hidden her oil and gas treasure troves under some strange and unlikely terrain. Caillou Island, a hundred miles south of New Orleans, was a good example. Caillou was more of a swamp than an island, although a hard-to-detect ridge does cut across the tidelands at this point. Years ago Caillou Island was a popular resort. Then a hurricane flattened every building. Nobody rebuilt anything until Union's crews set up their drilling platforms, derricks, tanks, and bunkhouses. Caillou became the habitat of water moccasins, muskrats, nutria, shore birds, and fish. Anglers caught fresh-water fish on one side of the island, ocean fish on the other. The swamp was so forbidding that Union's fifty wells were checked by teams traveling in boats. The service crews worked in shifts, five days on duty, five days off at home in towns to the north.

Finding these hidden oil and gas fields has proven to be a lot more than luck. Union's oil hunters rely on electronic eyes that can look two to three miles down through the swamps to "see" the layers of sand and rock that form the earth's crust. They can't see the oil, but they can map the strata that might trap oil and gas. Their Number 1 "eye" is seismic survey, which consists of bouncing little man-made earthquakes against the rocks below. The wriggling lines recorded electronically on long strips of paper tell their practiced eyes where salt domes or other upthrusts might have trapped a pool of oil. Another "eye" is gravity survey, a method of measuring the pull of heavy or light rocks far below the earth's surface. Then there is aeromagnetic survey, done by sweeping the area with a magnetometer dangling from a low-flying plane. Sometimes the oil hunters "see with their noses," as Lyman Stewart did when he bought or leased big blocks of California landscape because he could smell oil down below; this is known as geochemical survey, but today's oil hunter has instruments to do the work of Lyman Stewart's nose. Often Union's geologists can see signs of oil formations from aerial color pictures made from helicopters or slow-flying planes; this is called geophoto survey. After feeding all the information they can glean from their magic "eyes" into a computer, the oil hunters resort to the final "eye" in pinpointing the unseen oil field; they lay half a million dollars or more on the line and tell a drilling crew to "make hole here."

In Alaska, Union's geologists thought they saw oil beneath the Kenai Peninsula. In partnership with Marathon Oil, the company laid money on the line to drill holes. The first wildcat well blew out at 4,232 feet as a wild gasser. After a battle, the drillers brought the well under control, and continued drilling almost three miles until they had made the deepest hole in the biggest state. They found no oil, but had proved up a natural gas field, Alaska's first. Four more holes were prolific gassers. Luckily, the field was only eighty-two miles from Anchorage, Alaska's largest city. Pipeliners laid a line through forests,

UNION MAKES HISTORY IN AUSTRALIA

Discovery of Australia's first commercial oil field in Queensland in 1961 by Union Oil and its partners was appropriately commemorated by Queen Elizabeth II, who unveiled this plaque in 1963. Moonie No. 1, right, is the well that made history.

over rugged hills until they came to an arm of turbulent Turnagain Sound, which has 35-foot tides, swift and treacherous currents, and a bottom of abrasive silt washed down from a glacier. In Turnagain Sound, they met their match. The silt gripped the pipeline when they tried to pull it across the Sound; currents swept it far out of line when they tried to drop it from barges. By the end of 1961, winter's storms forced the pipeliners to give up the battle, in what is rated as one of the toughest pipeline-laying jobs in petroleum history.

That winter, the pipeliners towed a "Louisiana cruiser" from the Gulf of Mexico, through the Panama Canal, and up to Alaska. The "cruiser" was a behemoth barge, on which they welded pipe, X-rayed it, wrapped and coated it, and fed it out a long stern boom known as a "stinger." As the pipe touched the bottom of the Sound, hydraulic jets dug a bed for it. The shifting tides filled the trench, gratis. In twenty-six days, Turnagain Sound was conquered with a 10-inch gas pipeline. Then, as insurance against catastrophe, the pipeliners laid a duplicate line across the Sound from their Louisiana cruiser in eleven days. Anchorage citizens began cooking and heating with natural gas in 1962. Still on the hunt for oil, in 1963 Union's land men lined up 96,000 additional acres, most of them under the sea in Cook Inlet, off Kenai Peninsula. The Alaska oil hunt was in its infancy.

The catastrophe the pipeliners feared was not long in coming. It took the form of the violent earthquake that jolted the Alaskan coast on Good Friday of 1964. The pipelines held, but Anchorage itself was in shambles. So were Valdez, Whittier, and other terminals where Union lost wharves, docks, storage tanks, warehouses, and other marketing facilities. Luckily, Union's fifty employees and their families came through the disaster uninjured, though many of their homes suffered damage. Union Oilers in Seattle quickly launched a disaster fund to which hundreds of employees throughout the company contributed generously. Union's manager at Anchorage was able to disburse thousands of dollars to help repair the damaged homes. Within twenty-four hours after the temblor, Union trucks were delivering gasoline and heating oil in Anchorage from the few undamaged tanks. But rebuilding the storage facilities to carry the Alaska market through the next long winter was a major and hurry-up reconstruction project. Bulldozers, trucks, and operators worked around the clock building solid ground in the muck left by the earthquake along the Anchorage waterfront. Tanks, pipelines, and pumps, fabricated as far away as Pittsburgh, were loaded in pieces on flat cars, which in turn were loaded onto seagoing barges in Seattle, to be towed to Anchorage and shunted by rail to the tank farm sites. Welders had the parts joined together before the first winter storms struck.

Filling the new storage facilities with a winter's supply of products is remembered as a saga of battle with disaster and the elements. Bad luck struck in mid-October when the Union tanker *Santa Maria*, loaded with gasoline, heating oil, and other products, collided with another vessel a mile from the Anchorage waterfront. Flames engulfed the tanker, forcing the crew to abandon ship temporarily. But the captain rallied his crew, returned to battle the blaze, managing to save the tanker and most of her cargo. She was towed to Seattle for repairs. The accident made filling the Anchorage tanks an emergency operation. The tanker *Lompoc* took over the job. She arrived on her final voyage in early December with Arctic ice shrouding the rigging and catwalks. Deck winches had to be kept running to avoid freezing up. Cook Inlet was filled with a churning ice pack. A thick sheet of solid pan ice lay between the tanker and the new wharf. The tide rose and fell thirty feet daily. To complicate navigation a dense curtain of ice fog dropped over the area. Visibility was zero-zero. The *Lompoc* rammed ahead like an icebreaker, navigating by radar. On December 18, long after tugs had been frozen fast for the winter, the tanker miraculously reached the unloading wharf. In the bitter cold, it took four hours to pump the gasoline from the tanker's stern compartments—ordinarily a 45-minute operation. Then double-trouble hit. The heating-oil pipeline on the wharf was frozen solid. When steam failed to unfreeze it, a welding crew working all night strung an alternate line. Next day, the oil was moving into the tanks. Its removal raised the *Lompoc* in the water just as the falling tide, four feet lower than usual, was dropping the ship's hull dangerously close to the bottom of the Sound. Empty at last, the *Lompoc* fought free of the ice pack and back to California. Union's new Anchorage tanks were full with enough gasoline and oil to carry the customers through the winter.

By 1961, Union crews had drilled 175 exploratory wells through the frozen muskeg of northern Canada to score 22 oil fields and 21 gas field discoveries. Pipelines linked most of these fields in northern Alberta and British Columbia to the Dominion's centers of population. The Union wells were delivering over a million barrels of oil and 4-billion cubic feet of gas a year to these pipelines. In five Canadian territories, Union had more than 6-million acres of potential oil area to explore. Sizable discoveries had been made in the Virginia Hills

RIDING OUT HURRICANE HILDA

The rampaging elements Nature occasionally unleashes sometimes imperil offshore drilling operations. Here Hurricane Hilda's wind and water batter a Union Oil rig in the winter of 1964.

NEAR-DISASTER IN ALASKA

While attempting to replenish Alaska's supply of petroleum products after the 1964 earthquake, the Santa Maria *collided with another vessel just a mile from the Anchorage waterfront and caught fire. Quick action by her captain and crew saved the ship and much of her cargo.*

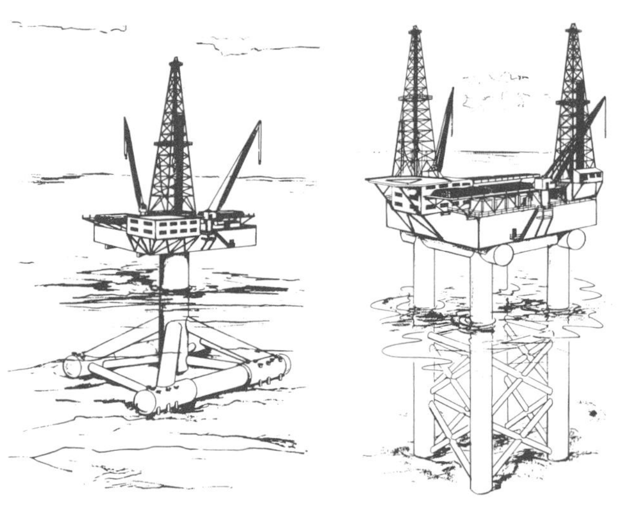

LEGS FOR OFFSHORE RIGS

Offshore drilling rigs may be supported on a forest of piling, as is the platform sketched above right, or on massive steel structures, such as those planned by Union and its partner for installation in Alaska's Cook Inlet, above left.

and Red Earth areas of central Alberta, and in the Milligan Creek, Wildmint, and Fort Nelson fields of northern British Columbia. The prospect for new discoveries on other leases was promising.

Union's Canadian Division, organized in 1949, was becoming a sizable oil company on its own. Canadians looked enviously at these rich oil finds made possible by venturous American capital and asked to share in their own oil bonanza. Union's directors thought they should. In 1961, the Canadian Division was spun off to form the nucleus of Union Oil Company of Canada Limited. Union Oil of California swapped its oil wells, facilities, and land leases for 3-million shares, roughly 83 per cent, of Union Oil of Canada. Canadians quickly snapped up the other 17 per cent of the shares. Union of Canada's directors and officers were part Canadian, part American. The new company expanded by buying smaller oil producers, began to make money in 1963 as output of crude leaped ahead 50 per cent. By 1965, its 280 wells were delivering over 12,000 barrels of crude daily to refineries, plus more than 10-million cubic feet of natural gas, reported W. A. Farrar, President of Union Oil of Canada.

The early sixties found Union's oil hunters set to launch risky wildcatting for oil under the ocean on the Pacific Coast continental shelf, which drops off abruptly to depths of 2,000 feet or more. Seismic crews had "shot" much of the shelf from Mexico to Alaska and reported favorable formations beneath the Pacific for trapping oil and gas. Unfortunately, the Pacific Ocean was anything but pacific much of the year. Off the Alaska coast weather permitted exploration only during the summer months. Off southern California the sea-going drillers

MOBILE EXPLORATORY PLATFORM

Little Eva (left) *is a conventional platform used in offshore oil production. More revolutionary is the mobile steel drilling platform* (above) *used in exploring for offshore oil. It is supported by four towers that rise high into the air while the platform is being towed to the drillsite* (right) *and are lowered to the floor of the sea when a site has been reached.*

could work all but during the two winter months. The deep sea drilling barges of Union's subsidiary, Global Marine Exploration, had cored exploratory holes. Union's geologists believed there might be oil pools out under the Pacific's swells perhaps comparable to those discovered on land in southern California. The only way to find out was to drill wells.

But there still remained the question of who owned the oceanic oil fields. Such ownership had been the subject of a series of hotly contested law suits between the federal government and several states. After decisions by the United States Supreme Court favoring federal ownership, the battle shifted to Congress. In 1953 Congress passed two bills, one giving Pacific Coast states title to lands three miles from shore, the balance of the Continental Shelf to the federal government. This action only intensified the controversy because the legislation failed specifically to settle the boundaries. In the case of California the problem was complicated by the Channel Islands lying over three miles from the mainland. This left the seaward boundary of the state in doubt. Nevertheless, Union's directors set up a Pacific offshore project in 1962 and allocated funds to wildcat the world's biggest ocean. In 1965 the United States Supreme Court handed down another decision covering California's offshore lands. In the main, the court held in favor of federal ownership.

The project called for a hefty layout of dollars. The first venture was 11,500 acres in three parcels off Santa Barbara County, for which Union paid the State of California a bonus of $3,620,660 for the mere right to spend more millions drilling for oil. The next step was to lease one of the strangest sea-going craft ever built, the *George F. Ferris*, an ungainly 6,000-ton barge resembling a weird water-bug with its four 275-foot legs sticking up 200 feet above its decks. The behemoth barge carried a 145-foot drilling tower, 80,000 gallons of diesel fuel, 100,000 gallons of fresh water, and ample living quarters for a crew. Towed to a precise anchorage two miles offshore, the *Ferris* pushed its stout steel legs down until they hit bottom in 180 feet of water, then hydraulically boosted its hull out of the sea forty feet to make a high and dry drilling platform. From a 60-foot slot in the rear of the platform, drillers could whipstock holes two miles deep to explore the expensive leases. If the geologists had guessed right, the drilling barge could pull up its legs and make room for a permanent platform. If they guessed wrong, the barge could lift its legs and plant them elsewhere for another try. The Santa Barbara offshore leases proved to be one of Union's bad guesses. By 1965, eight costly holes had been drilled through the briny deep. Only two of them tapped oil sands and these were not promising enough to justify building a costly island platform.

Another Pacific venture was a chapter out of science fiction. Union had bid over $6,000,000 for a 2,113-acre parcel seaward from the productive Huntington Beach oil field. A drilling barge drilled a 7,000-foot exploratory hole beneath 70 feet of ocean swell and found oil. So Union's management decided to gamble another $2,300,000 on a permanent drilling platform, known as Eva, after Little Eva, the lucky old houseboat from which Union drillers had carried out their first successful oil hunt in Louisiana. Platform Eva was fabricated in two parts in Houston, Texas. One part, called "the jacket," consisted of a framework with a dozen hollow steel legs welded airtight to make them float. The other part was a double-deck platform to be placed atop the legs after they had been planted on the Pacific's floor. Towed on barges through the Panama Canal, a month-long journey, the jacket of Platform Eva was toppled off its barge with a mighty splash. Floated into exact position, the legs were opened, allowing them to fill with water and sink to the bottom. Then steel pilings were driven through them seventy feet into the ocean floor. Hoisted on top by derricks, the 160-by-105-foot deck made a stable drilling platform for thirty whipstocked wells. The under-deck provided crew quarters, shops, other facilities. Platform Eva was a little oceanic island. From the shore, two miles distant, tugs snaked out an eight-inch line for oil, another for gas, a smaller line for water and a 12,000-watt power cable. Union had gambled $10,135,000 on this man-made island before the first barrel of crude flowed on January 17, 1964, from the watery new field to the oil-thirsty southern California market. By 1965, the field's daily output was almost 8,000 barrels and increasing steadily.

For the price of one of these expensive undersea holes, Union's drillers could put down three on-land wells. Although geologists thought that the great California oil reservoirs had been tapped, the company's wildcatters had amazing success with on-land exploration in the early sixties. On a 4,800-acre lease near Sacramento they brought in a new gas field in December, 1962. Under the Hacienda Country Club golf fairways, southeast of Los Angeles, they drilled a "nineteenth hole," then added twenty-eight more producing holes, with the wells

OIL IN DOWNTOWN LOS ANGELES *The brown circle areas above on the aerial of downtown Los Angeles are actually drilling sites in Union's Las Cienegas Field (shown in outlined area). Drilling rigs are skillfully silenced and artfully camouflaged. A dozen or more wells can be drilled from a single location.*

and pumps completely hidden in sumps and behind shrubbery. Beneath the Las Cienegas section of western Los Angeles, they brought in twenty-eight wells, screened by landscaped walls, that yielded thousands of barrels per day, only twenty miles by pipeline from the Los Angeles refinery. Known as the only oil field with a street address—4848 West Pico Boulevard—the Las Cienegas Field rated as a new petroleum discovery. The field's wells were whipstocked out from two sites that looked like home properties and over 20,000 lot owners shared the royalties. In 1963 an exploratory well in Ventura County hit a new petroleum pool beneath the 28,000-acre Simi property, originally purchased by Lyman Stewart, on which several other pools had previously been discovered. On 240 acres of fee simple land in the McKittrick Field in the San Joaquin Valley, bought in the early thirties, eleven deep wells yielded 8,000 barrels a day even under a voluntary curtailment program. The company was participating in 110 secondary recovery projects with astonishing returns. In Caprock Queen Field in New Mexico, for example, water flooding tripled the yield of crude.

Under K. C. Vaughan and Ray A. Burke, senior vice-president and vice-president respectively for Exploration and Production, drilling crews were bolstering Union reserves at the rate of 170 new wells in 1963, even more in 1964. Union was adding to its reserves in other ways, too. The purchase in 1962 of the Texas National Petroleum properties added 430 oil and gas wells and 350,000 acres of prospecting area in Texas, Colorado, Wyoming, and New Mexico. By 1965, Union was producing oil and gas in ten states, Canada, and

JUMBOIZED TANKER

To jumboize a tanker, its stern section with the propulsion gear is cut off and floated into a drydock where it is welded to a new stretched-out hull, thereby creating a new vessel of awe-inspiring dimensions. The jumboized Lake Palourde, *is nearly 1,000 feet long. Relative size and increased capacity of the ships (shaded areas) is shown below.*

Australia, on the Trucial Coast of Arabia, and in the Persian Gulf, where the company and four partners, one of them the Iranian government, made a spectacular discovery.

Moving more than 50-million barrels of crude yearly from oil fields to Union's six refineries and out of them to the markets called for some drastic transportation innovations. The big pipeline from the San Joaquin Valley to the Oleum refinery, and the network that fed crude into the Los Angeles refinery were examples. Both were electronic push-button operations that kept the rivers of oil flowing day and night. Early in 1965, the chartered super-tankers *Torrey Canyon* and *Lake Palourde* were "jumbo-ized" by widening and lengthening their hulls, thus increasing each vessel's capacity from 470,000 barrels to 850,000 barrels. Between 1960 and 1965, Union invested $1,300,000 in tanks alone to store these rivers of oil surging in relentlessly by tanker.

Sixty-million barrels of crude into the refineries meant almost as many barrels of products out of the refineries to the markets. Products lines, tankers, and trucks for transporting gasoline, diesel and fuel oils and other products likewise underwent revolution. Tanker trucks with lightweight aluminum bodies carried twenty per cent more fuel. Underground tanks at airports pushed jet fuel into airliners' wings at the rate of 2,000 gallons per minute. Marine service stations pumped fuel directly into motorboat tanks at more than a hundred harbors on lakes, bays, and sounds in the Western states. The revolution in marketing was sparked early in the sixties when the success of Fred L. Hartley, vice-president of research, in selling the patented unifining technique to other refineries, caught Reese Taylor's eye.

"You should be heading up all of our marketing," Taylor told Hartley one day in December of 1959. "This would be a radical change from your engineering and research work, so take your time in making a decision."

After an hour's discussion, Taylor said, "Well, let's have your decision."

"That's how I became a marketing man," recalled Hartley who spent months on the road, "learning marketing from dealers and the motoring public." Meantime, he asked a team of outside experts to survey Union's marketing setup. In May, 1962, following a sweeping reorganization of management authority and controls, a chain of "profit centers" were created. In effect the company was "divisionalized" into a group of separate businesses each with its own monthly profit and loss statement. Hartley was head of the Refining and Marketing Division encompassing everything downstream from the crude oil tanks to the collection of customer accounts. Over the Union sales empire, "76-Union" stations were refurbished or rebuilt and hundreds of new stations were opened. A bevy of sixteen Sparkle Corps girls checked them periodically for customer comforts. Union credit-card holders passed the million mark. Long-standing card customers were honored with new Gold Credit cards that required no year-to-year renewal. The familiar "76-Union" trade-mark was redesigned to put more emphasis on "Union," after a poll revealed that a good many patrons were referring to Union Oil Company as "the 76 Company."

"Our new marketing philosophy was simple," explained Hartley. "Instead of distributors of commodities, our dealers became merchandisers. In addition to gas and oil and services to motorists, we offered a line of sales impulse items carrying the 76-Union label. Our goal was to sell profitably, rather than volume for growth's sake. We eliminated unprofitable service stations and built more new and profitable stations in growth areas. We are making merchants out of one-time gas pumpers."

Vice-President C. E. Rathbone's 76-Union merchants had something extraordinary to sell. Union's research scientists and engineers had scored a breakthrough in refining "even better than finding a 4-million-barrel-a-year oil field right under the refinery," as Hartley put it, "because it gives us flexibility of products in an ever-changing market." The breakthrough was an almost unbelievable new refining process, known as Unicracking-JHC, a refiner's dream akin to the alchemist's age-old dream of turning base metals to gold. Unicracking-JHC actually converted base fuel oil into high-price top quality gasolines, aviation and diesel fuels. In the amazing chemical transformation, the process increased every 100 barrels of feed stock into 124 barrels of products.

A decade of most intensive research and engineering produced Unicracking-JHC. It was kicked off at a 1954 planning meeting of key men from Union's refining, research, and economics staffs. The economics experts warned that the 'sixties market for petroleum products in Union's marketing area would be topsy-turvy; demand for gasoline and jetliner fuel would skyrocket, fuel oil would be hard to sell.' They urged the researchers to find a way to turn the 55-barrel residue of fuel oil in every 100 barrels of crude into high-grade gasoline or diesel or jet fuel. All the researchers had to do was completely rebuild the atom structure of the hydrocarbons in crude petroleum!

This looked like something next door to the impossible, but the research team, under Fred Hartley and vice-president W. E. Bradley, agreed to do it anyway. Two dozen Union scientists devoted the next decade to the task. The process that looked most promising was one called "hydrocracking," by which petroleum molecules were cracked up under pressures ranging up to 10,000 pounds per square inch. Since it wasn't practical to build huge tanks strong enough to withstand these pressures, the Union scientists and engineers focused on a way to crack up molecules at a maximum 2,000 pound pressure. They found this could be done with an unusual and secret new catalyst which first achieved the molecule-cracking job in a bench-scale one-gallon-per-day model. This was a short leap forward; a full-scale hydrocracker for a modern refinery would have to crack the billions of molecules in 670,000 gallons of crude each day.

Development engineers made the next leap by building a 10-barrel-per-day hydrocracker. It provided the data for a slim 27-page book called "Design Basis." Over the years the slim book grew into twenty-five thick volumes of calculations and specifications. With all the questions answered, Union's directors approved in November, 1962, the expenditure of $22,000,000 to build the first "Unicracker" on a 3½-acre site at the Los Angeles Refinery. The huge reactors in which the catalysts, treated like crown jewels, worked their magic, had steel walls six inches thick. More than 500 skilled workers pooled their know-how on these reactors, the stock of catalysts, the valves, turbines, controls. After a count-down that started in mid-summer, the Unicracker went on stream on November 30, 1964, turning 12,000 barrels of feed stock daily into 16,000 barrels of products, "and with no residue," senior vice-president John W. Towler reported.

Union's Unicracker exceeded expectations. Within a year, ten similar plants were being built by other oil companies, on license from Union and Standard Oil of New Jersey, jointly. Esso researchers and engineers had hit on the same hydrocracking process simultaneously with Union's. The two managements decided to pool patents, and license the process to other companies on a royalty basis under the name of Unicracker-JHC. As Hartley explained, "We're getting a double return from this process, as we do from most of our research developments. First, the process improves the quality and output of our own products; second, royalties from licensing add to our revenues in future years."

By 1965, the company had 76 blends of "76-Union" gasolines, to meet the customers' needs for quick-start, continuous performance in such wide-ranging climates as the hot southern California deserts or Montana's and Alaska's frigid winters, or from below sea level to mile-high mountain service stations.

To replace the cumbersome batch system of gasoline blending in huge tanks, the company invested over $1.5 million in an electronic blending system that simultaneously mixed up to ten different stocks for the various gasolines, jet and diesel fuels, at the rate of 5,000 barrels per hour, in the pipelines that fed the storage tanks. Sitting at a console, resembling a pipe organ keyboard, the blender pressed keys, watched warning lights and measuring instruments, and electronically turned out the "Royal 76" or any of the other fuels needed to make engines purr smoothly in any climate.

By the mid-sixties Union had so many lively subsidiaries that Controller Max Lorimore was like the proverbial old woman who lived in a shoe. Some were growing as fast as the parent and their products were becoming world-wide commodities. To handle the booming demand for petroleum products throughout the Far East, the Unoco company was launched in January, 1962, with F. K. Cadwell as president. Unoco Limited, a wholly owned subsidiary based in Hong Kong, with branches in Singapore, Tokyo, Manila, and London, purchased and sold crude oil and petroleum products throughout the Far East and other world markets. The Far East door had been opened back in 1906 when W. L. Stewart made Union's first sale of fuel oil and refinery products in Japan. After 1933, Union's outlet in Nippon was Maruzen Oil Company, which built a small refinery near Osaka. Maruzen's spectacular growth came after World War II, under the leadership of President Kanji Wada. Following signing of the peace treaty, Union provided technical and financial cooperation in rebuilding refining, transportation, and marketing facilities. Maruzen engineers, technicians, and marketers came to the United States to study at Union facilities. Union dispatched teams to Japan to help Maruzen with on-job training. Maruzen's business mushroomed. By the sixties it was the third largest petroleum company in Japan. On May 7, 1963, Union purchased a 32.9 per cent interest in Maruzen Oil Company for $15,000,000, a transaction that involved 108,000,000 shares of newly issued Maruzen stock.

Meantime, Union Oil of Canada was thriving, as was Collier Carbon and Chemical, which had taken over Pacific Guano Company, marketer of agricultural products in Hawaii and California. In 1962, Collier teamed up with Tidewater Oil to build a 100-million-pound-per-year naphthalene plant in Delaware utilizing the new "Unidak" process developed by Union's research

CLEANLINESS PLEASES CUSTOMERS

The lively "Sparkle Girl" (left) *is one of the Union Oil Corps who check not only the condition of the rest rooms, but the entire service facility. Even very young ladies appreciate these services.*

THE REVOLUTIONARY UNICRACKER

Long range predictions that the market of the late 60's for gasoline and jet fuels would skyrocket while fuel oil demand would lessen led to the development of the Unicracker—an amazing research and engineering project that culminated in the construction of this efficient structure which delivers 120 barrels of gasoline for every 100 barrels of feed stock.

A LIBRARY OF SPECIFICATIONS

Specifications for the Unicracker filled 25 volumes, here lined up on a table in front of engineers C. D. Bradley, C. E. Gardner and R. A. McKean.

laboratories. That same year Collier joined Global Marine Exploration, then a Union subsidiary, in a veritable Jules Verne venture, the proposed mining of sulphate rock from 30,000 acres of sea bottom on the continental shelf forty miles west of San Diego. Unfortunately, this bonanza-in-the-sea had to be abandoned when it was found to be loaded with mines and shells left by the U. S. Navy, which had used the area for target practice. Meantime, Global Marine tackled a fantastic assignment from The National Academy of Sciences and the National Science Foundation, namely, drilling into the earth's mantle beneath the ocean to bring up cores revealing the planet's geographic history during the past two-billion years. In 1964, on the theory that the global explorers could serve industry better if they were not tagged as Union Oilers, Union's interest was sold back to Global Marine Exploration, which then offered its stock for sale to the public.

Important changes were taking place at headquarters in the Union Oil Center on the heights above downtown Los Angeles. On July 1, 1961, Chairman Taylor announced that Gulf Oil Company had agreed to sell back at par the $120-million chunk of Union Oil debentures it had bought in 1956, convertible if Gulf so chose into 2,700,000 shares of Union common stock, a move that would have given Gulf roughly one-fourth of Union's shares. The Gulf money had helped make possible Union's tremendous expansion program. The $120 million to pay off Gulf came from two new $60-million issues of 40-year debentures sold to the public, one issue convertible into 923,000 shares of common stock. The new issues removed the shadow of Gulf control from Union's horizon.

While this financial specter was being wiped out, another was casting its shadow over the company's future. For months Union Oil shares in large blocks of hundreds and thousands of shares were being purchased on both the New York and Pacific Coast stock exchanges. Efforts to learn who the purchasers might be were fruitless. Then a terse press release from Washington cleared up the mystery. In a letter to stockholders June 1, 1960, Reese Taylor wrote:

"Several days ago we received word that Phillips Petroleum Company had reported to the Securities and Exchange Commission in Washington, D. C., that it had purchased and now owned in excess of 1,000,000 common shares of Union Oil, or slightly over 12 per cent of the total outstanding. This is the first knowledge that your board of directors or management had of Phillips' acquisition of stock, as the shares had been purchased in other names and in such a manner as not to disclose the identity of the real owner. More recently, Phillips advised your management that it had purchased these shares solely as an investment, because of its confidence in their intrinsic value, and had no purpose or intention to seek any merger or consolidation."

Phillips continued to buy Union stock. In one month it purchased over 100,000 shares, bringing its total holdings in Union Oil to 1,111,100 shares, about 13 per cent of the total outstanding. By November 30, 1960, Phillips had brought its total holdings to 1,263,200 shares—15 per cent of the outstanding Union Oil shares—making it the company's largest stockholder. The U. S.

Department of Justice was keeping a close eye on the situation. Late in 1960, Taylor summarized the outlook in a letter to the stockholders:

"On December 9 the United States Department of Justice filed an antitrust action in the Federal Court at Los Angeles against Phillips Petroleum Company. It seeks an injunction to restrain Phillips from acquiring additional shares of Union Oil stock, from voting the shares it now holds, and to require Phillips to divest itself of its Union Oil shares. The government has also made Union a defendant in this action. Pending trial and final decision of the case, it seeks to compel Union to take no action which would enable Phillips to vote its Union Oil shares. . . . We will cooperate fully with the Department of Justice to help conclude this litigation as promptly as possible."

On January 13, 1961, Judge Peirson M. Hall, of the U. S. District Court, enjoined Phillips from (1) purchasing any additional Union Oil stock, (2) voting the shares it held, (3) soliciting proxies from any Union Oil stockholder, (4) seeking representation on the board of directors, and (5) selling Union Oil stock it held without meeting conditions specified in the injunction.

Union also went into court on December 22 to file a cross claim against Phillips in the action taken by the government a few days previously. Explained Taylor, "Union believed the filing of this cross claim was necessary to enable management to be in the best position to prevent Phillips from exercising any control, direct or indirect, over our company. If such control were exercised we believed it would be detrimental to the best interests of Union's shareholders, employees and the public." Phillips stipulated that a preliminary injunction be issued with the approval of the Court.

The Phillips "raid" came to an end two years later, when in June, 1963, Daniel K. Ludwig, president of National Bulk Carriers, Inc., after having given notice to the court purchased the 1,340,517 shares of Union Oil held by Phillips. Following this transaction, the antitrust action pending in Federal Court against Phillips was terminated. Ludwig was elected to the Union Oil board of directors July 29, 1963.

Rumors still persisted that other oil companies were dickering for control of Union, either by merger or purchase. On September 5, 1963, Union's then president, Cy Rubel, scotched these reports by declaring publicly: "Union Oil Company is not for sale in whole or in part, and there are no plans for merger or amalgamation with any other company. We believe that with present plans and future possibilities, stockholders of Union Oil will be better served by continuing our operations as an independent corporate entity."

Nevertheless, one year later Atlantic Refining Company suggested a possible merger into Union Oil. A consolidation of Atlantic and Union, operating at opposite ends of the country, would have created a nation-wide integrated oil company with annual revenues exceeding $1 billion. As Rubel explained these discussions:

"We did not approach Atlantic, they approached us. We both thought that there was an opportunity to combine our two companies to the benefit of both. We felt there was much to be gained by this combination. Unfortunately, long before the discussions got to a critical point there was a lot of premature publicity which upset things. When we were not able to get together on some of the fundamentals of the proposed arrangements, the discussions were called off. We parted in a very friendly way with no plans for resumption of discussions."

Purchase of the Phillips block made D. K. Ludwig Union's largest shareholder, outweighing even the Stewart family's interests in the company. The second largest shareholder was the group of Union Oilers participating in the Employees Incentive Plan, to which the company had contributed more than $13 million by late 1964; almost as much as the employees had paid for the million-plus shares owned by The Plan, four per cent of the company's outstanding stock. The company's contributions to The Plan were based on its yearly earnings, reflecting employee efforts to make Union prosper, vice-president N. T. Ugrin explained.

As it grew and prospered, Union Oil Company became a big neighbor in hundreds of communities throughout the Western states. Being a good neighbor had become a business in itself. In 1962, the company set up the Union Oil Company of California Foundation to handle the company's contributions for charitable, cultural, educational, and other civic responsibilities. One of the foundation's projects was matching up to $500 any gifts employees wished to make to colleges and universities. Outside the foundation, Union participated in scores of youth sports programs. The annual New Year's Day Union Oil floats in the Pasadena Tournament of Roses won numerous prizes. Reese Taylor took a personal hand in bringing major league baseball to Pacific Coast fans by having Union help finance the magnificent $20-million Dodger Stadium in Chavez Ravine, a short distance from the Union Oil Center in downtown Los Angeles.

By 1962, Union Oil was cashing in on Founder Lyman Stewart's obsession for buying up land under which he caught the scent of petroleum. Over the years, the company had accumulated in fee simple ownership, primarily for the mineral rights, more than 58,000 acres of land in California alone. As population surged into the state, several of these old fee simple properties, some of them still producing oil, were in the path of metropolitan development. Of 4,000 acres in northern Orange County, fastest growing Southern California area, 1,100 acres were sold for $15 million. In Santa Barbara County, 3,000 acres adjoining the Vandenberg Air Force Base were optioned to a developer for a 6,000-home community known as Vandenberg Village. Adjoining the Los Angeles refinery surface rights to 120 surplus acres brought another $3.6 million. At Union service stations the surveys revealed surplus areas readily leased for restaurants, motels, shops, and office buildings. The company was in the fortunate position in these land deals of "eating our cake and having it, too," because mineral rights and service station sites were jealously retained.

To keep pace with growth and be ready for the future, the full-grown giant required streamlining. Momentous changes occurred in Union's organizational structure. Early in 1962, following a searching scrutiny of Union's burgeoning divisions by both company officers and outside experts, chairman Reese Taylor announced regrouping of major operational activities into "profit centers," notably Exploration-Production, Refining-Marketing, Unoco Overseas Sales, and Collier Carbon and Chemical. Each profit center was an almost autonomous unit under a senior vice-president reporting to the president. Production and sales volume had more than doubled in the preceding decade.

In May, 1962, Dudley Tower resigned as President but continued until 1963 on Union's executive staff as senior vice-president of the newly formed Exploration and Production Division. The board of directors again called on Reese Taylor to pinch-hit as Union's president and chief executive officer. Less than two months later, on June 22, 1962, Taylor died suddenly and unexpectedly in the Hospital of the Good Samaritan in Los Angeles, ending a quarter-century role as the company's strong-willed guiding hand.

During the Reese Taylor era Union had grown steadily from the "Big Independent" and champion of the smaller independent producers to a big league company with more than one-half billion dollars in shareholders' equities, with over 60,000 shareholders, over 7,000 employees, $600 million in annual sales, $45 million in earnings, 546 million barrels in liquid hydrocarbon reserves, 5.3 trillion cubic feet of natural gas reserves. Taylor had given Union Oil a definite and potent personality by his corporate statesmanship, his championing of free enterprise, and by making the company an active participant in civic affairs wherever it did business. He had left his mark not only on Union Oil of California but on the entire petroleum industry. His philosophy was epitomized in one of his many homely talks:

"The success of a corporation depends on the individual and aggregate efforts of all its people; and the corporation's greatest responsibility is that of people—of human relations. . . .

"We must see that capital receives a decent wage for the risk of its savings. We must see that the people working for the company enjoy the highest standard of working and living conditions possible. We can do this only by satisfying our customers that we are giving them the best possible products at the lowest possible prices. . . ."

"His was an outstanding and useful life of lasting achievement as well as of warm friendship," the board of directors memorialized June 25. "He was a giant among men, and one of the great leaders in the petroleum industry, noted for his business statesmanship, courageous action, and enlightened farsightedness."

For a new helmsman, the Union directors sent out a hurried call for ex-president Cy Rubel, who was enjoying a leisurely fishing trip in a small boat off Vancouver Island, British Columbia. When Rubel put into Prince Rupert for fuel and supplies, a Canadian coastguard boat hailed him to answer an urgent telephone call from Los Angeles. As Rubel recalled later:

"When I finally reached a shoreside phone and received the shocking news I was urged to return immediately. There was no airport at Prince Rupert so we refueled and left before dawn for Ketchikan, Alaska. While we were enroute our people at Seattle arranged for a chartered seaplane to pick us up at Ketchikan and fly us to the nearest airport on Annette Island. Mrs. Rubel and I made a quick transfer at that point to a Union Oil plane which was waiting for us. We

FINGERTIP FUEL BLENDING *This Union Oiler sits at the "console" of Los Angeles refinery's electronic fuel blender. One section automatically blends jet, aviation and motor fuels at rates up to 210,000 gallons per hour; another blends turbine and diesel fuels at rates to 147,000 gallons per hour.*

reached Los Angeles around midnight, still in our dirty, smelly fishing togs."

When the directors urged Rubel to resume the presidency of Union Oil, he agreed under two conditions: (1) he was to be not only president but chief executive officer, and (2) he must have the unanimous backing of the board. The directors heartily concurred. W. L. Stewart, Jr. was called back from retirement to serve as chairman of the board. Since Rubel had continued on as a director and a member of the executive committee and Stewart was still a director, both were familiar with the company's current problems and projects. Rubel quickly scotched rumors that his was a caretaker administration. Answering reporters' queries, he replied:

"I am not an interim president nor do I expect to become one. I am and will be an active, operating president and if you don't think so, just watch. Bill Stewart and I will work together closely as we have for so many years."

The new president lost no time in making his position clear to Union Oilers. Calling the executive staff together, he declared that "Reese left us a financially sound and operationally progressive company. The basic policies which he established will be continued. To carry them out aggressively and successfully will involve the united effort and full cooperation of everyone. This will be a team effort. As a team we are going to make Reese's planned program work as he planned to make it work."

A dynamic new era was dawning for Union Oil. The company burgeoned into its most phenomenal years of expansion and earnings. Unfortunately, board chairman Stewart did not live to see this spectacular period of growth reach its apex. He passed away one year later, on August 30, 1963, in the same hospital as Reese Taylor, whom Bill Stewart had lured from the steel industry in the mid-thirties to become an oil man. Grandson of Union's founder, William Lyman Stewart, Jr., had devoted nearly four decades of his life to the company, after starting as a research assistant at the Los Angeles refinery in 1923, following an engineering training at Stanford University and Massachusetts Institute of Technology. Deep-voiced, rugged, at ease with rough oil field roustabouts, he liked to explain, "I'm gruff and tough on the outside but a softy inside." He also confessed to three loves—his family, Union Oil, and yachting—in that order. The Union directors paid tribute to Bill Stewart in a resolution which read:

"During his thirty-seven years of loyal and dedicated service as a member of the board—longest in the company's history—his uncompromising integrity, unswerving devotion, and warm-hearted sense of fairness left an indelible imprint in helping to shape the destiny of the company through its years of greatest growth and progress."

The Phillips "raid" and the Union-Atlantic merger talk served one unexpected purpose. They focused the attention of financial interests on Union Oil. The word spread that out in the West there was a "sleeper," a hard-driving, money-making oil company with topflight producing, refining, and marketing facilities in the country's fastest growing area. Union's officers were invited to tell the company's story at meetings of analysts and brokers and mutual fund stock purchasers in several financial centers. Several groups of analysts checked the company's California and Gulf operations firsthand. As a result, Union stock skyrocketed in three years from $40 to over $100, prompting the directors to declare a three-for-one stock split in late 1964, so that Union Oil Company shares would continue to be a people's investment. By 1965, Union Oil was owned by some 70,000 stockholders living in all fifty states and thirty-six foreign lands. Behind each share of stock was a reserve of thirty-five barrels of oil or its equivalent in natural gas.

A 1964 "State of the Union Message" to fellow Union Oilers by President Rubel revealed the lusty growth of the company during the first years of the sixties. Reserves of both oil and gas were the highest in Union's history,

UNION SCORES WITH BASEBALL FANS *Los Angeles Dodger fans appreciate the only service station in any major league ball park. Union provides fast service, a courtesy desk for tickets and messages, mechanical assistance.*

LOS ANGELES REFINERY TURNS BOOSTER *Pride in the Los Angeles baseball champions of 1965 was proclaimed by Union Oil with this decorated refinery storage sphere.*

547,400,000 potential barrels of crude, 5,908,600 million cubic feet of gas. "With our demonstrated exploratory ability we can substantially improve our reserve position," promised Rubel. Crude production totalled 125,000 barrels per day, gas output over 600-million cubic feet daily. Secondary recovery accounted for 14 per cent of this production. The new jumbo-ized tankers cut the cost of transporting Near East crude to Union's refineries. The efficient new Unicracker had replaced three older refinery units at Los Angeles, and was increasing the output of high-value products. Sales volume had jumped one-third even though Union's marketers were putting the emphasis on profitable sales rather than volume. The subsidiaries were thriving, particularly Union Oil of Canada, and lusty Collier Carbon and Chemical, whose President Craig Henderson had seven plants turning out petroleum by-products. Research under vice-president W. E. Bradley had new products in the works. The pilot plant in Colorado had demonstrated that Union's 3-billion-barrel reserve of shale was a mighty ace against future crude scarcity. The outlook was so promising that Union's directors earmarked $140 million for capital expenditures in 1965.

With this bright prospect ahead, Rubel decided that the time had come to turn the helm over to a younger president. On August 31, 1964, at his urging the directors chose executive vice-president Fred L. Hartley for Union's ninth president. Rubel was elected chairman of the board. Hartley was made chief executive officer on December 28, 1964.

CHAPTER TWELVE

Fred Hartley: The Making of the Man

WHEN A MAN COMES TO PROMINENCE in a corporation as a president or chief executive officer there are those who say "I saw it in him from the beginning." But there are also those who comment, "I never would have guessed."

Certainly if you had witnessed Fred Hartley's very early years at Union Oil you might never have guessed.

Born in Canada in 1917 but, as he is given to saying, "an American by choice," Hartley graduated from the University of British Columbia with a Bachelor of Applied Science in Chemical Engineering degree on Wednesday, the 13th of May, 1939, and started working in what is now Union's San Francisco Refinery five days later.

His impressive degree—which required five years of study—qualified him for the job of day laborer.

He had been, he admits, an unmotivated student in high school, with too many interests.

In college, he got progressively better, finishing his senior year with an A average. He worked two summers as a dish washer, working his way up to steward on a Canadian cruise ship running between Vancouver and Skagway, Alaska. A third summer he spent with a five-man survey party in the wilds of the Yukon, and his last summer in college he worked as a draftsman for Standard Oil Company of California's Canadian subsidiary.

He also had rounded out his pre-Union career by driving a truck for his dad in the day and working at night as a flunky in a drive-in restaurant called the White Spot Bar-b-que before starting in the university.

"There was a depression on and I needed the money to pay for college, in spite of a bursary I got in my first year," he explains.

BRIDGING THE GAP

Keeping in touch with youth, Fred Hartley strolls on the campus of Brigham Young University in Provo, Utah, after addressing students as a guest speaker.

How does a young Canadian get a job in America only five days after he graduated into a depression?

"My professor was a pretty sharp cookie by the name of Bill Seyer, dean of chemical engineering. He knew an Irishman named Bob Kenmuir, who was head of Union Oil Company of Canada. My professor talked him into interviewing our graduating class, suggesting that since British Columbia was being supplied with Union Oil products from California—gasoline and diesel—Kenmuir ought to think about taking some of the Canadian products back into the U.S. Dr. Seyer was referring, of course, to some of his students."

As a result, sometime later Hartley and several of his classmates were interviewed by John Rockfellow, Union's great recruiter at that time. A few days later Hartley was instructed to meet L. D. Metcalf, then manager of refineries.

"I bused to Seattle and met with Metcalf in the early evening," Hartley recalls. "We had dinner in his hotel room, and after dinner he or Rockfellow offered me a cigar. I didn't smoke, but I figured I had to smoke it or make a poor impression. Somehow I managed to get through it, and I don't know even to this day if I was hired because I could smoke a cigar or whether he thought I had enough ability to warrant being hired."

Hartley started at 75 cents an hour working in a labor gang at the Oleum—now San Francisco—Refinery.

"I got off the train with my suitcase of dirty clothes and $25, having traveled on the train for two days, and proceeded to the superintendent's office, identified myself, and was shortly thereafter on the payroll."

He spent his first two months hoeing weeds, cleaning out stills and tank cars, and cleaning out the bottoms of furnace stacks containing sodium sulfate.

"It was hard as rock, and you had to dig it out standing in water at about 120 degrees. You could only be down there for 15 or 20 minutes at a time, and then you got to breathe above for awhile, and then back down again."

He recalls that it seemed to him that most of his time was spent fixing the plants, instead of being involved in running them.

L.A. REFINERY
639

Research No. 639
Department

UNION OIL COMPANY
OF CALIFORNIA

EMPLOYEE PASS

Fred Lloyd Hartley
Name of Employee

Date Issued July 1 '41

Height 5' 10"
Weight 170
Eyes Hazel
Hair Fair

Signature of Employee

This card must be surrendered upon termination of employment.

Issued By

Authorized Signature.

IN THE BEGINNING

Employees pass issued to Fred Hartley at the time of his transfer to the Research Department, then located at Los Angeles Refinery.

NINTH PRESIDENT:
FRED L. HARTLEY

Fred L. Hartley joined Union Oil in 1939 as an engineering trainee at the Oleum refinery, following graduation from the University of British Columbia with a degree in chemical engineering. After executive experience in refining, research and marketing, he was named president August 31, 1964, and became chief executive officer December 28, 1964. In April, 1974, he was given the additional title of chairman of the board of directors.

His first promotion was to the inspection laboratory, where he participated in physical tests on petroleum products, API gravities, sulfurs, colors, pourpoints, etc. From there he went to the chemical lab where he took part in more sophisticated tests.

In 1940 Hartley felt confident enough of his career to marry his college sweetheart.

He had met Peggy Murphy through a friend at the University of British Columbia. She was in her third year and he was in his fifth. She graduated in physics and mathematics in May, came to California in November, and two days later they were married.

"We had an understanding when I left British Columbia that we were going to be married," Hartley explains. "On the other hand, we were mature enough to say that either one of us was free to make a better deal. I never could have, but you'd have to ask Peggy about her side of the bargain."

Openings came along in the research department at Wilmington. He had gone to an interview with a man who had seniority. Hartley had second choice. As fate would have it, the senior man chose lubricating oils, so the job of process engineer, where far more important action was soon to take place, fell to Hartley. In short order, he was running pilot plants, one of which was a forerunner in the manufacture of aviation gasoline.

By World War II, Hartley was totally involved in working on the design of plants for the manufacture of aviation gasoline and toluene for explosives. Both the American and Canadian armies decided he could be of most value doing what he was doing at Union Oil.

RELAXATION

As a form of relaxation and demonstration of versatility, Fred Hartley entertains at social gatherings with impromptu piano performances.

By the summer of 1942, at the age of 25, he was put in charge of the hydroformer's start-up at the Oleum Refinery.

As he tells it: "I just sort of fell into the job as the key man doing the initial work on the plant with the contractors. Having operated the pilot plant, I probably was one of the best informed men around regarding the commercial one.

"It was a tough job. But it was also the first opportunity I had to show I was capable of running an operation, working with the men at the plant, the men in the union, solving technological problems and keeping up the pressure and drive until we finally figured out what was wrong with the plant. We corrected the mistakes and made it run.

"That was a turning point in my career, I think, even though I was only in my mid-twenties. Part of the problem was that Union had bought the license for a process that seemed proven but wasn't. I decided then and there that if I had anything to do with it in the future, our company would have its own technology, based on solid, provable facts.

"Right after the war in 1945, we finally had to sell that plant to the junkman."

In 1943 Hartley had become process supervisor at the Oleum Refinery. It was a new concept, conceived to provide technological assistance to the refinery manager. By late 1943, he was transferred to the home office engineering department to serve as process supervisor in charge of the process engineering design of all of Union's new plants. He did so well that in 1950 he was moved to the Los Angeles Refinery as general superintendent of operations which further broadened his operating experience.

One measure of the man is that long before he had significant corporate authority, Hartley had the courage of his convictions.

While he was general superintendent of operations, a serious fire occurred in July of 1951. When Reese Taylor, then president, came down to survey the fire one night, he found Hartley on the scene. Taylor questioned him as to the problems involved. Hartley was blunt. He told Taylor that Union had built all its modern high-pressure technological equipment in the middle of this "junkyard" of old tank farms and cast iron piping systems—the worst possible place.

Taylor went back and did some scorching at higher refinery levels. But he was astute enough to tell Hartley privately that if he ever got in any trouble for his directness, he was to come and see Taylor. As Taylor put it: "If anybody wants to get rid of you, I want to know."

It took a little time, but eventually Hartley became aware that he was *persona non grata*, and should think of looking elsewhere for work. Hartley, as requested, informed Taylor of this predicament.

As a result, Bill Stewart—executive vice president—called Hartley to his office and introduced him to C. E. "Speedo" Swift, then head of research. Swift asked Hartley to establish a commercial development division to promote the licensing of Union's patents and technology to the industry.

That was how Hartley came in out of the cold in 1953 to begin a brilliant new career in research.

By then, he was a man marked for still larger challenges and still more responsibility.

He was put in charge of research in 1955.

Of marketing in 1960, and elected to the board of directors.

Of marketing and refining in 1962.

Of the total company as president and chief executive officer late in 1964.

Looking back, Hartley remembers that he joined the company as trainee the year after Reese Taylor became its president.

"I was a witness, and in my own part of the company, a participant in the dynamic change and growth of those Taylor years," he says. "When I finally came to the same job, he and Cy Rubel had left a company with a tremendous momentum operating at full speed ahead."

Hartley had scarcely settled into the presidential seat when he was faced with one of the most eventful decisions in Union Oil history. One day early in 1965, the phone rang and President Robert Milligan of the Pure Oil Company asked if Hartley was still interested in merging Union Oil with Pure Oil, with Union Oil Company to be the surviving corporation.

RECOGNITION

The Freedom Foundation's Honor Certificate award is presented to Fred Hartley for his speech "The Free Lunch Society." Mrs. George R. Hearst (center) and Mrs. Alex R. Jack made the presentation at the company's 1976 annual shareholder's meeting.

THE CHALLENGE OF CHANGE

"TIMING," SAID SOME WISE MAN, "IS EVERYTHING."

"I did not," said Fred Hartley, "become chief executive officer of Union Oil to see it remain a regional company."

He began his tenure with action: the Union-Pure Oil merger in July of 1965 was to make Union a national petroleum company.

But the political, social and economic climate in which this new company was to stretch its muscles was as trying and tumultuous as any in America's history.

It was the decade of the long and frustrating Vietnam war.

It was the decade of public suspicion and hostility.

It was the decade of government encroachment in private enterprise.

It was the decade of disbelief in government, media, education and industry.

It was the decade of Watergate, when for the first time in America's 200 years the nation's chief executive was forced from political office.

It was the decade of civil rights and civil unrest.

It was the decade of campus revolts, burned banks and political assassins.

It was the decade of double digit inflation and also the decade of the most serious depression since the early Thirties.

It was the decade which saw America's population pass the 200 million mark, the Gross National Product almost triple to $1.5 trillion and the Dow Jones Industrial Average finally break through 1,000.

It was the decade of consumerism.

It was the decade of environmentalism.

It was the decade of the Organization of Petroleum Exporting Countries (OPEC) and America's first non-wartime oil and gas shortage.

It was the decade when man walked on the moon, and earth-controlled robots landed on Mars.

There was no way to know, no way to anticipate much of this.

But looking back, you could hardly conclude this was the best of all possible worlds to expand a regional energy company into a national and international one, find new sources of oil, supply employment to thousands, pay a fair dividend to shareholders and still do well enough to have capital to plow back into new ventures.

But that's approximately what happened in Union Oil's eighth decade and Fred Hartley's first decade as the company's ninth president. It took some doing.

CHAPTER THIRTEEN

The Union Oil-Pure Oil Merger

ONE OF THE COUNTRY'S MOST RESPECTED OIL COMPANIES was in an economic squeeze: Pure Oil.

It was nurtured from small beginning to national significance by Beman Gates Dawes, the founder (1917) and first president, and was expanded into a multi-state integrated energy company by his younger brother, Henry May Dawes, who served as president from 1924 until 1947. It was then managed through vascillating gasoline markets by Rawleigh Warner until 1960 and by Robert L. Milligan until 1965, when Pure Oil found itself suddenly under siege.

While Pure was making preliminary plans in 1963 for its fiftieth anniversary to be celebrated the following year, President Milligan had unexpected visitors from New York. The visitors were Mark Millard and Robert Anderson, who were partners in the Wall Street brokerage firm of Carl M. Loeb, Rhoades & Company.

They told President Milligan and Chairman Rawleigh Warner of Pure Oil that their firm had been accumulating Pure stock since 1961 and, together with associates, had holdings of over 400,000 shares. They said they were interested in Pure from an investment standpoint only.

After preliminary overtures to the company, it was discovered that the Loeb, Rhoades group had increased its holdings to around 800,000 shares. In June, 1964, Pure received an offer from Loeb, Rhoades, Allied Chemical and Consolidation Coal to buy Pure outright.

SIGNING THE MERGER

Robert L. Milligan (left) *and Fred L. Hartley, Pure and Union presidents respectively, sign the merger agreement that formed a national oil company, "stronger and more successful than either could be separately."*

THE DAWES BROTHERS
Beman Gates Dawes (left) *was the founder and first president of the concern that grew into The Pure Oil Company. His brother, Henry May Dawes* (right) *became the company's second president in 1924, when Beman was elected chairman of the board. Henry Dawes remained as president until 1947.*

Milligan and Warner realized that Loeb, Rhoades had struck Pure when it was most vulnerable. Earnings were down. The "raid" was being made just before Pure's extensive new natural gas strikes could make a substantial contribution to earnings.

Someone had already tipped off *The Wall Street Journal* and other financial publications of the offer. The next day it was splashed all over the country, with the implication that Pure Oil was in trouble and on the bargain counter.

Milligan was galled by the Loeb, Rhoades power play. It was obvious to him that the purchasing syndicate could make an immense profit from the holdings of Pure's shareholders. Through the mechanism of a "reserved oil payment," the syndicate could borrow at least $500,000,000 on the company's large oil and gas reserves. By producing oil and gas from the reserves, the purchasers could pay off the $500,000,000 principal, together with interest, in about ten years. At the end of the period at least half the reserves would remain and the syndicate would have title to these valuable properties. For a relatively small investment, they would secure immediate ownership of Pure's refineries, transportation and marketing properties, working capital, and exploratory acreage.

Milligan was in trouble but far from helpless. He launched a series of effective moves to protect Pure's shareholders' interests. Within a short time a second offer for Pure's assets relieved the pressure. This proposition came from Laird & Company of Dallas, an oil and gas consulting firm. Later Francis I. du Pont & Company, another Wall Street brokerage and underwriting house, made a cash offer for Pure's assets, with the proposal that Pure's shareholders might participate in the new corporation to be organized.

Milligan wrote to the stockholders on July 6, explaining that the company had hired well-known reservoir engineers to evaluate its oil and gas reserves and that he was obtaining other appraisals of Pure's refining, transportation and marketing properties. In this letter he explained that Pure's management would not make any comment or recommendation regarding any of the offers until these studies had been completed.

The reservoir study would be an impartial scientific determination of Pure's reserves. It was essential to management in determining the company's worth and of great value to prospective bidders. The fact that the study would require several months gave him time to explore merger possibilities that might be best for both shareholders and employees.

Milligan favored a merger for two basic reasons: (1) Stockholders would not be forced to pay a capital gains tax as they would in a sellout and would be provided with a readily marketable security. (2) Pure Oil employees would become part of a strong corporate organization—a much better prospect than working for an oil company whose reserves had been stripped from it.

Pure's corporate situation had grown so complex that Milligan was forced to play his hand almost alone in merger conversations. On August 28 Milligan again wrote stockholders that the company had been approached "concerning other corporate suggestions" but that it would be premature to comment on them.

Several syndicates, hastily put together, sounded out the beleaguered Pure management with tentative offers that never quite jelled. In September, both Laird & Company and du Pont withdrew their offers. Almost immediately Loeb, Rhoades cancelled out, too. When the report on Pure's resources was issued on October 19, it revealed crude oil reserves of 539,000,000 barrels and natural gas reserves of 2.65 trillion cubic feet. By this time, Milligan had formed his own plan for a merger that might be most advantageous for Pure Oil employees and shareholders. Early in 1965, he called Hartley, who had just become president and chief executive officer of Union Oil. They had had prior friendly informal conversations about a possible mutually beneficial merger of the two companies. Now the two presidents discussed the principles and the broad outline of a formula for merging Pure Oil into Union Oil by utilizing a new issue of Union Oil preferred stock as the vehicle.

"I like the idea," Hartley said. "We'll go to work on it immediately."

The Milligan-Hartley plan called for a total fusion of the two companies and by an exchange of stock, Pure Oil would be merged into Union Oil, with the latter being the surviving corporation. The proposed amalgamation would create an oil company too big and strong to be destroyed by rivals or carved up by any of the financial syndicates such as had threatened both Union and Pure in years past. Luckily, the marketing areas of the two big independents were not overlapping. Instead of reducing competition, the merger would stimulate it, both in the consumer market and in the scramble for exploration acreage in this country and for overseas concessions. Pure's Texas refinery could handle Union's booming production of crude in the Texas, Louisiana, and Gulf oil fields. Spreading retail marketing over 37 states would give more protection against the whiplashing of regional gasoline price wars.

The merger moves added up to one of the exciting episodes in Union's long history. President Hartley lost no time in assigning Charles F. Parker, Union's senior vice president for finance, and Claude S. Brinegar, manager of economics and corporate planning, to make a preliminary but detailed study of the potential terms of the proposed consolidation. On January 11, 1965, Parker and Brinegar slipped quietly into the Brown Palace hotel in Denver, Colorado. Already there was Marshall McDonald, assistant to the president of Pure Oil Company. Presidents Hartley and Milligan stayed at their desks to throw inquisitive reporters off the scent, although both were in constant telephone contact with each other and with the negotiators, who agreed to lay all cards on the table. The possibilities for mutual stockholder benefit looked so promising on preliminary examination that Parker, Brinegar, and McDonald soon departed for their home offices to make their reports.

PURE OIL HEADQUARTERS *Aerial view of the Pure Oil Division headquarters at Palatine, Illinois; completed in 1960.*

On January 29, the Pure Oil board of directors at a special meeting in the Palatine headquarters of the company authorized Milligan to proceed with merger negotiations. This resulted in a new flurry of offers from bidders hungry to take over Pure Oil's assets. Several syndicates offered to buy the company outright, or to take it over by merger. Loeb, Rhoades & Company, the Wall Street brokerage firm that had been buying up large blocks of Pure shares for the past year or more, now teamed up with Allied Chemical Company, Lehman Brothers, and Lazard Freres & Company in a proposal to buy The Pure Oil Company lock, stock and oil derrick. Petrofina, S.A., the Belgian oil giant, had already entered a bid, so had Hercules Powder Company and Armour & Company in partnership with Houston oil magnate John W. Mecom. Atlantic Refining Company made a merger proposal somewhat similar to Union's, but of dubious practical value from an antitrust standpoint since Pure and Atlantic were direct competitors in several marketing areas. Ashland Oil Company of Kentucky, in partnership with the H. L. Hunt oil interests of Dallas, made headlines with a belated proposal. The Ashland feeler, which Milligan characterized as "only a proposal to negotiate on a variety of details," came after the Union-Pure deal had been wrapped up. Ashland and Pure were also direct competitors; hence the proposition appeared to be largely a smokescreen to confuse Pure shareholders. Loeb, Rhoades, as a major stockholder, had previously demanded two seats on the Pure Oil board of directors. When the Pure board offered one seat, it was turned down. Later, to avoid a showdown fight at Pure's annual meeting, Milligan said he would not object to Sandlin's going on the board, and so the Texas dissidents were offered one seat. This was accepted and Marlin Sandlin, an associate of director Jubal Parten, joined the Pure board in April.

Milligan fought off the buy-out proposals for two reasons. The most important was the conviction of Milligan and the vast majority of his board that Union's deal was both financially superior and specific, thus in the best interests of Pure's shareholders. The second reason was that the Pure stockholders would have to pay heavy capital gains taxes on an outright sale of the company, whereas in the Union merger plan they would receive shares of a new issue of stock, involving a "tax free" exchange of stock.

Hartley and Milligan had hoped to work the merger details out quietly, but the scramble for Pure Oil was soon splashed in the columns of *The Wall Street Journal* and other financial prints as "the battle of the giants." Pure Oil shares were suspended from trading for a brief period on the New York Stock Exchange. The Pure dissidents among its shareholders threatened lawsuits to scuttle the merger unless Union upped its bid. Hartley made it clear there would be no change in Union's offer, one that might have to be withdrawn entirely if too many of Pure's dissenters demanded cash instead of stock for their shares.

Meantime, Hartley and Milligan moved fast to close up a firm agreement. On February 4, they met, each flanked by four staffers, at the Pen & Quill, a secluded spot at Manhattan Beach near Los Angeles. Amazingly, no financial reporters found them during the two days in which they hammered out the basic terms of the merger. Hartley agreed to recommend that two of Pure's

DOLLAR BORROWERS PAR EXCELLENCE

Over a bank holiday Union treasurer Roy Houghton (left) *and senior vice-president Charles F. Parker telephoned heads of seventeen banks to raise $100 million to buy a block of 4 million Union shares—and secured pledges for $180 million.*

directors be added to the Union board. The Pure Oil board of directors would cease to exist at the consummation of the merger. Each Pure Oil share would be exchangeable for one share of a new Union Oil issue of cumulative preferred stock paying a $2.50 annual dividend. Each share of this Union convertible preferred could be exchanged at the owner's option for 1.3 shares of Union Oil common. After five years, the convertible shares could be called by Union's board at prices ranging downward from $67 to $65.

When the Manhattan Beach parley ended after two days of give and take, the merger appeared all wrapped up except for okays by the Union and Pure boards of directors and formal approval by the stockholders of the two companies. Then, one day in early February an unforeseen but significant development arose. Daniel K. Ludwig, the shipping magnate who had taken over the huge block of Union Oil shares accumulated by Phillips Petroleum Company, suddenly proposed selling his entire Union holdings to Union. Ludwig held some four million shares, worth approximately $146,000,000 at the then current market price of $35.50 per share. This was a big bite, on top of the merger. But on that same day, February 9, in a telephone conversation with Ludwig, Hartley concluded the purchase—subject to the approval of Union's directors—thereby reducing Union outstanding common shares fourteen per cent. On February 11, at a special meeting, the Union board voted to accept the Ludwig offer.

The Union board authorized Union's financial vice-president Parker and treasurer Roy Houghton, to borrow over a hundred million dollars in a hurry. The next day, Lincoln's birthday, was a bank holiday in most states. Nevertheless, Parker and Houghton manned long distance phones and dedicated their holiday to explaining Union's sudden money needs to the heads of seventeen of the country's largest banks, starting with California's Bank of America and Security First National Bank. Parker and Houghton had allocated a share of the huge loan to each bank, foresightedly allowing, in the best Lyman Stewart tradition, for a few turn-downs. They caught bankers at home, on golf courses and at holiday parties. When they had completed their phone calls, Parker and Houghton totalled up the dollars they could borrow in a hurry. The sum added up to $180,000,000 in five-year loans, many more millions than they needed, an amazing demonstration of confidence in Union Oil's management. Even two New York banks that had initially hesitated called back the next day offering more millions. Assistant Secretary C. E. Denton in New York promptly delivered a $146,000,000 check to shareholder Ludwig using $125 million from bank loans and the balance from Union's cash. The entire transaction started and ended in the elapsed time of nine days. Upon disposal of his holdings, Ludwig resigned his seat on the board.

Back at Palatine, Pure's President "Bill" Milligan was encountering difficulties with several shareholders who were opposed to the merger. The Number One hold-out was Major Jubal R. Parten, former president of Woodley Petroleum Company, which had merged into Pure Oil in 1960. On February 15, when the Pure directors voted 12 to 1 to accept the Union merger offer, Parten's was the negative vote. The anti-Union group launched a drive in the newspapers and financial publications to discredit the Union-Pure merger in the eyes of the Pure stockholders. A knock-down, drag-out proxy fight appeared in the making.

KEY MERGER NEGOTIATORS *Merger negotiations were facilitated by Marshall McDonald* (left), *assistant to the president of Pure Oil, who represented Pure in preliminary negotiations and helped plan proxy strategy; and L. A. Gibbons, Union vice-president and chief counsel, who handled all legal activities and relations with federal agencies.*

Prior to solicitation of proxies the dissidents were taking advantage of the fact that Milligan and Hartley were prevented by a Securities Exchange Commission ruling from answering their statements to the press.

Hartley and Milligan put into practice the old nursery rhyme "Sticks and stones may break my bones but names will never hurt me" and decided to ignore the protesters and push the merger to a conclusion as fast as possible. On February 18, Hartley and staff flew to Palatine to meet with the Pure Oil officers to explain how the Pure Oilers would be integrated into the Union scheme of things. Hartley appointed Claude Brinegar as "merger manager," his alter ego to smooth out merger details. He welcomed a study of Union's resources by Duff, Anderson & Clark, a Chicago-based investment banking firm, to assure Pure's stockholders that they would be exchanging their Pure shares for even better investment securities. Nevertheless, in March, *The Wall Street Journal* announced that both sides were preparing for a hot proxy fight. Apparently hoping to sabotage the merger, Atlantic Refining boosted its offer for Pure's stock.

The Pure Oil board met on April 29, in special meeting, to which Hartley and several of his advisors were invited. Hartley outlined Union Oil's extraordinary growth in recent years. Brinegar presented Union's long-range plans. Parker covered the financial outlook. Jack Vance of the McKinsey Company gave a round-up of the consultant's objective study of both Pure and Union Oil made by his firm. Summaries by New York investment bankers Frederic Brandi of Dillon Read & Company and Donald McDonnell of Blyth & Company assured the Pure Oil directors that the Union Oil offer was by far the best for all shareholders. Following these impressive reviews, Hartley revealed that the Union directors had already authorized him to execute the merger agreement. He also made it clear that Union's offer was its final one, adding that he expected the Pure directors to accept or reject it within four days.

The Union group then left the Pure board room. Without further delay, the Pure directors voted 11 to 2 to accept Union's offer. Only the Texas dissidents opposed it. A hurried phone call brought Union's assistant corporate secretary, Earl Cairns, winging from Los Angeles with the Union corporate seal. The merger document was signed at eleven o'clock that night on the dining room table of Milligan's home in Evanston, Illinois. This meant that any subsequent offers, such as the one from Ashland Oil, were too late—unless the shareholders of either Union or Pure formally voted down the merger.

On May 6, representatives of both companies met with proxy experts to plan the strategy for winning enough shareholders' votes to conclude the deal. An amusing sidelight was the comment of Pure's Marshall McDonald, who took a brief leave from the tense series of negotiations to get married. He was a widower with three offspring; his bride was a widow with four children. "We've completed our merger," he cracked to fellow negotiators. "Now let's finish this one." As the proxy fight loomed, the Pure dissidents almost daily bombarded the nation's financial editors with press releases attacking Pure's management. On May 27, a few hours after comprehensive proxy

CLAUDE S. BRINEGAR,
PRESIDENT OF THE NEW
PURE OIL DIVISION

Union's corporate planner, Claude Brinegar, was delegated by Union president Hartley as "merger manager" to work out details for combining the two companies, and after merger, he was appointed president of the new Pure Oil Division of Union Oil.

statements had been mailed to stockholders, Milligan, representing Pure Oil, and Parker, for Union Oil (Hartley being in Japan at the time), called a joint press conference in New York. They were free for the first time to answer all questions and innuendos. "If there is a proxy fight, we're ready for it and we expect to win it," Parker declared. Teams of Union and Pure officers took to the road to explain in personal calls on large Pure shareholders how the merger would enhance their earnings and the value of their holdings. These personal contacts were highly successful. Claude Brinegar and John Spence, Pure's vice-president and secretary, picked up proxies in New York for 1,300,000 Pure shares during two days.

On July 2, the Pure Oil stockholders held their meeting in Columbus, Ohio. Over 77 per cent of them voted to accept the Union merger offer. Only 4 per cent voted no; the rest of the shares didn't vote. The loud opposition had become only a whisper. And it later developed that only 59 Pure shareowners—holding less than one per cent of its outstanding shares—actually were full-fledged dissenters.

Two hours after the Pure Oil's meeting Union Oil shareholders gathered at the Union Oil Center in Los Angeles. When the ballots were tallied, Union's Secretary Robert F. Niven reported that 89 per cent of the shares had voted for the merger, less than one-half of one per cent against it. The big consolidation was virtually accomplished, except for one hurdle, the approval of the anti-trust officials of the U. S. Department of Justice. Union's vice-president and chief counsel, L. A. Gibbons, had kept both the Department and the Securities Exchange Commission completely posted on every step of the merger proceedings. The anti-trust officials declined to make a commitment, pending a clue from their new chief, Dr. Donald F. Turner, who had recently come from the Harvard Law School staff. When Dr. Turner, having completed his thorough evaluation of the facts, indicated that no action against the merger was presently contemplated, the way was cleared.

The formal merger agreement was filed simultaneously, after the close of both the New York and the Pacific Coast stock exchanges, with the secretaries of state in Ohio and California on July 16. This automatically put Pure Oil Company out of business as a corporate entity. To fill the void temporarily, Hartley had set up a financial and planning committee for Pure Oil with Claude Brinegar as acting chairman. On October 12, Brinegar was made president of the Pure Oil Division, with Milligan, who had reached retirement age, as chairman. Milligan and former Pure director Donold B. Lourie, chairman of the Quaker Oats Company, had already joined Union's board of directors.

Hartley and Brinegar moved fast to bring the Pure Oil Division into the Union orbit. Pure's exploration and production departments were quickly merged into Union's. The Pure research department migrated from Crystal Lake, Illinois, to Brea, California, to be merged into Union's Research Center. Pure's refining, transportation and marketing departments were kept intact and became another self-contained profit center under Brinegar's direction. Pure's subsidiaries became Union subsidiaries. Pure's properties in Canada were consolidated into Union Oil of Canada by the issuance of its common shares to Union Oil Company of California.

AGE DISPARITY—COMMON INTEREST

Eighty-nine percent of Union's stockholders voted for the merger with Pure. These two, Calvin Morrill (6), the youngest, and Fred H. Solomon (90), the oldest of the voting shareholders, are congratulating each other on having exercised their franchise.

In a report to the New York Society of Security Analysts on September 10, Hartley wrote, "The Union Oil Company I describe is the consolidation into a single national company of two fine regional oil companies. The resulting combination gives the new Union Oil Company greater competitive strength, broader geographic and product diversification, and increased financial and operating stability. The merger preserves and enhances competition in the industry."

He then pointed out some impressive figures revealing the strength of the new oil titan. After the merger, Union's assets were $1,700,000,000, making it the ninth largest company in the industry. Current sales were $1,400,000,000 a year. Common shareholders' equity topped $1,000,000,000. Union had 9,800 producing wells, a billion barrels of proven reserves (not counting Union's mountain of oil shale in Colorado), 9 trillion cubic feet of natural gas reserves. Its wells were yielding 226,000 barrels of crude daily, plus a billion cubic feet of natural gas. It had nine refineries in six states and a one-third interest in another. It operated 10,000 miles of product pipelines and had a large interest in 8,000 miles of raw material lines. Three supertankers and five product tankers flew the Union ensign, plus a fleet of barges. The company's subsidiaries were leaders in the manufacture of petrochemical products whose sales totalled $130,000,000 a year. Union's Unicracker was the last word in efficient refining; a new one was already on the drawing board for the Pure Division's refinery in Texas. Over 2,000,000 credit card holders patronized 17,000 service stations —for highway, truck, marine and air transport and travel—in 37 states. These Union-Pure outlets, along with hundreds of terminals, marketing stations, jobber and distributor outlets serving commercial and industrial accounts, handled 360,000 barrels of products daily.

Union's second post-merger board meeting, held at the Pure Oil headquarters in Palatine, Illinois, was followed by a dinner at the Chicago Club, where Bill Milligan introduced his new western colleagues to the heads of a hundred top Chicago enterprises. Next, appropriately, Hartley decided to call the company's seventy-fifth anniversary board meeting in the historic old building in Santa Paula where Lyman Stewart, Wallace Hardison and Thomas R. Bard launched the struggling Union Oil Company of California in 1890. The fine old structure still housed the Union Oil Museum and the company's district production headquarters. After the formal gathering, the directors and the local Union Oil staff celebrated the company's diamond anniversary at a luncheon, where descendants of all of the founders joined in the festivities. They and the stockholders of Union had plenty of reason to smile on that 25th day of October in 1965 for Union's common stock was trading in the area of $50 a share and the preferred in the area of $70 a share. Obviously the boards of the two companies had made a good decision for the mutual benefit of the shareholders of both companies.

Commenting on Union's fabulous growth, Hartley explained that the company aspired to be "not another Goliath in the oil industry, but a bigger David."

76
union 76
PURE

CHAPTER FOURTEEN

After the Honeymoon

MERGERS ARE A LITTLE BIT LIKE MARRIAGES.

After the courtship and honeymoon are over, both partners settle down to the business of living with each other harmoniously. Sometimes entered into for solving existing problems, they often create new ones.

Fred Hartley has said that this merger was certainly one of the single most important decisions in the history of Union Oil.

Merger Manager Claude Brinegar added that it opened new horizons, permitting Union to operate in a much larger arena. The new Union Oil Company had a much bigger "flywheel." By building on what the merger made possible, Union made more accelerated progress.

It enlarged Union's financial muscle. The company was no longer in the position of fearing that a lack of success in one particular venture would play havoc with earnings or its ability to attract new capital. For example, after the merger, Union could play the Indonesian game at more than several hundred million dollars, and the North Sea game at something very little less than that. The new Union Oil could undertake several or more large projects at the same time, and if one were not to turn out well, the company could move ahead solidly with the successes of other large projects.

In short it gave the company a depth and balance that had not existed in its regional past.

But like all experiences of value, making one company out of two was not without its problems.

Foremost, Brinegar explains, was the people problem.

"I found very early after the merger that Pure Oil people weren't sure what their futures were, and consequently they got very cautious. They often wanted to check with their potential boss in Los Angeles before they'd do anything."

IDENTITY CHANGE

The 76 sphere replaces the Pure emblem on a service station corner pole, completing the brand changeover program in the former Pure Oil marketing area.

CRANES STRAIN *A large process vessel is lifted into place in construction of the Chicago Refinery, completed in 1970.*

Brinegar constantly assured people that changes weren't going to happen overnight, but in a very orderly and studied fashion. It might take days, weeks, months, but it wasn't going to happen by people streaming across the mountains and taking over.

It was clear that Union did not have a surplus of executive talent. It had been running a company of its own, and obviously needed good Pure Oil people.

Brinegar at first took only one person from Union to commute with him to Palatine: Bob Creek, manager of supply and distribution planning. They were the vanguard.

Those early months were tense.

Competitors were trying to raid the commercial accounts in an effort to pirate Pure Oil jobbers. There was concern that valuable employees might panic and leave the company short on refining and marketing managers. Brinegar went into the field to talk to the jobbers and reassure them they were needed and wanted. Union lost almost none.

There was the continuing touchy problem of deciding who of the people on hand was going to help run the division. Pure had a far more complicated executive level than Union's—senior vice presidents and operations vice presidents, almost an extra layer of executives.

Study teams from both companies were formed and people from McKinsey & Company, an outside management consulting firm, brought specialists in problem-solving to the meetings. The work was done in such a way that everybody had a chance to look at the problems and participate in the solutions. The teams would take on various issues of the new organization over a period of weeks, sometimes months. For example, there might be 30 or more people performing a certain function. These questions would be raised: Do we need to do it at all? If so, do we need 30, 20, 15? If people were surplus how were they to be handled? Early retirement? Special termination allowances?

It was a tense and intensive period that lasted more than a year.

And while the people issue was going on, the new division also had another issue: How do you run this system? Exploration, production and research operations had been moved into the Union Oil orbit in the first few weeks, but the refining, marketing and distribution systems were quite different. They were, in fact, kept separate until 1968.

So there were vital questions: How do you decide what the refineries are doing and should be doing? What about the Pure pipeline systems? What about marketing policies in the new areas?

Bob Creek quickly set up a planning system that was similar to the one in Los Angeles, a system of which Pure had only the beginnings. There was a great struggle to put things together by December of 1965 for the first presentation to the Executive Committee which wanted to wire the Pure Oil division into the total Union Oil Company plan for 1966.

Brinegar challenged Senior Vice President John Towler, who was running the Refining and Marketing Division, as it was called. "I bet him that our Division would exceed our profit plan by more than his. We had a spirited contest in 1966—and we won! We bought a trophy that we awarded ourselves to help stir up the morale of our people."

AIR COOLERS

Massive air coolers which operate like the radiator in an automobile, greatly reduce requirements of the Chicago Refinery for water cooling.

LEADERS OF TWO REGIONS

C. E. "Ted" Rathbone (left) and W. S. "Bill" McConnor, refining and marketing vice presidents of the western and eastern regions respectively, implemented merger plans of the Union 76 Division.

The decision had not yet been made to build the Chicago Refinery, but there was talk about closing the Toledo and Heath Refineries. Rumors were floating around that the Palatine office was going to be turned into a junior college. The Research Center in Crystal Lake had been given to the Illinois Institute of Technology and some of the Pure folks were understandably uneasy about the future and their jobs.

Study teams were asked to consider what kind of marketing system could be evolved in the East where the market shares were low. There were tough questions to be answered: What is the future of the refining systems, of crude supplies? Much of 1966 was devoted to that kind of studies.

"Out of that it became clear that we could not profitably rebuild Heath or the Toledo Refineries; and the Lemont Refinery was really at the end of its economic life," Brinegar recalls. "If we kept those three small refineries going it would be in the nature of a holding action with high costs."

It finally was concluded to recommend to the Board that the three units be combined into a large grassroots refinery right next to Lemont. The Board said to go ahead.

That was the biggest single operational decision that had to be made. In point of fact, the $200,000,000 approval for expenditure that the refinery called for was, at the time, the biggest in Union Oil's history. The timing was perfect. When another company went down the street from the Chicago Refinery and built virtually the same plant 18 months later, its cost was about 50 percent more than Union's. In a year and a half Union had beaten the big boom and the enormous inflation in construction costs.

Meantime, in Los Angeles, Jerry Luboviski, director of corporate communications, was working with New York industrial designers Lippincott & Margulies on a new corporate identification program designed so that the company, its divisions and its subsidiaries could present a uniform look to the various publics. The total program, which involved a new corporate logotype, a marketing symbol, uniform packaging, a uniform printed materials system, and signage for service stations, buildings and rolling stock, was approved by the Board in mid-1967. It was introduced to company personnel as a complete package on September 1, 1967.

Joe Byrne, marketing vice president of the Refining and Marketing Division, recalls some of the trauma of the brand name changes. "It seemed to me that the most controversial things we did were to eliminate Union's purple motor oil and its Royal Triton brand name and Pure's Firebird brand for gasoline. We also dropped Minute Man service and Minute Man tires and batteries and went to the new Union star system for batteries and tires."

Many of the Pure people and Pure dealers who felt very strongly about the Firebird name and the company's advertising agency, The Leo Burnett Company, spent months trying to put a Firebird and a 76 together to make something out of them. The final conclusion: it wouldn't work.

At the time there also was concern whether the name Union would be offensive in the South because of the Civil War hangover. A survey revealed no particular ill feeling in the South over the name. It didn't bring back bad memories of the Civil War.

TESTING FOR THE CONSUMER *Officials observe braking test for a new model car, one of the criteria measured in annual Union/Pure Oil Performance Trials, a comprehensive evaluation of all popular auto models conducted for many years as a public service. Results were published.*

A GIFT FOR LEARNING *The Pure Oil Research Center at Crystal Lake, Illinois, was donated to the Illinois Institute of Technology in 1965 for use as a satellite campus.*

In the fall of 1968 with the retirement of Senior Vice President John Towler, Brinegar was named president of the newly formed Union 76 Division, responsible for Union's domestic refining, marketing and distribution. The Pure Oil Division was re-named the Eastern Region of the Union 76 Division and W. S. "Bill" McConnor was named vice president, refining and marketing, headquartered in Palatine. The Western Region, headquartered in Los Angeles, was headed by C. E. "Ted" Rathbone, vice president, refining and marketing.

In 1969, 400 people at the sales manager level and up arrived at the Arlington Park Tower hotel near Palatine for a great sales meeting.

"We had," says Joe Byrne, "bands and films, and we took some refiners from the West back there to this kickoff meeting of the general sales force. We wanted to get them to know each other to try to communicate that we were now one company. We even bought the rights to '76 Trombones' and later we took these filmed meetings to all the consignees and all the dealers. I heard the song so often I'm still tired of it."

Brinegar has high praise for the part Jim Egan, director of marketing, played in the changeover. "He did a fine job of being manager of the transition." Leo Spanuello, assistant to Brinegar, also played an important role. He took the responsibility of seeing that all the new signs were right for color and design and got to the right place at the right time.

"We actually 'feathered' the change into the Union Oil family as part of the normal station maintenance painting cycle so that the public could get used to our name gradually and we could spread the cost over a period of time. Certainly our costs were quite modest compared to what I have read that other companies went through," Brinegar says.

"As I look back now and reflect on the integration of the Pure system into ours, I realize we evolved certain management techniques which are common now. We used the task force to handle special assignments with some people having a special job for a while and then going to another assignment."

"But in the sense of the people making the decisions about how to do the transition, how to fit them in, there'd be a group working here and there. After their job was done we'd have them working some place else. We used this task force approach extensively for almost three years before we were finished."

Some special problems were encountered. Merging the benefit programs was almost tougher than merging the companies, but because the situation had been analyzed so well before the merger there were no serious negative surprises in most of the takeover.

"Our most pleasant surprise was the people we acquired, their quality, devotion and character. So many of them came to prominence later in the Union Oil family that I can't possibly name them all," Brinegar says.

Within a few years of the merger, all departments had been consolidated.

Manpower had been reassigned.

Station signing had been unified under the Union 76 brand.

A program for rebuilding Pure Oil stations had begun.

Pure's corporate functions had been moved to Union's headquarters in Los Angeles.

Union's budgetary procedures and related management control techniques had been extended through Pure's operations.

All research work was combined in a single location at Union's Research Center in Brea.

Pure's exploration and production activities were placed under the direction of Union's domestic and international divisions.

Pure's refining, marketing and distribution operations were organized into a new profit center located at Palatine.

A new $200 million refinery was built in the Chicago area.

Jack Vance, managing director of the Los Angeles office of McKinsey & Company, the management consultant firm which has served Union Oil for more than 15 years, makes a telling postscript to the Union-Pure merger:

"If you look at Union Oil, it was a question of survival or not. Union had to become a national, integrated oil company with sufficient resources to remain competitive and grow.

"The merger, then, was fantastically important to the company's future. That it was completed so successfully was a clear demonstration of good management strategy."

NEW
low-lead
regular
76
gasoline
76

CHAPTER FIFTEEN

Octanes and Environment

HISTORY OFTEN REPEATS, ALTHOUGH PEOPLE AND PLACES CHANGE. Back in the early days of this century, the salary of Judge Elbert H. Gary, chairman of the board of U.S. Steel, was $100,000.

The subject came up at a small dinner of business and political leaders.

"How can any man be worth that much?" exclaimed Senator Beveridge of Indiana.

"Senator," replied George W. Perkins, chairman of U.S. Steel's finance committee, "Judge Gary recently made a single decision which saved U.S. Steel enough to pay him that salary for the rest of his life."

Fred Hartley, during his first decade of command at Union Oil, made a similar decision. It substituted, for $80 million of undesirable expense, $80 million in profitable investment.

But that is getting ahead of the story.

Through the fifties and sixties, oil companies increasingly faced a serious problem in air pollution. The situation was especially acute in such local areas as the Los Angeles Basin, where prevailing winds and natural barriers, often combined with an inversion layer, tended to trap noxious fumes.

The discharge of various fumes into the air by refineries could be dealt with to a substantial extent. It largely was, as rapidly as was feasible. But refiners had another problem.

It became apparent that most of the noxious fumes were coming from automobiles.

Because combustion inevitably was imperfect, some pollutants were sneaking out of every exhaust—and pouring out of many. Among them were carbon

MONEY WELL SPENT

New Low-Lead Regular 76 gasoline sign, posted at the Union Oil Center service station, represents an $80 million profitable investment, instead of $80 million in undesirable expense.

monoxide, unburned hydrocarbons, oxides of nitrogen, and remnants of alkyl lead compounds.

Since the 1920's, one of these lead compounds had been added to gasoline to increase the octane rating and prevent engine ping or knock. Simply adding lead raised octane ratings inexpensively.

Declaring the automobile to be a major villain in the pollution story sparked efforts to end its menace.

The Federal government at first relied on state and local authorities. Its 1966 Motor Vehicle Air Pollution Control Act established auto emissions standards to be met by each state and the automobile makers.

California, with some acute local air pollution problems, took the initiative. An Air Resources Board (ARB) to set air quality standards and levels for automobile emissions was established in 1967.

Various proposals were made by regulatory bodies, politicians, and the industries affected. Often the debate was more emotional than rational.

General Motors President Edward Cole invited representatives of major oil companies separately to a series of meetings in Detroit in February, 1970. He told them that to comply with even some of the least exacting emissions standards proposed it would be necessary to install a catalytic converter in the exhaust line, and that this would require unleaded gasoline.

Cole recognized that it would be difficult and costly to produce a very high octane unleaded gasoline. So he suggested that cars be designed to operate on unleaded gasoline of 91 research octane by reducing the engines' compression ratio from an average of about 10 to about 8½. Refineries then could produce gasoline to meet the new cars' requirements.

On the way to the Detroit airport by car after the meeting, Fred Hartley, Claude Brinegar, Bill McConnor, vice president of refining and marketing of the 76 Division eastern region; Joe Byrne, marketing vice president of the 76 Division western region; and Dr. W. E. Bradley, vice president research, discussed the situation.

Unleaded gasoline was going to require more reformer capacity at the refineries. But 0.5 gram of lead per gallon could give a substantial octane boost, perhaps 40 percent of that provided by 3 grams of lead per gallon. Perhaps General Motors could find a way to live with 0.5 gram of lead per gallon, while capacity to produce unleaded was augmented.

Thus Union's "low-lead" idea was born in a limousine.

Within a month, the California ARB met to discuss fuel composition and emission control with representatives of the automobile, petroleum, and lead additive industries. Hartley and Dr. Bradley attended.

Hartley presented Union's proposal for "The Transition From Leaded to Unleaded Gasoline," but did not discuss low-lead because at this point it was only a concept to be analyzed further.

With proper technical supporting data, he called for an unleaded regular of 90-91 research octane and a leaded premium of 97 octane to replace the existing 94 octane regular and 100 octane premium. Not more than one grade of leaded

PRESS CONFERENCE *Fred Hartley, flanked by Dr. W. E. Bradley and Claude S. Brinegar, announces Union's Low-Lead Regular 76 gasoline plans at a well-attended press conference.*

could be offered, and not less than one grade of unleaded. 1971 cars would be designed to run on 90-91 octane unleaded gasoline. Dr. Bradley pointed out that Union's proposal would make a greater immediate reduction in lead pollution than would ARB's.

On April 9, 1970, Hartley outlined the low-lead idea in a letter to Secretary of Health, Education and Welfare Robert H. Finch. He suggested that after October 1, 1970:

(1) Marketers must offer at least one gasoline containing not more than 0.5 gram of lead per gallon, and could offer only one grade containing over 0.5 gram per gallon up to 4.0 grams per gallon.

(2) Unleaded gasoline must be made available, subject "to technical and economic confirmation of necessity."

(3) New cars should require gasoline of no more than 91 research octane rating.

Hartley's proposal stressed immediate reduction of the amount of lead going into the atmosphere from automobile exhausts. He promised that Union was ready to go as far as possible as soon as possible in meeting environmental needs.

"The public is demanding action to end pollution, and we agree," he said.

Other proposals being discussed would have permitted two grades of gasoline containing substantial amounts of lead, as long as unleaded was offered. It was feared that this would practically compel the sale of three grades.

The Union proposal would permit only one grade with a high lead content, presumably premium, and encourage the use of a low-lead or unleaded regular suitable for most cars using this grade. The amount of lead entering the atmosphere would be reduced. At the same time, to install a third set of pumps for a second grade of leaded gasoline would cost Union about $80 million—and the industry well over $1 billion—so the Hartley proposal had economic as well as environmental merit. Most other companies, however, went the three pump route.

Practicing what Hartley preached, Union in May, 1970 introduced 93.5 octane Low-Lead Regular 76 gasoline in Los Angeles and Orange counties and Sacra-

PUMP TOPPER
Cleaner air capabilities of Low-Lead Regular 76 are advertised on the top of gasoline pumps.

mento, California. Within 90 days supplies reached all of California, Hawaii and major population centers in Arizona and Nevada. Because of a variety of distribution and other problems low-lead was not marketed in the eastern area.

Union was one of the first oil companies to sell low-lead gasoline as its house brand.

The State of California specified low-lead gasoline for all state cars, and Union was successful in its competitive bid to supply it for 1971.

Low-Lead Regular 76 contained 0.5 gram of lead per gallon, 80 percent less than the old Regular 76 and most other regulars. Reflecting only Union's additional manufacturing costs, it was priced at 1¢ more than regular had been. And its quality was high enough to satisfy practically every car then using regular, as well as the new 1971 models which did not have catalytic converters. Additionally, many customers could recover the extra penny in reduced maintenance costs.

In February, 1972 the Federal Environmental Protection Agency (EPA) proposed making unleaded gasoline available for 1974 model automobiles.

Auto makers advised, however, that they would not be ready with catalytic converters requiring unleaded gasoline until 1975 models.

In the meantime Hartley addressed himself to another aspect of EPA's proposed regulations. In an important speech in April, 1972 in Dallas, Texas, he suggested the establishment of an average amount of lead per gallon which a refinery could use, setting it at less than the current average being used. Then let the refiner determine how he would distribute among grades the amount of lead available.

This would avoid limiting the flexibility needed to optimize efficiency in refinery operation, he said. It would avoid processing as much as 100,000 extra barrels of crude daily, required by inefficient operation. And it would be far easier to police several hundred refineries than several hundred thousand service stations.

After further hearings, EPA adopted lead averaging.

Meanwhile the Union board of directors had authorized creating refinery capacity for substantial production of unleaded gasoline, which Hartley was convinced would be necessary.

As early as October, 1966 Hartley had told the board of directors he thought gasoline would be unleaded within 10 years.

Reforming was the key to unleaded production. It created more "high octane" molecules. The process required more crude oil than when the octane rating was raised simply by adding lead. It was expensive; unleaded gasoline would cost more than an equivalent leaded, and Hartley knew this.

He had been in charge of research during initial development of Union's Unicracking-JHC process, which dramatically increases the amount of gasoline obtainable from a barrel of crude.

He realized that any unleaded gasoline would have to overcome price competition from leaded gasoline of similar octane.

But, contrary to criticism that business is concerned only with maximizing immediate profit, he took the long view.

With the elimination of lead from gasoline obviously a social goal, it was felt that the sooner Union adapted to the situation the better.

And Union, investing in long-term advantages rather than stopgap measures, also would benefit in the end.

"Let's get the lead out!" Hartley said.

Eighty million dollars was to be—or had been—invested to complete reforming capacity and associated facilities at Union's four major refineries. By the latter part of 1974 the company was set to meet any lead reduction requirements that might be imposed.

And just in time.

Detroit had finally announced that the 1975 models would have catalytic converters and operate on unleaded gasoline of 91 research octane. And this time the decision was definite.

The EPA on January 10, 1973, announced that effective July 1, 1974 there would have to be unleaded gasoline available at 60 percent of a company's service stations and at all stations pumping over 200,000 gallons a year. (The ruling further proposed some regulations gradually to decrease the amount of lead permitted in grades other than unleaded over a several year period. Final regulations on this became effective in mid-1976 when the U.S. Supreme Court agreed with EPA's position.)

In the meantime Union had further prepared to introduce an unleaded regular. Lead had to be purged from facilities that would handle the grade: storage tanks, pipelines, truck tanks, even service station hoses, on which a special nozzle would be required to fit the smaller size gas inlet on the new cars.

It was a $3.3 million clean-out program.

CHICAGO REFINERY DEDICATION *Dignitaries on stage at dedication of Union's Chicago Refinery, from left, Fred Hartley; C. S. Brinegar, president of the Union 76 Division; Illinois Governor Richard Ogilvie; Lee DuBridge, science advisor to the President; Mayor John F. O'Hara of Romeoville, site of the refinery; Kazuo Miyamori, president of Maruzen Oil Company; and John Braun of C. F. Braun and Company.*

July 1, 1974, Union Unleaded Regular was introduced. It was sold at most of Union's retail outlets nationwide, many more than required by EPA regulations.

In the West, it was 94.5 research octane, sufficient to take care not only of the new models but of most older cars—over 70 percent of all cars on the road. And Union's premium leaded gasoline satisfied almost all the rest.

In the East, distribution problems made more interchange of gasoline between marketers necessary. H. Dorn Stewart, Eastern Region refining and marketing vice president, pointed out that largely because of this, 76 Unleaded Regular's octane had to be held to 91, as was the case with competitors. This satisfied all new cars and about 25 percent of the older models. 76 Unleaded Regular was available in whatever quantity the market might demand. Most competitors offered an unleaded of about 91 octane, available in comparatively limited quantities.

Union 76 Unleaded Regular had an octane rating in the West comparable to most competitive leaded regulars, and in addition to cleaning up the air, the company's advertising pointed out it could save up to 2¢ a gallon due to decreased maintenance costs. With lead absent, spark plugs, mufflers and tail pipes last longer, and tune ups are not needed as often.

By the end of 1976 Unleaded Regular constituted about 60 percent of Union's branded gasoline sales, compared with about 20 percent for the rest of the industry.

The importance of the decision to create ample capacity for unleaded gasoline production was underlined by a Union Research Department study in February, 1976. It estimated that cars needing unleaded fuel were responsible for 11.4 percent of market volume in 1976, while this would be 65 percent in 1980 and

95 percent by 1986. What then would happen to the third pumps other companies had installed?

Hartley's decision to really get the lead out—to put $80 million in refineries instead of gasoline pumps and tanks—assuredly was one of the decade's developments most vitally important to the company in spite of the attendant problems.

During the decade the company showed only a slight increase in refinery capacity but vastly improved the caliber of its operations while maintaining an outstanding safety record. The increased capacity was due primarily to the new Chicago Refinery's 140,000 barrels a day, 40,000 more than the three obsolete Pure Oil refineries it replaced: Lemont (located on adjoining property), Heath, and Toledo.

The new refinery cost over $200 million, including $37 million for environmental controls. This was Union's largest such investment to date.

A dramatic touch occurred during the dedication of the new Chicago Refinery on June 20, 1970 attended by hundreds of guests including Hartley, Claude Brinegar, then president of the Union 76 Division; and the then Governor of Illinois, Richard Ogilvie.

The refinery, located beside the Chicago Sanitary and Ship Canal, draws contaminated water from the canal, uses it in processing, purifies it and returns it to the canal.

To demonstrate the effectiveness of the purifying process, Brinegar produced a cup and drank some of this effluent water. Not to be outdone, the governor did likewise. In addition, his dedicatory speech referred to the fact that the "massive commitment which you have made at this refinery to preserving the quality of our precious natural resources of air and water provide an example for other industries to emulate."

CONTROL ROOM *Robert Bungay, vice president engineering and construction (left), explains Chicago Refinery controls to Lee DuBridge, science advisor to President Nixon and John Braun of C. F. Braun.*

REFINERY ENTRANCE *The Union Oil logotype graces the entrance to the company's $200,000,000 Chicago Refinery, embodiment of latest manufacturing and environmental developments.*

Numerous tough decisions had to be made before planning the Chicago Refinery. Should the Toledo Refinery be modernized, with Lemont and Heath eliminated, and refining capacity reduced accordingly?

Where would the crude come from? Initially the thought was to use crude from Canada, including some produced by Union's Canadian subsidiary, via a nearby pipeline. (Several years later Canadian export restrictions made this impractical.) Fortunately the refinery was located near virtually every major pipeline system so other crude oil also was available in sufficient quantity.

What processing units should be included? For octane capacity there was a reformer, as well as a catalytic cracker and other units. But what facilities should be provided for Amsco, which had relied heavily on the Toledo Refinery to supply naphthas for Amsco solvents?

Facilities to produce a substantial volume of environmentally acceptable solvents were provided. A coker was installed to control production of residual fuel and asphalt. This gave Collier a supply of carbon, and it later added a calcining unit.

The coker also gave the refinery flexibility to handle heavy crude oils, many from the Middle East. It even was prepared to handle oil from shale.

The naphtha supply proved more than adequate for Amsco, as well as reforming requirements.

But Union 76 Division President Bill McConnor has noted: "From a barrel of crude you always end up with something you don't want. If there is no market for it you have to find a way to convert it or find a market. That is where ingenuity comes in."

So in 1972 a 10 year deal was made with Peoples Gas Co. for delivery of 10,000 barrels per day of low octane naphtha to be used as feed stock in producing SNG—synthetic natural gas. Delivery started in 1975.

At other refineries an all-out program to improve efficiency was underway. To again quote McConnor: "It is one thing to be able to make the product and something else again to make it economically."

At Beaumont, a major renovation was undertaken.

By early 1969 a Union Oil developed Unisar unit came on stream, making it possible to reduce the aromatic content in solvents and in turbine fuels.

A Udex unit also increased the supply of aromatics—benzene, toluene and zylene—available for sale to companies making petrochemical products.

A reformer was completed at Beaumont in 1972 to upgrade its ability to make unleaded gasoline.

In modernizing Beaumont, according to Walt Jameson, Eastern Region vice president of refining and supply, it was decided to continue limiting feed stocks to so-called sweet, light crude oils since the facility was located at a gateway where such crudes arrive from Texas and abroad.

In the West, capacity to handle so-called sour, heavy crudes was essential since many California crudes with high sulfur content fell into this category. Alloy steel facilities were needed to resist corrosion, as they were in the Chicago Refinery with its general purpose flexibility.

The Santa Maria Refinery for many years had been processing sour, high sulfur crudes, producing coke for Collier and distillates for further processing at San Francisco.

But the principal objective of modernization in the West was increasingly efficient production of gasoline and reduction of non-saleable resids. R. F. "Bob" Nootbaar, director of planning for the 76 Division, has repeatedly emphasized these factors both within the company and within industry as well as to governmental groups.

Computerized analysis and control continued their important function in refinery operations. The new Chicago Refinery was fully computerized from the time of its start-up in 1970. The computers were programmed to compare actual with planned conditions, and report or correct any differences. Yields were improved and manpower saved.

Analytically the computers could do in an hour things that would take a man a year, said Barney Barnett, Western Region vice president of refining and supply. They could, for example, reveal all effects, including profitability, of a change in the type of crude oil run.

At San Francisco, Alaskan crude oil began arriving in September, 1967 in the remarkably short time of only two years after Union's big Cook Inlet discovery. Unlike most of the California supply, this was sweet, low sulfur crude, ideal for gasoline and lube oil production.

In September, 1971 an $85 million Unicracker-reformer complex was completed at San Francisco Refinery, providing capacity for the unleaded gasoline to come. Also included was a Unisar unit to provide aircraft turbine fuel with a low aromatic content to meet airline standards.

Then, to meet increasingly strict clean air standards, Beavon sulfur recovery units, which Union had co-developed with another company, were added to all three sulfur plants. This removed an amazing 99.9% of the sulfur from stack gases.

To assure the quality of processed water returned to the bay from the San Francisco Refinery, California's Regional Water Quality Control Board had established a random testing procedure of the effluent water, at the point of discharge, that was practically foolproof. This was done by checking the ability of a common small fish of the area—the threespine stickleback—to live in it.

Refinery Manager Bill Stark and Environmental Engineer Forrest Bottomley wanted to make sure the test results always were accurate. A bad test could shut down the plant until the condition presumably causing it was found or corrected.

They decided to bypass all of the costly scientific equipment on hand. Instead three small aquariums were set up with sticklebacks in residence. Effluent water on its way to the bay went through two of them. As a control, pure water ran through the other.

Any erratic behavior by the fish in "effluent tanks" provided prompt warning that something might be wrong. The control fish indicated whether it was the effluent at fault or psychosomatic sticklebacks. The aquariums and the sticklebacks proved more accurate than the computer!

At Los Angeles, where Alaskan crude also began arriving in 1967, the refinery's alkylation capacity was doubled in 1969. This made it possible to produce substantially larger quantities of premium and aviation gasolines.

Also in 1969, a deal was made that added the equivalent of 30,000 barrels a day additional refining capacity.

The Union Pacific Railroad had some heavy crude oil production from the Wilmington field which did not justify a full-scale refinery. It offered to build a topping and coking plant if Union would buy the distillates and Collier buy the coke.

A 10-year contract was signed. Union Pacific built its plant and connecting pipelines to Union's Los Angeles Refinery.

Construction of a $35 million reformer unit to increase the Los Angeles Refinery's unleaded production capacity was begun in 1973, and completed in late 1974. This, with reformers already installed at the other three major refineries, gave Union ample capacity for producing high octane unleaded gasoline.

While the reformer was being started, two sulfur plants were built, complete with two Beavon units.

Union found itself trapped in an illogical regulatory maze when two 300,000 barrel crude oil storage tanks were to be added routinely to the seven existing at the San Pedro Outer Harbor Terminal. Extra capacity was needed for crude to come from Alaska, Indonesia and the Persian Gulf.

Designing and engineering were completed, and the first application filed May 21, 1974.

There followed 12 personal appearances before 10 different Federal, state and local boards or commissions.

Not until January 21, 1976 was final approval granted by the California Coastal Conservation Commission. All approvals had been granted unanimously, yet nearly two years transpired.

UNLEADED GASOLINE UNIT *This $35 million Unionfiner Reformer, designed to increase production of unleaded gasoline, went "on stream" at the Los Angeles Refinery in March, 1975.*

In the same month Union authorized abandonment of its four million barrel earthen bunker fuel reservoir—one of the largest in the world—at the Torrance Tank Farm. In the late 1960's a similar authorization had to be withdrawn hastily when Union suddenly found itself with a fuel oil glut, and it was not possible to slow down the L.A. Refinery fast enough to take care of it. Subsequently a resid reduction program had been completed, and so this mid-1920 facility finally had outlived its usefulness.

By 1976 the input of crude oil to Union's refinery processing units was up by one-third over the combined Union/Pure figure at the time of the merger. The industry's increase was slightly higher. In the same period Union's net crude oil production as a percentage of crude oil runs to refineries was over 70 percent as compared with only 60 percent for the earlier period, thus improving its profits because of being able to buy a smaller proportion of its total crude oil requirements.

Two-thirds of Union's refinery runs were coming from domestic produced and purchased sources, and only one-third from foreign imports, thus establishing a relatively strong stability of raw material sources. The comparable industry foreign import figure was over 40 percent for 1976. This reflected the apparent willingness of America's energy users to rely more—rather than less—on foreign imports, most of which came from the Organization of Petroleum Exporting Countries (OPEC).

During the decade, stringent environmental regulations had reduced the use of fuel oil by utility companies. But the demand for gasoline in the U.S. increased nearly 50 percent. Union's refinery operators increased the yield of gasoline and reduced that of fuel oil through new facilities and modifying operations, while significantly reducing costs.

In mid-December, 1970 sale was completed of Union's 3,800 barrel per day refinery in Cut Bank, Montana, together with the adjoining absorption plant. The majority of employees at the plants elected to remain at Cut Bank. The rest transferred to the company's operations in California and Alaska.

Refineries typified the very difficult problems which even reasonable environmental regulations imposed on industry—including petroleum. Union and its subsidiaries were no exception, and their combined total cash outlay since 1970 for environmental expenditures has exceeded $300 million—or more than $100,000 a day. Over half of this involved oil refineries and chemical plants.

As much as two-thirds of the $300 million could be considered as required and necessary, such as preventing sulfur and nitrogen compounds as well as other contaminants from entering the air, purifying plant waste water discharges, and building new facilities that minimize the impact on local environment. Some regulations, however, required attempts to comply with standards that even nature herself often violates.

Union's environmental policy was set forth strongly and clearly early in Hartley's stewardship. This included compliance with, and wherever possible, exceeding governmental regulations on pollution control. Operations were to be conducted to minimize air and water contamination. The most modern pollution control equipment was planned into all new facilities. But Hartley also pointed out the balance between risk to health and welfare on the one hand and risk to jobs and economic stability on the other hand.

As environmental pressure built up from all sides, an environmental sciences department was formed early in 1972 reporting to Administrative Vice President M. S. Thomson. It was headed by Dr. C. B. "Bud" Scott, formerly manager of development for Collier Carbon and Chemical Corporation. He was to be responsible for implementing the company's environmental policy, and coordinat-

PAPER, PAPER EVERYWHERE *Dr. C. B. Scott, director of environmental sciences, is overwhelmed by the mass of paperwork created by a morass of environmental regulations.*

ing conservation programs and the company's compliance with governmental regulations concerning environmental matters.

Dr. Scott's initial staff was three and during 1976 had quadrupled. In addition, operating divisions had assigned personnel the day-to-day responsibilities for compliance, and the legal department had assigned three lawyers plus outside counsel.

The environmental sciences group had to concern itself with the four basic environmental areas of air, water, solid waste and noise. It had to involve itself with each operating department's specific problems. It had to negotiate and consult with a myriad of governmental bureaucracies at all levels.

Scott recalls one case where a bureau chief outlined the course of action necessary to secure approval for a large installation. Implementation was well under way when a vacation brought a deputy into the act. He suggested an entirely different approach. When the chief returned from vacation both he and the deputy were replaced and the program started all over.

By 1975 two large and powerful Federal agencies seemed to be running on a collision course, the Environmental Protection Agency (EPA) and the Federal Energy Administration (FEA).

The FEA was encouraging the oil industry, through price incentives and otherwise, to increase its domestic supply of crude oil to avoid further reliance on crude oil imports. But the New Source Review rules at the Federal, state and local levels were seemingly making it either difficult or impossible even to bring available new oil out of the ground for public consumption.

When the environmental sciences group runs across what obviously seems highly unreasonable or duplicative environmental requirements, the first step is discussion of the facts with the governmental agencies involved. Then comes negotiation with, and testimony before, these same agencies. If all this proves futile the company does not hesitate to go to court.

The environmental sciences group has helped make possible a significant decline in contaminants released by Union's operations to air and water, has sharpened awareness at operating management levels of environmental constraints, has emphasized the facts of economic life with governmental agencies leading to more reasonable regulations, and has saved the company millions of dollars in terms of regulations that were modified at the company's suggestion.

Environmental matters were only one of several of the governmental encroachments into the affairs of corporate activities. There were also price controls, production quality controls, operating methods, safety regulations, new tax regulations, etc. All of these, of course, involved new laws and regulations and the brunt of interpreting them and complying with them from a legal standpoint fell to the legal department. George Bond had succeeded Doug Gregg as vice president and general counsel late in 1973, and in the following three years the expanding reach of government forced him to significantly increase the legal staff.

An oil import quota system had been in effect since 1959, and had become the subject of considerable and continuing criticism both within the oil industry and by a good many legislators. Special privileges and special deals abounded. In a 1968 speech to the National Petroleum Refiners Association, Hartley emphasized this by referring to the benefits then being derived from plants of other companies in Puerto Rico and the Virgin Islands.

Product shortages, which developed early in the Spring of 1973, were a primary cause for ending the long-time crude oil import quota system as it then existed. Its original purpose had been to encourage domestic production increases.

On the political front, President Nixon, by proclamation on May 1, 1973 substituted import fees for the quota system. In August the Cost of Living Council—in existence since 1971—issued regulations that were to have a significantly adverse impact on Union—and many others in the petroleum industry.

It imposed new price controls on the industry's raw materials, dealers' margins, gasoline pump prices, etc., based on May, 1973 prices.

It gave birth to a two-level domestic crude oil pricing system which eventually led to three levels later on. This involved the controlling of prices of "old oil" (1972 level of production as to each company) and removing price controls on all other domestic crude oil production with the hope of stimulating discoveries of crude oil.

It also initiated regulations that marketers could "pass through" most—but not all—cost increases to consumers. Large and small alike, they had to keep "bank books" on both cost and price variations.

The effect of these regulations had barely been felt when the October Arab oil embargo hit the industrialized nations, followed by OPEC's sharp increases in crude oil prices. By the beginning of 1974 prices had more than quadrupled over those in effect one year earlier.

As a result of the OPEC embargo, by the end of 1973 most of the nation's almost 300 refineries were without an assured supply of crude, and products for consumers also were short. To protect both groups the Emergency Petroleum Allocation Act was passed, to be administered by the newly created Federal Energy Office (FEO). It took over all pricing matters of the petroleum industry from the Cost of Living Council, and also established allocation priority systems. By now regulations and rulings had become so voluminous and complex that Accountant Lowell Way was appointed manager of pricing and allocation in the 76 Division's Palatine office to devote total time to these matters.

By March of 1974 the Arab embargo was lifted, and in May the FEO was replaced by the Federal Energy Administration (FEA) to control the oil industry's pricing of products as well as raw materials. Under FEA the crude oil buy/sell program continued, even though its reason for existence (the abandoned embargo) had become non-existent. Under the program small and independent refiners were allowed to purchase crude oil from other oil companies. This gave the small refiners an economic advantage because they purchased crude at the supplier's average price even though the latter's delivered crude may have been its most expensive. The large companies still had to replace their low cost, forced sales with higher priced foreign oil. Two years later—in February of 1976—the FEA finally corrected this expensive inequity, mini-

TELLING THE STORY *The energy shortage was explained by Union Oil management people at every opportunity. Here Tom Monroe, area sales manager in Toledo, Ohio, addresses a Kiwanis Club luncheon.*

mizing its effect, although continuing its availability in event of any future oil embargo.

But one inequity leads to another. The FEA instituted an "entitlements" program effective in November of 1974, designed to equalize the raw material costs of all refiners. It was a sister regulation to the buy/sell program.

Under entitlements Union paid out millions of dollars per month to its competitors for the right to refine its own domestic crude oil in its own refineries. In one month Union paid over $4 million to one of the world's largest oil companies. In 1975, and again in 1976, it paid approximately $130 million, or about 2¢ per gallon on domestic product sales.

Subsequently refiners with less than 100,000 barrels per day capacity were exempted from purchasing entitlements as to their first 50,000 barrels per day. Such small independents could process the latter, regardless of how much "over" they might be.

This meant lower raw material costs and the ability to sell for less to their own stations or other independent marketers. The market share of independents continued to increase at the expense of the majors, and rose from roughly 20 percent to more than 30 percent during the five year period of price controls, which were still in effect in 1976.

The method of allocating crude oil supplies and controlling their cost had since 1973 included a "pass through" program. Its purpose was to make sure the oil industry would not "pass through" to consumers in increased prices more than was justified by certain increased costs. At the same time it enabled the industry to recover these cost increases only if market conditions permitted, which was not always the case.

KOREAN DEDICATION *President Park Chung Hee of the Republic of Korea cuts ribbon at dedication ceremony of Kyung In Energy Company refinery power plant. He is flanked by Union's President Fred Hartley and Kim Chong Hee, president of Korea Explosives Company, partners in the joint venture.*

In December, 1975 the Energy Policy and Conservation Act was passed. Its title ran somewhat counter to its content. There was very little policy and only some conservation. But there was more government control. Prior to its passage there were two price levels—controlled (domestic "old" oil) and uncontrolled (other domestic and foreign oil). The Act continued price controls on "old" oil (now called lower tier) but brought all other domestic production back under the price controls, calling it upper tier and establishing a mandated national average price of the two tiers at $7.66 per barrel—subject to some future adjustments—maybe. That left foreign oil without price controls as a third tier.

If all this sounds complicated, it was. FEA regulations fill four thick volumes. Sometimes the local FEA office didn't have the same volumes as its national office. One morning in April of 1975 Union was served with a $45 million Notice of Probable Violation (NOPV) for mispricing. Hartley was confident this was not the case, but not so confident of bureaucratic correction. He asked Vice President Tom Sleeman—whose staff was following FEA matters closely—to investigate, but did not tell Treasurer Bill Craig to write a check.

Sleeman got in touch with John Allen and Bill Cole in Union's Washington office for an urgent appointment with FEA's review office. Its rules and Union's interpretation were the same, and so the $45 million NOPV was withdrawn in the remarkably short time of only one week from when it was served.

Union's accounting and computer costs for handling FEA requirements in 1975 were $3 million, and roughly the same in 1976. One major oil company had a computer tape 636 miles long on which was stored the information it had to supply to the FEA.

Union's refining interests were not all in the United States. In 1967 Union's 87 percent owned subsidiary—Union Oil Company of Canada—built a new refinery at Prince George, British Columbia. The original cost of the 8,000 barrel per day plant was $8.2 million, with another $2.5 million in asphalt facilities added in 1969. Many service stations were built and some were bought, all being located in British Columbia, Alberta, and the Yukon Territory.

The refining and marketing end of the business did not prove adequately profitable. In 1976 the refinery and the company's 110 marketing outlets were sold to Husky Oil Company (Alberta) Ltd. for $38 million plus an adjustment for inventory evaluation. The almost $7 million capital gain helped make the initial decision look better, and provided cash for the expanding activities of Union Oil of Canada in petroleum exploration and production, as well as in minerals and coal.

Across the Pacific Ocean in South Korea, Union had a 50 percent interest in Kyung In Energy Company, Ltd. It had been formed in 1969 jointly by a Korean partner—Korea Explosives Company, Ltd. and Unoco Limited—Union's Hong Kong based, wholly owned subsidiary.

Kyung In, of which George Snyder (formerly manager of the San Francisco Refinery) was executive vice president, constructed a 325,000 kilowatt electric power plant and a 50,000 barrel a day crude oil topping plant in the Seoul-Inchon area. The topping plant's function was to make fuel oil from crude oil supplied by Unoco under long-term contracts. Subsequently additional facilities were added to the topping plant, thereby converting it to a full product line 60,000 barrel a day refinery. Marine and other loading facilities, trucks, and service stations were also established to serve this rapidly developing country.

Total investment ran well over $100 million, largely from funds loaned by private banks, Unoco, and others. The investments were substantially insured by Overseas Private Investment Corporation (OPIC), a U.S. government corporation, against many of the risks associated with overseas enterprises.

The facilities were dedicated in April, 1972 on the same tidal flats where General Douglas MacArthur made his daring Inchon landing in 1950. Republic of Korea President Park Chung Hee cut the ribbon in a formal ceremony complete with traditional white gloves and white-wrapped scissors. Sharing honors with him were Hartley and Kim Chong Hee, better known as "Dynamite" Kim, president of Korea Explosives Company.

NERVE CENTER
Control room of the Kyung In Energy Company power plant at Inchon, Republic of Korea.

At the time the power plant was first put into commercial operation, Senior Vice President Charles Parker was having dinner with "Dynamite" Kim at his house in Seoul, which is supplied in part with electricity from the new plant. Parker had arranged to be telephoned there by the plant manager when the startup had been completed. The phone call came in just as the lights went out. The plant manager reported that all had gone well and its electricity was flowing into the system, and couldn't understand why the Kim house lights were off. The solution came when it turned out that "Dynamite" Kim—a practical joker of sorts—was found at the house switch, turning the lights back on!

Dan Waldorf, formerly general superintendent of operations at the Los Angeles Refinery, was elected executive vice president of Kyung In when George Snyder returned to Union to become director and later vice president of engineering and construction. Shortly thereafter the OPEC induced worldwide crude oil price increases occurred. They were not matched by Korean government controlled product price increases, and this had a temporary but adverse effect on Kyung In's operations.

In the 1960's huge supplies of cheap Middle Eastern oil made tankers a vital part of the supply lines for the industry's refineries in the United States. Union had three large ones at 70,000 deadweight tons each, *Sansinena*, *Lake Palourde*, and *Torrey Canyon*. The latter two were jumboized in 1965 to 123,000 deadweight tons. All three were under foreign flag to minimize operating costs and to remain competitive. Their principal job was to transport crude oil to Union's U.S. refineries from the Middle East, and later from Indonesia.

By 1967 the two jumboized tankers were still among the largest in the world. And one went on the rocks.

The 123,000 deadweight ton supertanker *Torrey Canyon*, with a cargo of 880,000 barrels of crude oil, was wrecked on March 18, 1967 on the Seven Stones reef off Land's End in Cornwall, England, due to navigational error. The ship was only 100 miles from her destination after an 11,300 mile trip.

While under long term charter to Union, the ship at the time was sub-

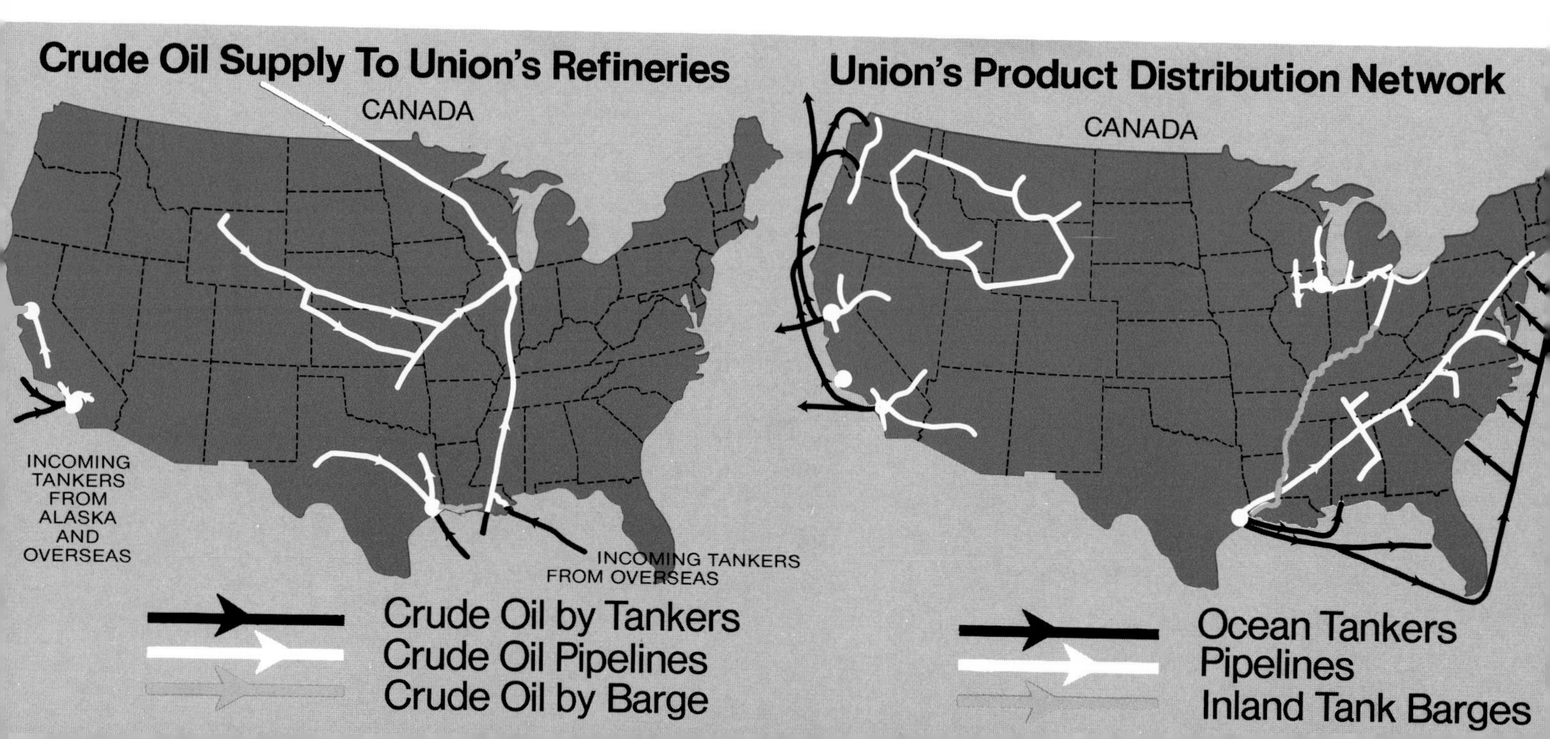

chartered to British Petroleum Company and was carrying cargo for it from the Middle East to the British Isles.

The crude spread to 120 miles of Cornwall's beaches, and part of the French Coast. Salvage turned out to be impossible, and the ship finally was bombed and set afire by British planes.

People from Union, British Petroleum, and British armed forces all turned to in an effort to minimize the spreading of oil and clean up the beaches. A year later Cornishmen were quoted as saying, "You'd hardly notice a thing had happened." Another source indicated the beaches were clean within three months. Vice President M. S. Thomson flew to England as Hartley's personal representative.

Union was covered by insurance for both the loss of the $17 million ship and the $7 million spent for cleanup and other costs. The disaster, however, had an effect on worldwide marine insurance coverage. Lloyds of London for some time eliminated coverage on oil spills and ocean pollution from its policies. Operators of tankers, including Union, formed private insurance groups to cover future liability.

The third tanker, *Sansinena*, was needed by Union in domestic service to bring crude oil from Alaska's Cook Inlet to its West Coast refineries. However, under the Jones Act this could only be done by tankers built in and registered in the U.S., and manned by U.S. crews. The *Sansinena* did not meet the latter two conditions, although Union was willing to make the necessary changes.

This created a politically produced "play" in 1970, with Union cast in a villain's role.

During the "Buy American" days of the late 1950's Union had built the *Sansinena* in the United States. Intended initially for foreign trade, it was registered in Liberia and chartered through its legal owner, Barracuda Tanker Corporation.

Under existing law the Secretary of the Treasury could grant a waiver permitting a vessel built in the U.S. but registered abroad to be brought back under the U.S. flag and given domestic trading privileges. But this had to be in the interest of national defense.

In 1967 Union requested such a waiver for the *Sansinena*. The application argued that the vessel would strengthen the U.S. Merchant Marine should an emergency arise, and U.S. crews would be used and U.S. taxes paid. The application was denied.

In 1970 the need had become more acute, and the request for a waiver was renewed. This time it was granted on March 2.

Then came the storm.

The March 5 *Weekly Bulletin* of the Shipbuilders' Council of America charged that the waiver had been granted on national defense grounds with "no explanation, no reason, no rationale, and no justification."

The International Union of Marine and Shipbuilding Workers of America, AFL-CIO, especially, was aroused, indicating this might deprive U.S. citizens of shipbuilding jobs.

PROW BEATING
Mrs. Fred Hartley breaks the traditional bottle of champagne on the prow of Sansinena II, a 70,000-ton tanker launched in 1971.

Maryland Senator Joseph Tydings, on the floor of the Senate, took a very strong position against the waiver. After a maelstrom of charges, explanations and more charges, it was withdrawn by the Treasury Department.

Union's position had been clear: It wanted the *Sansinena* to bring needed crude oil from Alaska to California, and would use U.S. crews, thus creating more jobs. The ship would simply pass from Union's foreign service to Union's domestic service, and be operated by a U.S. crew at greater cost.

On May 16, 1971 a 70,000 ton tanker was launched at Baltimore, with Mrs. Fred Hartley breaking the traditional bottle of champagne across the bow. Its capacity was 560,000 barrels of crude. Following sea trials, it began regular Alaska-California runs in the fall. It was named *Sansinena II*, on the premise that a Sansinena should have been making that run all along.

In December, 1976 the original *Sansinena*, on long-term charter to the company, exploded in Los Angeles Harbor from unknown causes. The explosion resulted in the deaths of eight persons, total loss of the vessel, and damage to the adjacent dock and nearby buildings. Insurance to cover most of the property and other losses was carried by Union as well as by the tanker's owners.

In 1972 and 1973, charters were arranged for two 35,000 ton tankers to carry products between West Coast refineries and terminals. They were named the *Santa Paula* and the *Santa Clara*. The latter was put on a "triangle route" replacing a chartered ship previously on that route.

As explained by Marine Manager Glen Burk, this was an innovation to decrease costs. Tankers normally had carried products to Hawaii and come back in ballast, or carried crude from Alaska and returned there in ballast.

The *Santa Clara*, after discharging products in Hawaii, went in ballast to Alaska and carried crude from there to California. Tanks then were cleaned out so products could be loaded, and the process repeated. The ship was operated in ballast only one third instead of one half the time.

Then came a super bargain in supertankers. Demand in the early and mid

'70's had created a tanker glut. More and more huge supertankers were built. Where the 123,000 deadweight ton *Lake Palourde* had been one of the world's largest in 1967, by 1975 there were tankers in service of more than 480,000 deadweight tons. By December, 1975 there was an estimated 45 million tons of idle tanker capacity worldwide.

Union had an opportunity and took it. In mid-1976 a four year old 266,000 ton VLCC (Very Large Crude Carrier) was bought at about 50¢ on the dollar, a real bargain at $17 million. Marine Supervisor Tom Sheehan reported that it would be named *S.S. Coalinga* after one of Union's large California oil fields. It had a 1909 counterpart by the same name, the comparative sizes being shown below:

	S.S. Coalinga	
	1909	1976
Capacity in bbls.	80,000	2,000,000
Deadweight tons (DWT)	10,000	266,000
Length	485 feet	1,086 feet
Speed	10 knots	15 knots
Draft	27 feet	72 feet

Due for service early in 1977, it is scheduled to carry foreign crude to terminal facilities leased at Curacao, Netherlands Antilles, pending completion of U.S. facilities capable of handling such ships offshore Louisiana. Meanwhile, two 50,000 ton tankers were chartered to transship the crude from Curacao to East Coast and Gulf of Mexico ports.

By the end of 1976 the company's marine fleet consisted of 13 owned and chartered tankers and supertankers, plus other smaller vessels, with the capacity to carry about 7 million barrels. The 266,000 deadweight ton *Coalinga* would replace one of the chartered supertankers in 1977.

Another basic factor in Union's transportation system was the pipeline for carrying crude to refineries and products to marketing terminals.

Here there were important differences between the Union and Pure Oil systems.

DOWN THE WAYS *The Sansinena II, built in Maryland to carry crude oil between Alaska and California, slides into the water after launching.*

Oil companies in the West developed their own pipeline systems. There were subsequent additions, though none of great length. Among them was a new pipeline from the Los Angeles Refinery to Los Angeles International Airport, completed in 1966. Loren Grandey, manager of pipelines for the 76 Division's Western Region, reported that this increased efficiency and improved service to jet fuel customers.

The old Pure Oil refineries and marketing terminals were served primarily by a network of common carrier pipelines, both crude oil and product, that had developed east of the Rockies. Also involved was a nationwide network of natural gas pipelines.

The company was able not only to supply its own requirements but also to trade crude oil when advisable virtually all over the United States.

Claude Brinegar has said that knowledge of the national logistical supply and demand system gained at Pure Oil was a tremendous asset to Bill McConnor at the time he was named president of the Union 76 Division in 1973, when Brinegar resigned to become Secretary of Transportation in President Nixon's Cabinet. Brinegar returned to Union in February, 1975, as senior vice president, corporate affairs, after resigning from then President Ford's Cabinet.

As explained by Jim Baird, manager of pipelines and marine for the Union 76 Division's Eastern Region, common carrier pipelines normally have been joint ventures with several potential users sharing construction and operations costs in established proportions, as well as any profits.

The largest diameter crude oil pipeline in the western hemisphere, called Capline, runs from southern Louisiana to central Illinois. This 40-inch line with a current capacity of 600,000 barrels per day was completed in 1968, and Union has a 13.2 percent interest. Lines also were completed connecting it with Union's offshore Louisiana production and the Chicago Refinery, for which it subsequently supplied 40 percent of the crude required.

Capline's capacity was increased by about 50 percent in 1974, by adding six new pumping stations and enlarging others. A second dock capable of accommodating 80,000 ton tankers also was added at the southern end of the line at St. James, Louisiana. A third such dock was completed in 1976.

Capacity of the 26-inch, 205-mile line connecting Capline's northern end with Chicago area refineries also was increased by over 50 percent, through new pumping facilities, to over 400,000 barrels a day.

Provision was being made to accommodate the huge supertankers in operation during the '70's. A consortium of twelve (six by 1976) oil companies—including Union—was planning to build the Louisiana Offshore Oil Port (LOOP). Included in the project was a 78-mile pipeline connecting LOOP with Capline. But first a governmental permit was needed, and the application for this weighed in at 60 pounds of paper!

Capacity of a key pipeline designed to move products between Texas and New Jersey, the Colonial Pipeline, in which Union had a 4.4 percent interest, was increased by 1968 to over one million barrels per day.

Then in 1969 Union acquired a 26 percent interest in the Wolverine pipeline,

MAIN ARTERY *Giant pipes are part of the Capline project which moves crude oil from the Louisiana gulf coast to Illinois.*

a 16-inch products line from Hammond, Indiana to Detroit and Toledo. During the year a 40-mile extension was completed to connect this line with the Chicago Refinery and compensate for disposing of Pure's Toledo Refinery.

By 1976 these and other pipelines—both east and west—had created a transportation system of 9,100 miles of raw material lines, and 7,100 miles of product pipelines, of which Union either was the owner or had an interest.

And this did not include a 1⅔ percent interest in the $7 billion, 800-mile pipeline being constructed by Alyeska (a group of oil companies) from Alaska's North Slope to Valdez, an ice-free port on the state's southern coast. This line was conceived in 1969 and originally scheduled for 1972 completion for just under $900 million. Environmental, governmental, and other delays plus inflation septupled the cost and delayed completion for at least five years. In 1970 Kenny Vaughan, then a senior vice president before retiring in 1972, foresaw this when he told the Executive Committee one day that "we won't have to worry about the engineering problems of crossing the Yukon nearly so much as the political problems of crossing the Potomac."

In 1969 Union's minority interest in the Minnesota Pipeline Company and Great Northern Oil Company was sold for $30 million, an after tax gain of $19 million.

Efficiently transporting quality products to market is important. But as sales managers in a wide variety of industries keep reminding salesmen, nothing really happens until a sale is made.

The demand for gasoline was increasing rapidly until the OPEC countries created the crisis of late 1973. New cars grew bigger and thirstier and there were more of them. People drove more. Pollution controls and safety devices caused lower miles per gallon.

Between 1965 and 1972 U.S. demand for gasoline increased 39 percent. Service stations construction boomed, and by the end of 1972 there were 228,000

PROMOTION CRAZE
Receptionist Cathy Wilson shows off a multitude of "76 satellites," a spectacularly successful marketing promotion.

service stations across the nation. Union followed this building trend, and many of its stations were in the "300R" residential style which Mrs. Lyndon B. (Lady Bird) Johnson, when heading the national "Keep America Beautiful" campaign, had called "an inspiration to travelers and residents alike."

An important element in the station building program was expansion of the Auto/Truckstop system inherited from Pure Oil. The one in Calumet, Illinois likewise received the commendation of Lady Bird Johnson, this time in the form of an award she presented to Bill McConnor.

These large, expensive (upwards of $2,500,000) specialized facilities are located on 10 to 20 acre parcels mostly at interstate highway interchanges about 200 miles apart. Volume of diesel fuel, gasoline and other petroleum products usually exceeds 500,000 gallons per month for a good station. In addition to repair facilities and message service there is a restaurant, store and place to sleep. By 1976 Union had more than 300 Auto/Truckstops on major highways.

Combination gasoline-car washes also were becoming increasingly important as a means of selling gasoline as were stations located in major shopping centers.

Gasoline price wars flared intermittently until the early 1970's, and giveaways and games became a competitive necessity.

A "satellite promotion" was perhaps the most spectacular. Customers in the West, when stopping at Union stations, received small orange styrofoam balls emblazoned with a blue "76 Union" emblem. Motorists sported these reminders of space-age enthusiasm on their cars' radio antennas.

"One of the hottest crazes to hit the West since hula hoops," reported *Seventy Six* magazine.

Another Union promotional program, inherited from Pure Oil, has been termed "an investment in safe driving." This was the Performance Trials held since 1959 at Florida's Daytona International Speedway under the supervision of the National Association of Stock Cars, Inc. (NASCAR). New car models competed against each other in braking, acceleration and fuel economy. The cars were grouped by classes, based on similar price and performance characteristics. Three days of exacting tests simulated actual driving conditions. Complete comparative test results were published as a service to the public.

In 1974, responding to the concern for automobile fuel economy that had been created by the Arab oil embargo, Union introduced a special fuel economy test under actual road and highway conditions and published the results. This provided valuable data for comparison with the published results of EPA testing done in laboratories.

In 1970 credit card processing was centralized and further computerized in San Francisco. Rental car and motel arrangements via credit card were expanded, and mail order merchandise and insurance were made available to credit card customers.

But meantime the energy crisis was developing.

The main problem, as Fred Hartley pointed out, was energy consumption.

In the five years ending with 1967, gasoline demand had increased at an annual growth rate of 3.3 percent. During the next five years demand spurted at an annual growth rate of 5.2 percent, an increase of 57 percent over the previous rate.

Motor gasoline usually hovered around 50 percent of Union's refinery production, but it was not the only factor in the marketplace. Sales of fuel oil were decreasing, as environmental regulations restricted power plants' burning of high sulfur fuel. The sale of diesel fuel and lubricants to transportation firms and others was increasing. Heating oil remained a substantial seasonal factor in the East, according to R. E. "Bob" Robbins, Eastern Region marketing vice

SELF SERVING *Reflecting changing trends in retail marketing, this service station has been especially designed to test self service, although major emphasis remains on full service.*

president. But it was the marketplace gyrations of motor gasoline of which the public was most aware. At Union there were some 14,000 retail outlets marketing gasoline in approximately 45 states by 1976.

With the shortage resulting from gasoline demand increasing faster than supply, by April, 1973 Union had instituted an allocation program as had other major oil companies. It was based on a percentage of a customer's purchases in a like period of 1972.

Rigid controls on gasoline prices made it unprofitable to import extra supplies of gasoline. Tankers in service would continue to bring in their cargoes of crude, but shipping was short and transportation costs way up. Chartering additional tankers to bring in more crude at extra cost to produce government price controlled gasoline did not make economic sense.

Then the public seemed to suspect a shortage, and to demand "fill 'er up" at every service stop.

Had the industry been able to raise prices, consumption might have been slowed. But Joe Byrne, Union's Western Region marketing vice president, related an incident that reflected the mood of some.

With gasoline short, a dealer on California's State Highway No. 1 was about out. He put up 89.9¢ on his price sign rather than "no gas," figuring that if customers came in needing a gallon to go a few miles to someone else he'd explain and sell a gallon.

TRAFFIC JAM *This was a common scene at service stations everywhere in the wake of gasoline shortages brought about by the Arab oil embargo in the fall of 1973.*

A Continental rolled in and the driver said "fill 'er up."
"Did you look at the price?" the dealer asked.
"I'm in a helluva hurry," the man said. "I don't care if it's a dollar a gallon, fill 'er up!"
And the dealer did.
Why didn't the oil companies warn the nation of the impending shortage? They did, and had for years. But few listened. There seemed to be plenty of gasoline and other petroleum products. And all cheap.
Union, for example, in its 1970 Annual Shareholders Report pointed out the impending supply shortage as it related to low crude oil and product prices.
Few listened as the chorus of warnings swelled until October, 1973, when Arab states at war with Israel announced an embargo of shipments of oil to nations that were Israel's friends.
During the embargo the gasoline shortage became acute and lines were forming at service stations. License plate numbers determined which day gasoline could be purchased. Stations closed. With the lifting of the embargo in March of 1974 gasoline lines and memories were shortened. Later in 1974 shortages had disappeared, there was an ample though costly—because of high crude oil prices—supply of crude oil and gasoline.
Prior to the imposition of new price controls on the oil industry in 1973, retail pump prices for regular grade gasoline had hovered around the 35¢-40¢ per gallon level. By 1976 they had risen to the 60¢-65¢ per gallon level. Every penny of that substantial increase had been controlled under Federal regulations. Those who accused the oil industry of blame for the high prices had forgotten that OPEC's crude oil prices were five times higher over the same period.
Hartley, in a 1975 interview, told of a customer's finding and sending in a 1916 sales slip showing 19¢ a gallon. Union's economists were instructed to compute what 19¢ currently would be, allowing for inflation. They came up with 95¢.
"That, adding 13¢ for taxes, would make gas sell today for over $1.00 per gallon," Hartley said. "Our men of science and engineering are responsible for the fact that gasoline prices are not that high today."
While there were some advocates for removing price controls from the only industry which still had them, there was much Congressional opposition based largely on fear of runaway gasoline price increases. Hartley pledged in August, 1975 that Union would not increase the price of gasoline for the rest of the year by more than 2¢ a gallon if the government would eliminate price controls and the tariff on crude oil. This pledge was quoted by President Ford and in Congress and widely applauded, but the government took no positive action.
During periods of gasoline shortages, Union's policy was not to advertise gasoline but rather advocate efficient utilization of fuel, citing the excellence of Union products and services, including the benefits of using unleaded gasoline.
Union brand tires, batteries and accessories, and the Union Certified Service program received increased stress. The latter was a major marketing program in which Union led the industry. Developed by Ted Rathbone working with Fred

OVERSEAS OPERATOR

M. S. Thomson, corporate administrative vice president, also serves as president of the Union 76 Overseas Division, responsible for marketing crude oil and petroleum products outside the North American continent.

Hartley when he was in charge of marketing in the early 1960's, they built a dealer's backroom business. This meant more volume and profit for both dealer and company.

Two other basic marketing trends developed during the decade.

Independent marketers were taking an increasing share of the retail gasoline market. To reduce costs, many offered only minimum facilities and virtually no services. They simply pumped gas and sold lots of it, sometimes at less than a major brand dealer's cost. Regulations gave them a big advantage.

When the shoe pinched during the Arab boycott, many closed their stations temporarily.

One survey estimated that independents' share of the market increased from about 20 percent in 1971 to over 30 percent in 1976.

Such independents had existed long before the 1960's, and with the idea of beating by joining, secondary outlets were formed by many majors.

Several secondary outlets selling lower grades of gasoline were formed by Union at various times. They included Harbor, Super Par and Westway.

Harbor was the largest with 100 stations in California, Oregon and Washington. In the early 1960's, over $5 million was spent on new buildings and improvements. The operation nevertheless was unprofitable. In 1969, a decision was made to sell.

No buyer for the complete package was found. So sales were made piecemeal.

The other trend of the decade was to self-service whose buyer filled his own tank.

In some areas, chains of huge self-service stations developed, with some stations pumping as much as 300,000 gallons a month. Highly automated facilities were designed, with one cashier controlling all operations and collecting as drivers left.

More commonly, one pump island at a major service station was devoted to self-service.

The emergence of self-service was probably the decade's most striking change in the retail marketing of gasoline. Authorities estimated that only six percent of the nation's service stations were offering self-service in 1974, but by 1976 almost one-third were doing so.

In addition to its domestic marketing, Union also is active on a smaller scale in the Orient. It has developed a substantial market in Japan, where A. R. "Oz" Ousdahl is president of Unoco (Japan) Ltd. Maruzen Oil Company, Ltd., a major Japanese refiner and marketer in which Union owns a substantial minority interest, is the principal customer, although there are others. During the 1970's more than 130,000 barrels of crude oil a day were sold to Maruzen, much of it from non-Union production.

Another subsidiary, Unoco Limited, is under the direction of president J. H. "Jim" McGee. Its business activities consist primarily of buying and selling crude oil from various suppliers and customers, including its parent company. Over the decade its sales by volume.more than doubled, and its total revenues in 1976 exceeded one billion dollars, over 10 times what they were in 1965, largely as a result of OPEC price increases.

With Kyung In Energy Co., Union is involved in selling fuel oil to power plants in Korea, and also in the retail service station business there. More than 100 outlets in Korea bear the sign of the 76. Jack Robertson, former Union retail sales manager in Phoenix, Arizona headed the operation as vice president, marketing.

Overall responsibility for marketing crude oil and petroleum products outside the North American continent has been assigned to the Union 76 Overseas Division, of which M. S. Thomson, corporate administrative vice president, is president.

EVOLUTION OF A TRADEMARK
Successive steps in the evolution of Union Oil's trademark, all in orange and blue, are shown. The current logotype was adopted in 1967.

CHAPTER SIXTEEN

Pushing Into Petrochemicals

IN THE PETROCHEMICAL FIELD, two Union Oil subsidiaries are using natural gas or refinery products in producing various chemicals.

Collier Carbon & Chemical Corporation has been a wholly owned subsidiary for many years. In the sale of fertilizers and other agricultural chemicals especially, it has built an enviable position in west coast markets.

American Mineral Spirits Company, or Amsco, previously a Pure Oil division, is a leading marketer of solvents derived from refinery naphthas, and also offers such basics in petrochemical production as benzene, toluene and xylene.

Both of them are upgrading the value of products obtained from other Union divisions. They thus are not only providing markets but also augmenting Union profitability.

Equally important, they provide chemical expertise and market contacts that established a sound base for further expansion of the fast growing petrochemical field. Their combined revenues in this field are over $500 million annually, about five times higher than ten years earlier, with pre-tax profits keeping pace.

In 1965 Union had indicated natural gas reserves of more than one trillion cubic feet on the Kenai Peninsula in Alaska, but virtually no market that could be reached by pipeline. In a joint venture with Marathon Oil Company, a huge gas field had been discovered, but only comparatively small amounts could be used locally, some by the City of Anchorage, some by oil producers for repressurizing. There were two additional alternatives for its use:

It could be liquefied to natural gas and shipped by tanker to foreign markets, but not to the U.S., where the costs of producing and delivering the liquefied

DEDICATION

Fred Hartley is at the rostrum at dedication of Kenai, Alaska, chemical fertilizer plant of subsidiary Collier Carbon and Chemical Corporation. Seated on stage are Walter Hickel, Secretary of the Interior (left), and T. C. Henderson, president of Collier.

natural gas to the west coast were higher than the prices allowed by the Federal Power Commission for interstate gas.

Or it could be used to produce ammonia and urea, basic ingredients in many fertilizers.

Both possibilities were thoroughly explored, and the partners reached different conclusions. Marathon teamed with another company, which also had natural gas production in the area, in building a gas liquefaction plant.

Union's subsidiary, Collier, had a strong position in the west coast fertilizer market, and proven manufacturing and marketing capability was there ready to use.

Hartley recommended the fertilizer route. Both Union's and Collier's boards of directors agreed. Contracts were let in 1966 for a 1,500 tons-per-day ammonia plant and a 1,000 tons-per-day urea plant. The latter was a joint venture with Japan Gas-Chemical Company. The plants were designed to use, when operating at full capacity, over 60 million cubic feet of natural gas per day from Union's Kenai Field.

Collier originally had operated an ammonia plant at Brea, California. Its capacity was 375 tons per day. By 1964 it had become obsolete and a new 750 tons-per-day ammonia and urea plant, using an improved centrifugal process, was completed in 1966.

This marked Collier's entry into the urea market. Urea, processed from ammonia, is an increasingly important form of fertilizer and an important animal feed protein supplement. Further processed, it also is used to make adhesives and a variety of molded articles.

The Alaska plants were completed late in 1969. Over half of its employees were already residents of Alaska, although senior technical people were brought in from the "lower 48." Additional housing in Kenai was built by a subsidiary formed for the purpose, Woodland Development Company. It was administered for Collier by the Union real estate division.

At first the Kenai plant had some start-up problems, but operations had improved by 1972 and by 1974 were operating satisfactorily. With worldwide supplies of fertilizer short, export prices had more than tripled by 1974, and with the end of price controls in November, 1973, domestic prices also rose.

To serve the important Northwest market, a 480-foot barge of 15,500-ton capacity, the *Kenai*, was built and terminals were established on the Columbia River near Portland and at Hedges, Washington.

Some members of the Union board of directors felt in 1971 that the company should carefully consider whether or not to sell off Collier's fertilizer operations. It would be a major divestiture, since fertilizers constituted over two-thirds of Collier's business. The directors making the suggestion argued that Collier capital expenditures had been heavy, the rate of return on investment was low, the fertilizer market was depressed and many major oil companies were getting out of the business.

T. C. "Craig" Henderson, Collier president (and by 1976 a Union Oil Director), and John Abel, Union manager of corporate planning and evaluation,

COLLIER PRESIDENT

T. C. Henderson joined Union in 1949 and after serving in various management positions with Union and its chemical subsidiary, Collier Carbon and Chemical Corporation, was named Collier president in June, 1964. He was elected to Union's board of directors in February, 1976.

made a presentation to the board on July 26, 1971. They pointed out that capital expenditures had been heavy in relation to sales volume because new plants were being built. Start-up expenses for the new plants had reduced earnings. Price controls had minimized profit margins.

But Collier was the largest supplier of fertilizer on the West Coast, a market using over 1.5 million tons per year of contained nitrogen and growing at a rate of about 100,000 tons per year. With the area's largest and most modern plants and most efficient distribution system, Collier should be able to sell profitably despite the usual price fluctuations in the market. In addition, Henderson had recommended, and Hartley had authorized, expansion of the profitable company-owned and franchised fertilizer retail outlets. Collier also had developed substantial export capability to take care of domestic surplus.

As he had when the no-lead gasoline problem arose, Hartley argued against following the example of others in the industry. Most of them, he pointed out, were heavily involved in the middle west and south. Collier was strong on the West Coast, had a more than ample supply of natural gas in Alaska and had the industry's newest and most efficient plant to process it. The directors agreed.

In 1972, Collier's operating profit set a new record. It increased substantially in succeeding years. And the final portion of Collier's once substantial long-term debt to Union was retired in 1974.

In 1974, Union's directors authorized construction of a second plant at Kenai, more than doubling production of ammonia and urea there. It initially was projected to cost $165 million, more than twice the $65 million cost of the comparable first plant. Before completion, this was to be up to over $235 million, considerably more than Collier's total capital expenditures since 1965.

Virtually all of the original plant had been built in Alaska. Contracts for the second plant specified modular construction at Anacortes, Washington. Over 100

MODULAR CONSTRUCTION

Modular units for an expanded Collier plant in Alaska are loaded on a barge at Anacortes, Washington, for assembly at the new site.

modular units approximately 40 feet by 100 feet and weighing from 400 to 600 tons each were shipped by barge to Kenai, where they would be placed on foundations and welded together. This pleased the local population, which had no desire to be inundated by a flood of construction workers.

Prior to opening the new plant a training program was established in cooperation with the Kenai Community College, to prepare existing employees for more complex jobs and to develop new technicians from the local area.

Meanwhile environmental problems had appeared at the first plant which was discharging small amounts of nitrogen into waste water. The amount had been carefully planned. Research had determined that the upper portion of Cook Inlet, on which the plant was located, was very short of nitrogen needed for abundant growth of marine life. The 9,600 pounds of nitrogen discharged per day should be beneficial. To make sure the effect was beneficial, for several years young salmon were grown and thrived in pens at the waste water outlet. In some areas of the world, nitrogen is deliberately fed to breeding waters.

In 1975, however, EPA ruled that a blanket regulation limiting nitrogen discharge to 3,200 pounds per day would apply by 1977, regardless of the local situation and needs of marine life. To comply meant that Collier would have to spend nearly $3 million for additional treatment facilities, with the strong probability it ultimately would be called upon to return to a higher nitrogen discharge to aid marine life.

On October 15, 1974 the barge *Kenai*, under tow off Baranof Island, broke loose in heavy seas, drifted ashore and was wrecked on the rocks. Collier had lost its means of transporting ammonia and urea to the fertilizer-hungry Northwest. Nor was a suitable replacement immediately available under terms of the Jones Act. The *Kenai* had been designed to carry both ammonia and urea. U.S. vessels were available to handle the granular urea but only foreign vessels were available to handle ammonia which is liquefied at about –28 degrees F. With the loss of the *Kenai*, a waiver of the Jones Act was requested of the Treasury Department with strong farmer backing, until a ship to handle both ammonia and urea could be built. It was granted.

Construction of a 23,000-ton refrigerated tanker was ordered for completion late in 1977, at a cost of approximately $70 million. It would supply the Portland terminal and a new terminal being built at Sacramento to better serve California's Sacramento and San Joaquin valleys. A ten-year contract also was entered into under which Pacific Inland Navigation Co. would operate a pair of barges to transport Collier urea between Kenai and West Coast ports.

When the Union-Pure Oil merger was completed, Collier's marketing area was greatly expanded through a Pure Oil subsidiary, Pure Gas & Chemical Co., selling fertilizer in the Midwest under the brand name of PureGro. In the early 1960's Collier had acquired a fertilizer marketer, the Pacific Guano Company. The PureGro name fit both operations perfectly, so the businesses were combined as the PureGro Company.

Collier sells through PureGro independent retailers and Brea Agricultural Service; the latter conducts a franchise type operation with dealerships managed by independent businessmen under contract to Collier. Both aggressively and successfully sought new outlets. By 1976 PureGro territory included the West Coast, Rocky Mountain states, and some of the Midwest. Brea Agricultural Service units were selling from Texas through the West Coast. By 1976 sales had increased over 500 percent for the two, representing more than 50 percent of the dollar value of all Collier chemical sales.

Animal feed supplements are designed to comprise 5 percent to 10 percent of the diet of cattle while simultaneously improving the nutritional quality of the feed. Working with scientists at the Research Center, Collier developed a group of feed supplements tailor-made to fit the particular requirements of cattle in various parts of the West Coast and Rocky Mountain states. These supplements

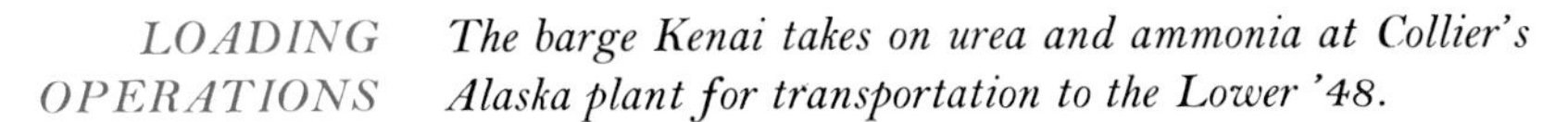
LOADING OPERATIONS *The barge Kenai takes on urea and ammonia at Collier's Alaska plant for transportation to the Lower '48.*

permit the animals to put on considerably more weight in a shorter time and at less cost.

Also working with Research, effective anti-crustants for problem soils were developed by Collier. Many western soils have a high clay and silt content. When they dry after watering, a hard, cement-like layer forms atop the soil. Farmers call it "crusting." Often seedlings cannot penetrate the crust and die. Even survivors grow slowly. The yield is smaller. Bio-degradable latex emulsions using Amsco latex were developed to solve the problem. Sprayed on the seed bed at or after planting, they form a porous, plastic film which prevents crusting, yet is easily penetrated by seedlings.

Sulfur produced as a waste product at Union refineries was being sold to industrial users by Collier. Sales of the normal commercial forms declined during the 1970's, but a unique and profitable product called POPCORN® sulfur was showing gratifying sales increases.

Developed in 1971 with Research, it had advantages over common "ground" sulfur for both agricultural and industrial use. Formed in tiny balls, like popcorn, it eliminated severe dusting problems as well as the danger of fire through spontaneous combustion, both of which are experienced in handling the conventional form. It also proved especially good for use in acidifying soil to improve yields.

Collier's original business, carbon products, continued to grow during the decade, with sales approximately quadrupled. It completed calcining kilns at Union's Santa Maria Refinery in 1966, at its Rodeo, California plant near Union's San Francisco Refinery in 1968, and adjacent to Union's Chicago Refinery in 1971.

Other plant additions included a 300-ton per day liquid carbon dioxide plant adjacent to Union's Los Angeles Refinery and additions for nitric acid, ammonium nitrate and urea at Brea.

Chemicals, including agricultural fertilizers, were an increasingly important part of Collier's sales and contributed about 85 percent of total sales in 1976.

Once regarded as a laboratory oddity, a "super carbon" of outstanding properties is produced by Poco Graphite, Inc., a Collier subsidiary in Decatur, Texas, headed by Vice President Robert Carlson.

This product has many uses that are as diverse as its unusual characteristics—it can be found in digital watches and calculators, jewelers' benches, on the moon and Mars, in machine shops and even inside human bodies. Since the "super carbon" can withstand enormous heat and pressures, its original use was intended for the manufacturing of shields to protect space vehicle nose cones during re-entry to the earth's atmosphere.

Most carbons have a tendency to swell when bombarded with radioactive particles, but Poco graphite has a great resistance to this. Since it has three times the strength of ordinary graphite, it was also used in the case for the compact atomic generators left on the moon and Mars which power the equipment used in transmitting signals back to earth.

Many other technologically advanced uses have been found for Poco graphite by Poco scientists working with Union Research. There are eight major markets

THANK YOU, POCO

Hillis O. Folkins, a developer of Poco graphite at Union's Research Center, utilizes a synthetic heart valve made from the material he helped create.

where the properties of the multifaceted carbon are inestimable—in electronics, metallurgy, opto-electronics (the application of graphite in lasers), mechanical carbons, nuclear projects, electro-chemical, aerospace and in electrical discharge machines.

Because of its high strength and uniformity, Poco graphite is used as the basic material in manufacturing artificial heart valves. Hillis O. Folkins, one of the scientists originally involved in the research and subsequent development of Poco graphite at the Research Center, found that one of the lives the substance has saved is his own. In 1973 a damaged aortic valve in Folkins' heart was found to be defective. It was replaced with a synthetic valve made from the material he had helped develop—Poco graphite.

Today Poco graphite is being used throughout the United States and Europe and in such countries as Japan, New Zealand, Mexico, Venezuela and Australia.

The production of Poco graphite involves the most esoteric technology in which Union Oil is involved.

Union's Amsco Division, which became part of the company with the Pure merger, already was a leading marketer of solvents widely used in many industries. Since then it has been making an expanding contribution to Union's operations. Amsco is a highly specialized marketer, developing from a tank car broker of petroleum solvents to a customized seller of industrial solvents. No longer is it necessary for solvent users to choose from the limited number of solvents offered by petroleum refiners primarily interested in simplifying operations and developing the fast growing gasoline market.

Amsco marketing men and technicians work to provide a product tailored to the customers' needs, and in any size or quantity from a small container to large bulk shipments. It is a customizing operation, and Union refineries back it up by producing the specialized solvents needed.

In 1966 over a score of basic solvents were offered. By 1976 the number of blends offered ran into the hundreds. In 1965 there were 22 sales offices across the country, increasing to 36 by 1976. Distribution was handled through 40 storage points, served by more than 450 tank cars.

A substantial export business had been done for many years from Amsco headquarters in Murray Hill, New Jersey. When headquarters was moved to Palatine in 1967, an export office was established in New York City. By the early 1970's Amsco's international division was marketing in 25 countries under the leadership of then president Dorn Stewart, later vice president, refining and marketing, for Union's 76 Division Eastern Region.

After reorganization of the Pure refinery system following the merger, Amsco products were produced principally by Union's Chicago and Beaumont refineries. Prior to 1969, sales in the western United States had been handled by Amsco Western, a joint venture with another company that was supplied primarily by its refineries. Late that year Union bought it out.

About 30 percent of Amsco's volume was sold to manufacturers of chemicals in 1966. This included such basic chemicals as benzene, toluene and zylene. About another 30 percent went to makers of paints and other protective coatings. The balance was scattered among makers of nearly everything from adhesives and metals to rubber and textiles, including even printing ink.

These percentages were about the same in 1976, said President Jack Schrage. But an important change had taken place. Air pollution regulations greatly

CUSTOMER CUSTOMIZER *The Amsco Division of Union Oil provides customized solvents, emulsions and hot melt adhesives to customers throughout the U.S. and 25 foreign countries.*

limited the percentages of aromatic hydrocarbons that could be emitted into the air in solvent vapors. The Chicago and Beaumont refineries installed Unisar hydrogenation units developed by Union's Research Department which made it possible to greatly reduce the aromatics and also to create more highly refined and stable solvents for sale by Amsco.

Another dramatic change took place in the products sold to paint manufacturers. Air pollution regulations were discouraging the use of petroleum solvents in paint, and manufacturers increasingly turned to water-based paints made with polymer emulsions. An Amsco Development Committee recommended that long-range strategy indicated Amsco should get into the polymer emulsion business. The Union Research Department was handed the problem of developing superior emulsions, and Amsco was authorized to determine how its potential in the field should be developed. It was decided to start with a small existing plant and expand from that base. In October 1966, a newly constructed polymer emulsion plant in Charlotte, North Carolina, was purchased.

By 1968, Research under Dr. Joe Walker, former Pure director of research and later an associate research director of Union, produced a real breakthrough in latex paint emulsion technology with introduction of a product that enhanced many of the desirable properties of earlier emulsions without their drawbacks. This provided exceptional durability and flexibility, good tint acceptance and color retention, good adhesion and surface protection. Subsequent products created a family of vinyl acrylic emulsions suitable for use in a wide variety of coatings, from highest quality exterior paints to economy-grade interior finishes.

Almost infinite variations were possible. Presently AMSCO-RES 3011 is being substituted in formulas developed for other polymers by more than 100 paint manufacturers. By 1972, production of vinyl acrylic polymers was ten times that in 1968, and it continued to grow. Plants built in Charlotte and in La Mirada, California, had their capacity tripled in a 1973 expansion.

Amsco also diversified its product line with development of improved hot melt adhesives for virtually every packaging application, from sealing packing cases to wrapping frozen foods. The line further was expanded into many other fields: book binding, carpet seaming tape, pressure sensitive labels, product assembly, lamination, construction. Amsco's type of customized customer service presented different problems in the solvents and polymer fields. When coating polymer emulsions first were developed, it was thought that the new products could be handled by Amsco's existing solvents sales force. "But when we got the polymer plants going and sales under way," said Schrage, "we soon found that a separate specialty sales force would be needed to handle the polymer products properly."

He also pointed out that Amsco's progress in customized chemical sales was providing a sound base on which to build in the chemical field during ensuing years. To which Union 76 Division President Bill McConnor added, "I think Amsco has growth opportunity in every one of its areas: solvents, polymer emulsions and hot melts." Amsco is making an expanding contribution to the successful operation of Union.

Being a chemical customizer definitely pays.

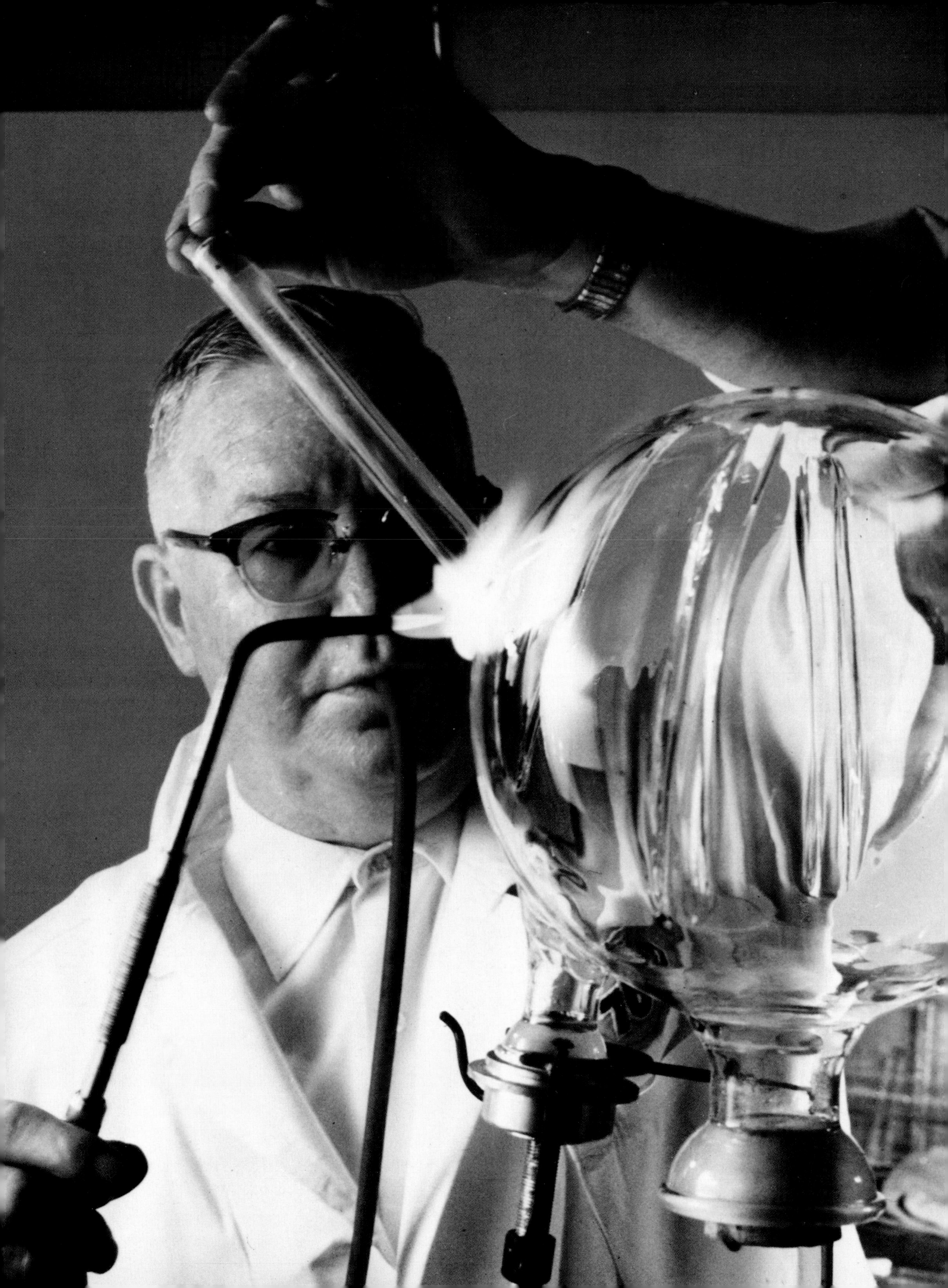

CHAPTER SEVENTEEN

Fueling Union's Forward Thrust

RESEARCH IS THE SCIENTIFIC CRYSTAL BALL of an energy company.

Research always has been a key to Union Oil's success.

The first petroleum laboratory in the West was organized by Union in 1891. In that year the principal reason for research was to remove odors and soot from kerosene.

Today, Union's Research Center stands on 40 acres at Brea, California, east of Los Angeles. The complex is manned by 600 research scientists, engineers and supportive personnel.

The center has fathered a steady stream of sophisticated processes and new products.

Union research scientists have received almost 4,600 United States and foreign patents. Two thousand of these still are active.

Other firms have been licensed to use Union processes. With still others, Union has arranged profitable exchanges of licenses.

By 1976 more than 550 Union-developed process units were licensed in 20 countries. Associate Director Bill Baral traveled the world over to discuss Union processes with prospective licensees, as Fred Hartley had done before him.

Income from this covered a substantial part of the Research Department's budget, thus materially reducing its costs. In addition, Union Oil divisions and subsidiaries enjoyed the fruits of this research.

One of the department's principal and most productive activities since 1965 was further development of Union's patented Unicracking process which was bringing in about half of Union's licensing revenue in 1976. The process, developed by a team headed by Hartley, then vice president of research, and Dr. W. E. Bradley, who succeeded him in the job, in simple language converts four barrels of low-grade crude oil into five barrels of gasoline. A basic objective of

DELICATE TOUCH

One of the many skilled technicians and scientists at the Union Research Center demonstrates glass blowing skill for shaping scientific apparatus.

the new development was to develop ways of processing heavier and heavier stocks and to remove sulfur from them.

With Unicracking-HGO (subsequently called Gofining) in 1967, the ability to remove sulfur from gasoline, jet fuel, and diesel fuel was expanded to heavy distillates. Fuel oil could be produced which would meet the specifications of utilities compelled to use low-sulfur fuel by environmental restrictions.

A plan employing the Unisar process, developed by a team headed by Dr. H. C. "Hal" Huffman, then associate director of research, came on stream at the Beaumont Refinery in 1969. It was of special significance in a pollution-conscious world as it reduced the quantity of highly volatile aromatics present in paint solvents and jet fuel.

The Beavon process came in 1971. It was named for David Beavon, of the Ralph M. Parsons Company, whose idea Research helped to develop. Existing processes removed about 90 percent of the sulfur from gases escaping to the atmosphere. Beavon increased this to 99.9 percent.

In 1976 a start-up of the world's first Unicracking-HDS (formerly called RESIDfining) was completed at Maruzen Oil Company's Chiba Refinery in Japan. The plant, developed in cooperation with Exxon, was designed to desulfurize 60,000 barrels of high sulfur content resid per day. At the heart of this

UNICRACKER

The 30,000 barrel per day Unicracker while under construction at San Francisco Refinery. Union and another company have licensed the process to other oil companies for use throughout the world.

RESEARCH HEADS

Dr. W. E. Bradley (left) who joined Union in 1931, was elected vice president of research in 1960 and a director in 1971. Dr. H.C. "Hal" Huffman, who joined the company in 1940, succeeded Dr. Bradley as vice president in December, 1973.

process is a new catalyst (RF-11) developed to convert the sulfur compounds in the feed stock to hydrogen sulfide and hydrocarbons. The hydrogen sulfide is then converted to elemental sulfur plus water. C. B. "Bud" Scott, director of environmental sciences, has noted that Union processes for removing sulfur and nitrogen—Unicracking, Unionfining, Gofining, Unisar, and Beavon—may be taking more of these pollutants out of atmosphere than almost any other company's processes.

Through all of this, expertise in catalysis was vital. Numerous profitable catalysts were created. A good example is N-100, developed in 1975 for the existing Unionfining process which desulfurizes light distillates. It was 35 to 55 percent more active and lasted far longer than the widely used N-21, vastly increasing refining efficiency and product profitability.

To Dr. Rowland C. Hansford, consultant, and Dr. John W. Ward, research associate, go much of the credit for catalysts used in hydrocracking. In 1976 The American Institute of Chemists presented Hansford with one of its annual distinguished awards, citing his work in that field.

The department, spurred on by President Hartley, also went a bit afield in 1975 and developed a catalyst for automobile exhausts. Its purpose: to convert noxious nitrogen oxide to the elemental nitrogen breathed in clean air. Automobile manufacturer tests proved it the most effective such catalyst developed to date.

In December 1973, Dr. Huffman succeeded Dr. Bradley as vice president of research. Back in the 1950's, Dr. Huffman had been an instigator of an important change in the department's procedures. Often, to make sure products were "the finest," unnecessarily high and costly specifications had been set. Product qualities were called for from which the customer received no real benefit.

CATALYST EXPERT *Dr. Rowland C. Hansford, research consultant, is seated behind a molecular model of the Unicracking-JHC catalyst. An international expert in the field of refining catalysts, Dr. Hansford has 73 patents in the U.S. and abroad.*

"Now let's determine what the customer actually needs for top performance," Dr. Huffman said. "Sometimes this is much less than our specifications call for. We'll be able to give the customer a more than satisfactory product and save both of us money." Just as improved refining processes created products that could be sold more profitably, so did more realistic specifications.

For marketing, research acted as a watchdog of quality, furnishing technical services required by marketers or customers and helping to maintain Union's reputation as a knowledgeable, progressive company.

Once, when environmental requirements backfired, Research came to the rescue. A special nozzle required to minimize vapors escaping when gasoline was pumped into an automobile, inadvertently permitted gasoline to flow back through the line so that the gasoline pump meter sometimes registered more gasoline delivered than actually reached the car's tank.

Associate Research Director Cloyd Reeg turned the problem over to Products Research Manager Bob Askevold and his assistant, Jim Keller. They came up with a nozzle with a rotating orifice which would prevent backflow by remaining in the proper position regardless of how it was inserted.

Research continued to be organized with a division counterpart for every major operating division of the company, each headed by an associate director. Divisions were set up for exploration and production, refining and products, engineering and development, petrochemicals, analytical and corrosion research, and technology sales.

Dr. Huffman summarized the department's objectives:

- To improve the company's ability to find and produce more crude oil and natural gas.
- To develop non-petroleum sources of materials to supply Union manufacturing plants.
- Conduct process and product research aimed at further economically attractive expansion and development of Union Oil Company.
- To furnish technical services to operating divisions, departments, and subsidiary companies.
- To sell Union technology to others.
- To serve as a training area for technical personnel.

Introduction of computer technology to both oil exploration and production problems made it possible to undertake and complete jobs that would have been impossible on a man-hour basis. John Sherborne, formerly an associate director, was one of the first to recognize its potential in these areas.

A more sophisticated use was the development of Union's patented UNISRCH or Unisearch, developed in the early '70's. It stands for Union Search and Retrieval System, developed by Dr. Homer Rea, a research engineer. Unisearch includes a filing system for storing an index of all scientific publications in a computer's "memory," and a "program" for telling the computer what information is wanted. The computer searches its memory for the wanted information. Then it displays the appropriate references on a cathode ray tube like a TV screen. The computer can handle up to 50,000 characters a second. (The standard teletype system prints 15 characters a second.)

NEEDLE IN THE HAYSTACK

UNISRCH is the name for Union's patented search and retrieval system for thousands of technical papers and articles. Dr. Homer Rea, who developed the system, holds a printout produced by the system.

Instead of toiling through a printed index and then calling for wanted files for manual delivery, Union scientists can in seconds search through more than 250,000 documents dating back more than 10 years.

The computer also is used to plot maps derived from aeromagnetic, geochemical, geophoto, gravity and seismic surveys which help to indicate where oil might be found.

By 1976, sophisticated technology from the nation's space program was being applied. Data regarding the earth's structure from surveys and electronic drilling logs were being fed to computers. High-speed tabulation and correlation of the stupendous amount of data then produces a three-dimensional geophysical map which enables the geophysicist to "see" below the surface and determine where oil or gas is most likely to be present.

Associate Director Dick Crog's exploration and production division used the science of palynology in helping exploration for oil. This becomes valuable when oil has evolved from organic matter deposited in fresh rather than salt water.

In the latter case, ancient seashells indicate possible oil-bearing strata, but they are absent when fresh water is involved, as is usually true in Alaska. Here fossil spores and pollens help to identify strata and their ages. This in turn facilitates proper identification of the geologic zones in an area, and the possibility of oil.

A technique which Research developed during the early 1970's working with production engineers often saves over $100,000 in drilling a single Gulf Coast well. In many wells, packer rings are put around the tubing to separate well zone intervals. These may become stuck to the casing, making recovery of the tubing difficult and costly. The technique involves Packawell, an oil base packer fluid developed by Research that solved the problem. Tubing can be pulled with less effort.

Another major production aid has been the development of unibeads. Researchers David Watanabe, Paul Fischer and Roland Krueger were instrumental in this process designed during the late 1960's to get more oil out of existing wells where "formation fracturing" is involved. In "fracturing," fluid is injected into a well at a rate so great the oil or gas-bearing formation is broken apart, or fractured, to permit increased flow to the well. Then sand is pumped in to hold the fracture open while permitting oil or gas to flow. Unibeads are tiny waxy beads pumped in with the sand to help "seal" the fracture and are formulated to last just long enough for the fracturing process to be completed. They are then dissolved by the oil or gas, which now can enter the well and surface in greater quantities.

Even after primary and secondary recovery techniques have been applied, it is estimated that between a half and two-thirds of the oil still remains in the ground, so major efforts continue in numerous techniques from injecting acids to use of steam and fire.

Perhaps the most promising method is Union's recently patented "Uniflood" process. This first injects chemicals that free the oil from the sand or rock grains to which it clings. Next water thickened by gelatin-like materials is pumped in to sweep the oil away. Finally water is injected under pressure to drive the viscous mass to the recovery wells.

Initial tests showed the Uniflood process produced up to 65 percent more oil than would have been recovered with water flooding.

In 1972, research on shale oil potential was intensified, principally under Associate Director of Research Arnold Kelley.

This meant improving the recovery method previously tested. Any recovery method must heat the shale to separate oil from it. Union researchers in years past had determined that upflow retorting is most efficient. This forces shale up through a retort by means of a solids pump.

Improvements had been designed in the laboratory. In October, 1973, a new experimental retort capable of processing three tons of shale a day was started. Designated "Retort B," it overcame problems of excessive heat and a tendency to fuse the raw shale particles together which resulted in the low yield present in the previous Retort A.

In another improved version of the retort, designated SGR (Steam Gas Recirculation), heat from a separate combustor was used to heat the retort. It also was used to generate steam to operate compressors and pumps.

The SGR process gave a liquid yield of 100 percent versus 75 percent from Retort A. Thermal efficiency, the percentage of energy in the oil shale that ends up in the form of oil and gas after deducting the energy required to operate the retort, was increased to 83 percent from the 73 percent of Retort B.

Also included was a hydrogenation process which, using a new research-developed catalyst, made it possible for the plant to produce refinery feed stock similar to crude oil directly from the raw shale oil. This eliminated intermediate refining that otherwise was necessary.

By 1976 the design basis had been completed for a commercial plant capable of processing 10,000 tons of oil shale a day to produce 7,300 barrels a day of shale oil.

ENHANCED RECOVERY *Union's Uniflood process to get more oil out of a reservoir employs chemicals to free oil from rock or sand grains. Treated water is pumped into the well to sweep the oil away and water under pressure then moves it to recovery well.*

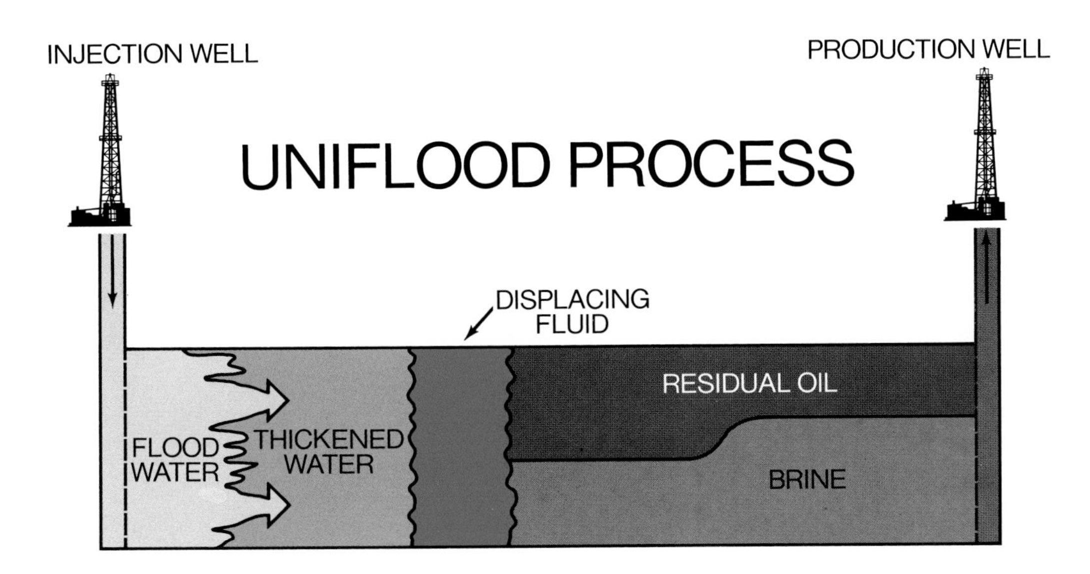

The petrochemicals division under Dr. Joe Walker recognized the changing nature of opportunities offered energy companies. The market for petrochemicals was booming; Union already was a factor in this through Collier Carbon & Chemical Company and American Mineral Spirits Company. Expanding market penetration was in order.

An important product development for Collier resulted from removal of sulfur in oil refining. Initially it comes out as elemental sulfur, and as molten sulfur can be transported only short distances by pipeline. When cast into slabs there are handling problems, as there are problems with dust from powdered form.

Senior Research Associate Dr. Don Young, working with the Collier Sales Service Engineering group in the early 1970's, found a way to process the sulfur into little balls that look like yellow popcorn. In the Union patented process, molten sulfur and water are pumped through a "gun." As they are sprayed out, the sulfur solidifies and the water runs off. This creates an easily handled, virtually dust-free form of sulfur, with particles that can be tailored in size from 1/16 inch up to ½ inch. It is called POPCORN® sulfur. In agriculture, POPCORN® sulfur proved ideal for acidifying soil. Another research team with Dr. Alex

POPCORN® SULFUR *Dr. Don Young, holder of many patents in the agricultural field, was instrumental in the development of this improved method for acidifying soil.*

Miller was helping Collier develop cattle feed supplements to improve the feed's nutritional qualities.

Working with the Poco Graphite operating staff, research develops new carbons, raw material resources and uses for its super strong product.

Some of the most intensive research activity in the petrochemical field has been carried on in association with American Mineral Spirits Company, a subsidiary of the Union 76 Division, in the development of polymer emulsions and hot melt adhesives.

With an eye to the future, Cloyd Reeg and his group also were seeking low-cost means of removing sulfur from coal, the most abundant fossil fuel.

Removing sulfur would permit much greater use of coal in electric power plants. By 1976 they had achieved removal of 65 percent of the sulfur in high-sulfur coal, using water solutions of compounds that take up sulfur. Economic feasibility had yet to be demonstrated.

They also attacked the problem from a different angle. Instead of costly removal of sulfur from coal, why not remove it from the stack gases after coal is burned? By 1976 a process had been developed in the laboratory that removed 90 percent of the sulfur dioxide and nitrogen oxides from stack gases when high-sulfur coal is burned. Again, economic feasibility remained to be demonstrated.

Expanding supplies of uranium—other than by traditional open-pit mining—for developing nuclear power is another research charge. Working with a Union subsidiary, Minerals Exploration Company, Dick Crog and his group in the early '70's came up with a leaching technique called "solution mining," a chemical method for extracting uranium from low-grade, buried ores that cannot be mined economically by open-pit methods. Injection wells carry a chemical into the ore body, separate the uranium from the ore and transport it in solution to a central recovery well. Solution from the well then is processed to recover the uranium.

There are times, in fact, when Union scientists are called upon to answer unusual cries for help. One came from San Francisco Refinery Manager Bill Stark in February, 1976.

A bulldozer was slicing off a hilltop on Union-owned land, to get fill dirt, when some members of the American Indian movement showed. An old Indian burial ground was being defiled, they claimed, and the work should stop.

Rather than start a new Indian war, Stark phoned Research for help.

Dr. Cortez Hoskins, manager of exploration research, whose hobby is archeology, was sent from Brea to the rescue. He demonstrated that there was an old burial ground nearby, but not where the bulldozer was digging. Shellfish had been a major part of the Indian diet in the area. Quantities of shells had littered the spots where they lived. Though buried by time, many were brought up by the digging of gophers and other animals.

Hoskins found such a location, with evidence of a burial ground nearby; far from the bulldozer's work site. The Indians were satisfied, Stark was thankful, work proceeded.

Once again Research had come up with the answer.

CHAPTER EIGHTEEN

Unearthing Buried Riches

OIL AND GAS EXPLORATION IS A GAMBLE, but a gamble worth the taking, because exploration and production provide the very lifeblood of the industry. That is where over $3 billion has been spent by Union during the Hartley years, representing more than two-thirds of its capital expenditures for that period. This compares with about 60 percent for the industry.

During the 1965-1976 period Union Oil produced 1.3 billion barrels of crude oil and 6.1 trillion cubic feet of natural gas. Production levels for 1976 were about 50 percent higher than they were at the beginning of the period.

As the demand for oil and gas has increased, so has the search for it. The hunt has grown worldwide, moving it more and more into offshore areas requiring ever greater drilling depths and skills.

One of Hartley's early actions as chief executive officer was to form an International Division to handle exploration and production abroad. This was in February, 1966.

He named 44-year-old Ray Burke, then vice president of exploration and production, to head up the new division. The Board promptly elected Burke a director, member of the executive committee, and a senior vice president. In 1973 he was put in charge of a newly formed Energy Resources group to be responsible for worldwide exploration and production activities for oil and gas, as well as geothermal.

"The decision to create the International Division," Hartley explains, "reflects our belief that oil and gas discoveries of the future are more likely to be made overseas, and in most cases offshore, where exploration techniques have reached a high state of development."

SYMBOL OF SEARCH

The only answer to whether oil or gas lies deep in the ground is what the drilling bit discovers. The worn three-cone, mill tooth bit (opposite page) symbolizes the continuing search to unearth buried riches.

FIRST INTERNATIONAL HEAD

Ray Burke, vice president of exploration and production, was promoted in 1966 to head Union's first International Division. He subsequently was elected a director and senior vice president in charge of all Energy Resources.

Union already was well represented in all major oil and gas provinces in the United States, and following the Pure Oil merger was ready to attain the same status in overseas areas. Soon its exploratory activities would surround the globe. And under the leadership of Burke and his two successors as head of the International Division, John Sloat and H.M. "Hal" Lian, there was a considerable degree of success.

Pre-tax profits from foreign operations were almost 30 percent of Union's total in 1976, up from roughly five percent 10 years earlier.

Indonesia's steaming jungles were a far cry from Union's domestic theater of operations. But it was here, off the east coast of Kalimantan (formerly Borneo), that Union would spend more than one-half billion dollars in the first seven years of one of its most successful overseas exploratory ventures. In oil production Union's east Kalimantan output is comparable to its output from the state of Louisiana, onshore and offshore.

The first well Union drilled offshore east Kalimantan found oil in August, 1970. It was located 12 miles offshore in the Balikpapan Basin, and tested at daily rates of 11,300 barrels of high gravity, low sulfur crude oil and 26 million cubic feet of gas from six zones. The 72,000 acre discovery block was held 50-50 with Japex Indonesia Limited, Union being the operator.

Negotiations for exploration activities in Indonesia had begun as early as 1959, when Francis Barker of the exploration and production division investigated opportunities.

The time was not ripe, but contacts continued. Later on, Hank Brandon, a general representative of the foreign operations department, was asked by Indonesian officials to originate a new type of agreement that would be a "first" for Indonesia. He suggested a "contract of work" arrangement.

In a speech on Indonesian Independence Day in August, 1961, then President Sukarno talked at some length about "production sharing," which included some of Brandon's suggestions. Other Indonesians made significant revisions in the

ATTAKA DEDICATION

C. M. "Chuck" Schwartz (center), head of Union's Indonesian operations, explains a model of the Attaka field to President Soeharto of Indonesia and General Ibnu Sutowo, president of Pertamina, Indonesia's state-owned oil company, at dedication ceremonies in 1973.

type of contracts to be offered to companies wanting to do exploration work in Indonesia. One of those most instrumental was General Ibnu Sutowo, later to become president of Pertamina, Indonesia's large and powerful state-owned oil company.

The most important new feature was that ownership of all oil and gas remained with the Indonesians. As contractors, however, oil companies had the right to a specified share of production over a period of time. Such share would be larger in the early stages to permit faster recovery of capital and operating costs, but considerably lower thereafter. This assured the Indonesians of a larger share of oil and gas than under former concession arrangements.

Final details of Union's production-sharing contracts with Pertamina were hammered out by Burke and his staff. Two contracts were signed. One early in 1968 covered the offshore north Sumatra area, and the other, later that year, covered east Kalimantan, both offshore and onshore.

C. M. "Chuck" Schwartz, who had been resident manager of Union's Australian operations, took over the Indonesian activities also, along with R. J. "Dick" Stegemeier. Schwartz has since become vice president for exploration of the International Division and Stegemeier vice president for southeast Asia.

The contracts remained in effect without material change until the drastic OPEC-inspired crude oil price increases which occurred in late 1973 and early 1974, and revisions to the contracts were made shortly thereafter. Then in 1976 further changes were agreed to after negotiations with General Piet Haryona, who had succeeded Sutowo as president of Pertamina, Minister of Mines Mohammad Sadli, and their staffs. The principal effect of the changes would be to stretch out the period over which costs are recoverable. This adverse development resulted in reduced exploratory activity.

After the original contract had been signed, a drilling barge left Long Beach, California in September, 1969, on a two month voyage to begin exploratory drilling in Indonesia. First assignment: offshore northern Sumatra. By March of 1970 a small natural gas discovery had been made. The rig moved to the east Kalimantan offshore area to make the initial large oil discovery there in August.

More wells confirmed the discovery. "Attaka" was suggested as a name for the field. It was the Indonesian name for a reef in the vicinity. Union's Japanese partners quickly agreed. In their language it meant something quite similar to the ancient Greek word, *Eureka* (I have found it).

By 1976 the Attaka field's 52 wells were producing over 100,000 barrels of crude a day from six platforms, and a cumulative total of well over 100 million barrels had been produced since the field came on in 1972.

"And," said W. K. "Bill" Lewright, vice president of operations for the International Division, "the field is still going strong." Additional drilling in the field continues.

Several other discoveries on the east coast of Kalimantan were made from 1972 to 1976. The Kerindingan, Melahin, Sepinggan and Yakin fields were producing small quantities of high grade, low sulfur crude by 1976. In these fields Union had a 100 percent interest in the contractor's share of the production-sharing contract.

The Santan Terminal, handling production primarily from Attaka field, was dedicated January 22, 1973 by President Soeharto, who succeeded Sukarno as head of state in 1965. Hartley and Burke were present for the opening ceremonies as were General Sutowo and the late H. Okada, president of Japex. Crude was pumped from offshore platforms through a pipeline to onshore storage at the terminal. Tankers of up to 125,000 deadweight tons then loaded from a monobuoy located some five miles offshore.

The relatively short two year time lag between discovery and delivery compares favorably with Union's Cook Inlet performance in Alaska five years earlier.

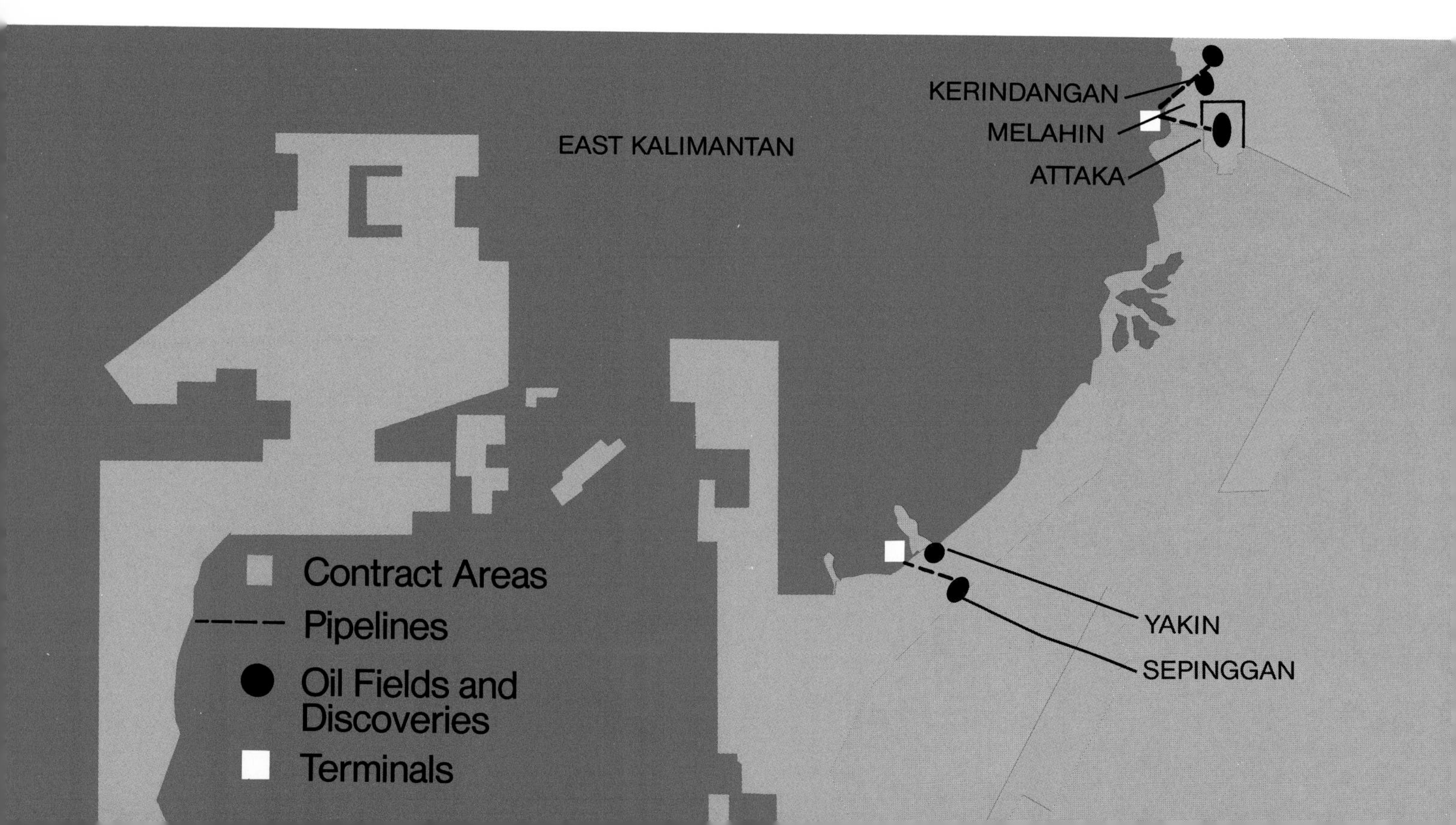

ON LOCATION *A helicopter view of the Wodeco VI drilling ship on location offshore East Kalimantan, Indonesia.*

Other discoveries on Union's Indonesian acreage were being made, the significance of which has not been evaluated.

A follow-up well to one of these had a bizarre background. It was accidentally drilled three miles away from the reef location decided upon, and was dry. The drilling platform was then set again, this time where it belonged. It dutifully confirmed an original gas discovery.

Burke recognized, even before commercial production had been established in the offshore east Kalimantan area, that adequate housing would be needed for both Indonesian and American personnel.

On a flight over the area he spotted Pasir Ridge, a former Japanese anti-aircraft base.

"That's the place," he said.

An entire community was designed—housing, water system, generating plant, schools, fire department and police facilities.

"I felt," Burke said, "that we should build a facility that would be attractive, serve its purpose, and be entirely compatible to the climate and neighborhood in which it was built."

Some 1,300 miles northwest of east Kalimantan, Union had an 80 percent interest in a five million acre concession off the east coast of Thailand. A gas and condensate discovery was made in January, 1973, followed by five more successful wells on several different structures. A 45 percent interest in 2.6 million additional acres was acquired in 1976.

Yet the future for successful production in the area remained cloudy. In 1976 Hartley and Burke held exploratory talks with the Thai industry minister and other officials to discuss their interest in piping gas to Bangkok from wells in the Gulf of Thailand capable of producing gas and condensate. If feasible, the gas would replace the fuel oil being used to generate electric power. Union's Japanese partner, Southeast Asia Petroleum Exploration Company (SEAPEC), also would share in the venture.

No final decision has been made because commercial gas reserves have not yet been proven. R. R. Roethke, vice president for natural gas of the International Division, is following the project. Additional exploration and appraisal wells are under way.

In the Andaman Sea off Thailand's west coast Union has a 24 percent interest in a five million acre block. Five exploratory wells were drilled without success in 1976 in depths of between 1,300 and 2,000 feet. These water depths are the deepest ever for Union Oil.

In the Persian Gulf, nearly halfway around the world from Union's headquarters, Union's oil seekers also were busy in the mid-1960's.

Iran was known to offer concessions on a 50-50 sharing basis, calculated on the highest bonus bids received.

Burke, then vice president of exploration and production, and John Sloat, then head of geophysical activities, had directed a study of geological possibilities. From their subsequent discussions with other companies a partnership evolved.

The partners' bid was successful, $25 million successful. Two other areas in Iranian waters of the Persian Gulf also were obtained. The three areas totaled some 3,100 square miles. The concession was for 25 years, with three five-year extensions. Union had a 12½ percent interest.

In December, 1965 a discovery well was completed by Lavan Petroleum

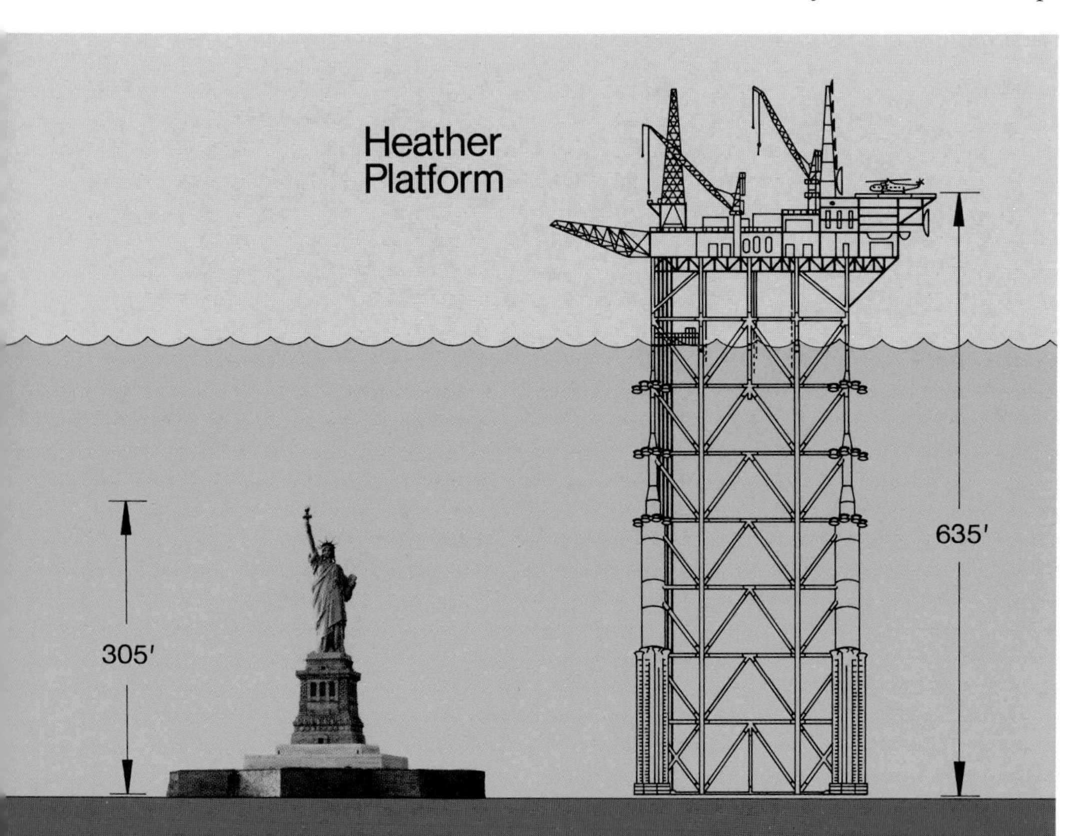

BIG, BIG, BIG!

The tremendous size of the Heather platform for the North Sea is indicated by an artist's conception comparing it to the Statue of Liberty.

Company as operator for the National Iranian Oil Company, Union and its three U.S. partners. It subsequently was rated by the *Oil & Gas Journal* as the 39th largest oil field in the free world, with crude oil reserves exceeding one billion barrels. It was named Sassan after an early Persian empire.

Sixteen wells had been drilled by 1968 to complete the initial development program, and 88 miles of 22-inch pipeline laid from the field to Lavan Island. During 1968 a tanker terminal was completed on the island. In November the first shipment of 506,000 barrels of crude oil was made.

Bachelor quarters for employees were constructed on the island. The men would fly in from Tehran for a two-week tour of duty, then fly back for a week off. Conditions for carefree living weren't exactly ideal. The island was barren and its weather mostly hot.

While Sassan was being developed another discovery was made in the Gulf. Sixty-five miles away a well came in in November, 1967. A second well came in early in 1968. By 1976 plans were being made to develop this field (Bahram) and lay a pipeline to Lavan Island.

The Sassan field produced about 200,000 barrels a day for several years, declining to around 160,000 by 1976. A program is underway to drill additional development wells, plus water injection wells for pressure maintenance, to restore the field's 200,000 barrel per day production.

The North Sea was not as hot as Iran. But it was the wildest exploration area with the wildest weather Union had encountered. And the wildest dollar costs, too.

Here in 1973, Union and three partners were awarded four blocks in the United Kingdom sector. They added up to about 200,000 acres in which Union had a 31 percent interest, and was to act as operator.

But in the North Sea nature seemed determined to prevent exploring for oil.

In winter, temperatures drop well below freezing and winter storms hurl huge waves across the waters, battering everything in their path. The force of some giant waves has been calculated as great as 6,000 pounds per square foot. They have been known to lift a concrete block weighing 2,600 tons. Only during the summer are there sufficient periods of the calm needed for seismic exploration. And when it comes to costs, even a 12,000-foot exploratory well can exceed $5 million.

One of the most promising blocks on which Union was to be operator was located at 61° north latitude, about the same as Union's Cook Inlet fields offshore Alaska. Under W. A. "Bill" Sax, resident manager of Unionoil Company of Great Britain, Union and its partners arranged for the leasing of a semi-submersible, $35 million drilling rig, West Venture, owned by a Norwegian company. It would be towed to the drilling location. Positioned there, it would sink lower in the water for stability, be anchored and get to work.

This nautical giant's legs are 30 feet thick. Her drilling derrick stands 160 feet up, 70 feet higher than the more normal rigs used in the Gulf of Mexico. The 23,400 ton heavyweight could drill in water up to 1,000 feet deep and operate in rugged seas.

"From up there," said Exploration Manager Ed East, "it was like being up on the Eiffel Tower and looking down into the middle of the ocean!"

The West Venture's first venture was successful. In December, 1973 a discovery was made on 49,800-acre Block 2/5 about 76 miles off the Shetland Islands in 472 feet of water. It tested 9,000 barrels a day from two zones from a depth of roughly 10,000 feet. The next well was even better, but the third was dry. The fourth was productive and proved up the field, which was named Heather.

A production platform was ordered, to stand in nearly 500 feet of water. Production was expected in early 1978, and to increase to about 50,000 barrels a day in 1979. Union's share would be about 15,000 barrels per day. And like its Trading Bay counterpart in Alaska's Cook Inlet, secondary recovery by water injection was to be used at the outset to increase oil recovery to the maximum efficient rate.

In August, 1976 an agreement was signed to take a 10.25 percent interest in the pipeline from Ninian field to the Shetland Islands, with an interest in the oil terminal at Sullom Voe in the Shetlands. A feeder pipeline would be built to connect the Heather field with the Ninian's central platform.

Rough weather and angry seas were not new to several of the men who did the Heather field job. Drilling superintendent Fred Simmons, John Imle, platform project manager, and East all had served with Union in Alaska.

A second discovery was made March 4, 1975 on Block 9/12, 75 miles south of the Heather field. Development of this second block was delayed until some political and economic questions were settled. With the size of the new field undetermined, and a platform cost of $100 million, further Heather field development made more sense.

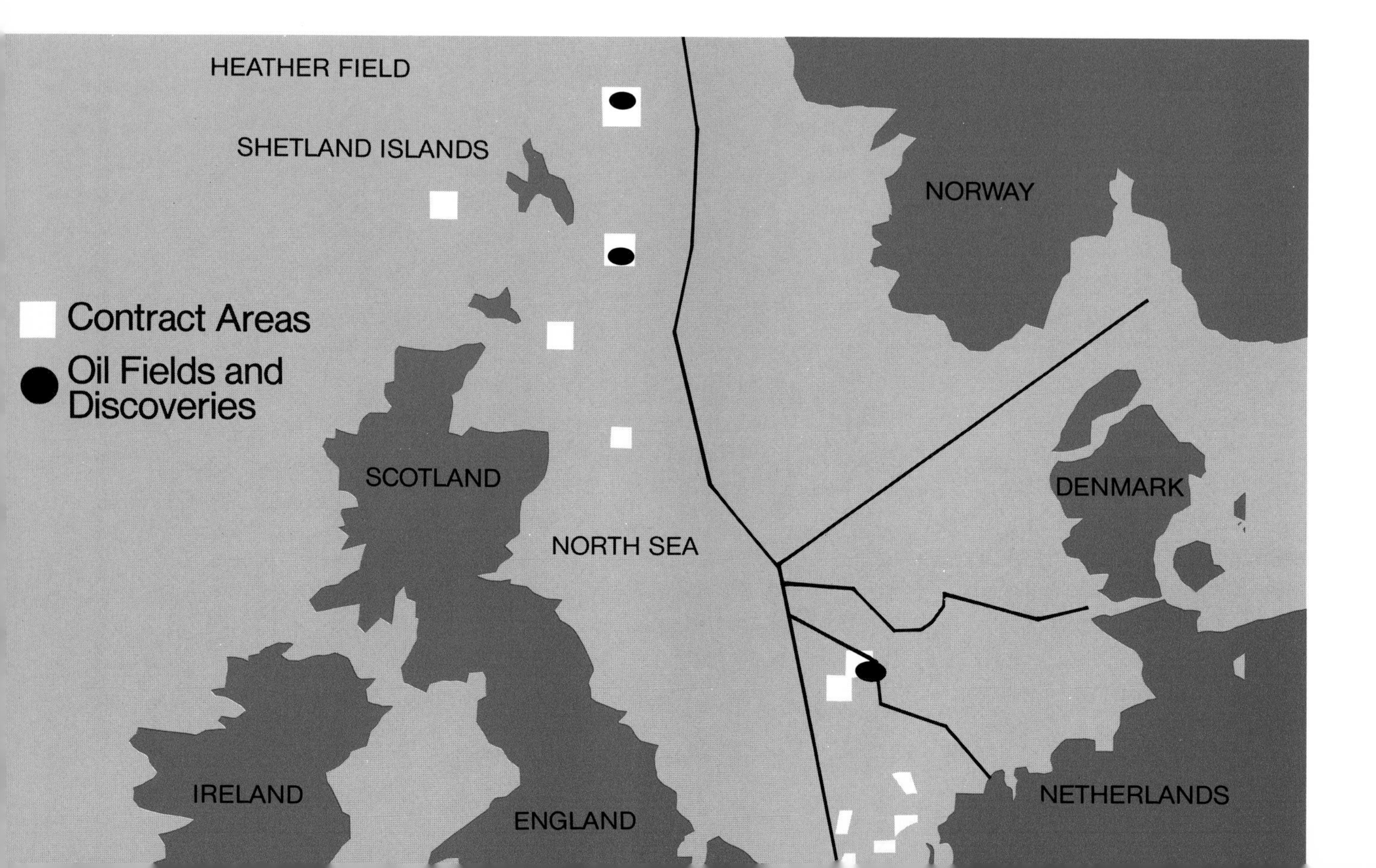

A new government in the United Kingdom decided to institute a Petroleum Revenue Tax on oil revenues, and also requested the right to participate in commercial oil fields in the British sector of the North Sea. Discussions resulted in establishing an understanding whereby Britain would have the right to buy up to 51 percent of the oil produced there at a true market price. In that way they were able to satisfy their demands for a 51 percent participation without adverse economic impact on Union.

Union had interests in several tracts in the Dutch sector south of its British leases in the North Sea. By 1969 three dry holes had been drilled. Seven years later Union made a discovery on its 80 percent held 98,000-acre Block F/2 some 120 miles offshore The Netherlands in 146 feet of water from below a 10,000-foot depth. Commerciality remains to be proven.

Much of the other drilling overseas resulted in discoveries that were not commercial, considering existing prices, quantities and physical conditions involved.

In Africa, wells were drilled in Dahomey, Libya and Nigeria.

Aside from the spectacular success in Iran, Union's Middle East exploration in Dhofar, Qatar, Ras al-Khaimah, Sharjah, and Umm al-Qaiwain proved noncommercial.

In South America, drilling in Argentina, Bolivia, Ecuador, Honduras and Peru proved disappointing.

In 1975 Union's Lake Maracaibo interest in Venezuela, which it had obtained from the Pure merger, was delivering 4,000 barrels of crude a day as Union's share. On December 31, 1975 Venezuelan oil resources were nationalized. Some $3.1 million in bonds were to be paid for Union's assets that had an actual value exceeding the amount of the settlement.

Australia's Moonie Field, which had been declining since 1969, was sold at a profit to Australian interests in 1973.

Starting in 1973, Far Eastern activity expanded from Indonesia to Pakistan, Papua, New Guinea and Bangladesh.

In Egypt, an agreement was signed April 18, 1974, covering 2.4 million acres in the Red Sea off Cape Ras Benes. With the completion of seismic surveys and other exploratory techniques, a several million dollar well was spudded in the latter part of 1976 but was dry. A second well encountered substantial sands and further drilling will be undertaken.

In September, 1975 agreements were made with Japan Petroleum Exploration Company and Mitsui Exploration Company for joint exploration and development of a total of 13.3 million acres off northern Hokkaido, Japan.

Three promising blocks totaling 184,000 acres were obtained, with two partners, in the Atlantic Ocean west of Ireland in 1976.

On the North American continent Union's only foreign activity is conducted by its 87 percent owned subsidiary, Union Oil Company of Canada Limited, and its over 300 employees. Shortly after the Pure Oil merger Union of Canada acquired Pure's Canadian oil and gas properties from Union of California by issuing to it 1.2 million shares of its own stock.

Over the 10-year period since then, Union of Canada's revenues have almost quadrupled and its earnings more than tripled to over $20 million in 1976. Crude production declined while natural gas more than doubled. Reserves followed roughly the same pattern.

At the end of 1975 Union Oil of Canada had almost 7 million net acres under lease or exploration permit. Its exploration activities include the far northern area of the Northwest Territories as well as the Beaufort Sea.

No commercial discoveries in these remote areas had been made by Union by the end of 1976, and new tax, royalty and pricing measures by the Canadian government had discouraged any costly search for oil in high risk, frontier areas. The decision: limit exploration virtually to Alberta and British Columbia until regulations are clarified, except for a 25 percent interest in a production-sharing agreement with the Bangladesh government covering offshore acreage at the mouth of the Ganges River on the Bay of Bengal. Union Oil Company of California has the remaining 75 percent interest.

By 1976 the Province of Alberta was the source of most of Union of Canada's oil and gas production. Crude oil had fallen off sharply during the decade in both British Columbia and Saskatchewan.

In Alberta, construction of the Kaybob South gas processing plant in 1968, in which Union of Canada's interest was 35 percent, had an important impact on the company's growth, reported then president W. E. Farrar. It marked entry into condensate, liquefied petroleum gas, and sulfur sales. The plant has a design capacity to treat 170 million cubic feet per day of wet sour gas. Daily average product recoveries are over 12,000 barrels of condensate, 7,000 barrels of liquefied petroleum gases and 1,000 long tons of sulfur. Products are transported by pipeline and rail directly from the plant to Canadian, international and U.S. markets.

GAS PROCESSOR *The Kaybob South gas processing plant 150 miles northwest of Edmonton, 35 percent owned by Union Oil Company of Canada, Ltd., has the capacity to process 170 million cubic feet of gas per day.*

Production personnel were alert to technical developments under Vice President C. W. "Clem" Dumett, Jr. who succeeded Farrar as president in 1975. For example, they were testing in a Saskatchewan field a new application of combustion as a tertiary recovery method following a waterflood. Most of the company's productive fields are, and have been for much of the past decade, under some form of secondary recovery operations.

As future insurance for a long term energy supply, leases were taken in 1972 on 50,000 acres in the Athabasca oil sands area of northeastern Alberta, and in 1974 an 80 percent interest was obtained in a coal discovery, also in Alberta. Preliminary evaluation in 1975 indicated a significant reserve approximating 100 million tons of coal, the equivalent of about 250 million barrels of oil on a BTU basis.

By the end of 1975 retained earnings of over $77 million had accumulated in addition to a contributed surplus of over $73 million. Early in 1976 a capital reorganization was effected relating to contributed surplus, all of which was distributed later that year to shareholders. As the largest one, Union Oil Company of California received over $63 million.

Overall, in spite of many disappointments, Union's foreign exploration and production operations had done well. During the past decade both foreign crude oil production and foreign crude oil reserves had more than tripled, and foreign reserves had jumped to roughly one-third of Union's total reserves as compared with one-tenth at the beginning of the period.

The situation in the U.S., however, was different, even though from an incentive standpoint a domestic barrel of crude production continued to be generally more profitable than a foreign one. Industry reserves for both domestic crude and natural gas, excluding the as yet untapped Prudhoe Bay reserves on Alaska's North Slope, had been steadily declining for several years.

Over the past decade Union's reserves also had declined, slightly more than the industry for crude oil and slightly less for natural gas. Exploration was losing ground. Domestic production by both the industry and Union, on the other hand, did show strong increases over the decade in helping to satisfy consumer demand. Union's production was up by a third as to crude oil and by a half as to natural gas, in both cases somewhat better than the industry's increases.

Harry Keegan, president of the Union Oil and Gas Division after Kenny Vaughan's retirement in 1972, pointed out that Union's biggest domestic exploratory successes over the decade were in offshore areas, principally the Gulf of Mexico, Alaska, and California.

Onshore discoveries of somewhat less importance were made in those three areas plus Alabama, Mississippi, New Mexico, Texas and Wyoming. And yet Union had not de-emphasized its domestic exploration, as some others had. Its almost one million net acres of proved oil and gas lands in the U.S. at the end of 1976 were at about the same level as 10 years before. It maintained district exploration offices in all key areas in the U.S.

Ray Burke explained why: to make sure that Union "would have a position in

CHUNCHULA DISCOVERY *Crew prepare to chemically treat a well in the Chunchula field, Alabama, a significant gas producer for the company.*

the historic basins that had remaining oil and gas possibilities."

In a major effort to find new resources, Union continued its heavy reliance on the offshore areas of the Gulf of Mexico, and to a lesser extent on the adjoining onshore areas. Over the past decade the two areas combined have proved to be one of Union's most productive, and also one of the most profitable.

During that period Union has invested over $365 million to acquire more than 225,000 net acres on federal leases in the offshore Louisiana and Texas areas. In addition the company spent $240 million for drilling wells and for installing some 50 production platforms. Thus Union's total 10 year investment in these offshore Gulf of Mexico areas amounted to more than one-half billion dollars, of which two-thirds was spent in the past several years. As a footnote, the industry has paid $20 billion to the federal government over the last 20 years or so for bonuses, rentals, etc.

The company has varying interests in over 100 offshore platforms in the Gulf of Mexico. From them, Union's net production in 1976 amounted to almost 20,000 barrels a day of crude oil and 530 million cubic feet per day of natural gas. In both cases this was about double the levels from a lesser number of wells 10 years before.

There are growing markets for natural gas in the U.S., and an efficient pipeline system to distribute it. This has particular significance to Union in that by 1976 its domestic natural gas production, on an energy basis, was exceeding its domestic crude oil production.

The price of natural gas used in interstate markets has been regulated by the Federal Power Commission (FPC) since 1954. Under its regulations prices had been kept so low compared to the oil equivalent as to encourage wasteful usage for over 20 years. For example, as late as year end 1976 the federal ceiling price on substantial sources of natural gas was still significantly less than the market price of the crude oil equivalent. And this in spite of FPC having allowed the price of natural gas to increase somewhat, particularly in the early and mid-1970's.

Because natural gas was not only more desirable environmentally but also cheaper, demand grew rapidly, outpacing a supply that was not being replenished nearly fast enough. It seemed paradoxical that foreign gas, imported to the U.S. in liquid form, is allowed by the FPC to be sold at prices considerably higher than permitted to U.S. companies for their own domestic gas. Francis Barker, vice president for natural gas and gas liquids of the Oil and Gas Division, has called the movement of this liquefied natural gas from source to market one of the most important developments in the natural gas field over the past decade. Another foreign impact was the fact that Canadian gas imports were slowing down and their prices were going up, a combination which added to U.S. shortages.

Prices of natural gas for use in intrastate markets were becoming more comparable with oil, and this tended to channel much of the non-federally owned onshore gas away from interstate pipelines. But pipeline companies badly needed natural gas for interstate lines. With FPC permission they used their own capital for several years to help oil companies drill exploratory and development wells, thus speeding up natural gas availability to the consuming public. Union Oil had numerous transactions of this type. In 1976 the FPC sharply limited these transactions, although still allowing pipeline companies to participate in exploratory plays for their own account, as is the case with Union and Texas Gas Transmission Company on the High Island play offshore Texas.

Production of both oil and natural gas was coming from old fields as well as new fields. C. F. "Chuck" Bowden, vice president of the Gulf Region of the Oil and Gas Division until his retirement in mid-1975, pointed out that additional drilling into fault blocks on leases which Union had held for some years developed other productive zones. This resulted in significant new reserves in such areas as Caillou Island and West Cameron as well as Vermilion parishes.

J. W. "Joe" Luckett, vice president for exploration of the Oil and Gas Division, explains that this is not unusual in the history of offshore drilling. In fact, he recalls Executive Committee approval in June, 1976 for an exploratory well on Eugene Island Block 276, one of Union's outstanding offshore fields, acquired in 1962. On a nearby block in the same field some 17 miles into the Gulf of Mexico the former Pure Oil Company had made one of the industry's first offshore Louisiana discoveries over 25 years ago.

Success in exploration often comes in bunches. This was certainly the case in 1975 when Union drilled some two dozen wells offshore Louisiana and Texas, with a remarkable 80 percent indicated success ratio. Several platforms to develop reserves are planned, according to T. W. "Tom" Stoy, Jr., who replaced Bowden upon the latter's retirement as vice president of the Gulf Region.

Among Union's discoveries were several in the High Island area offshore Texas, according to W. C. "Bill" Raymer, manager of exploration for the Gulf Region. Union had acquired leases on 45,000 net acres at federal lease sales over a several year period for $160 million.

Not far from the Gulf of Mexico a significant onshore gas-condensate discovery was made in late 1973 in an area where several companies had drilled a

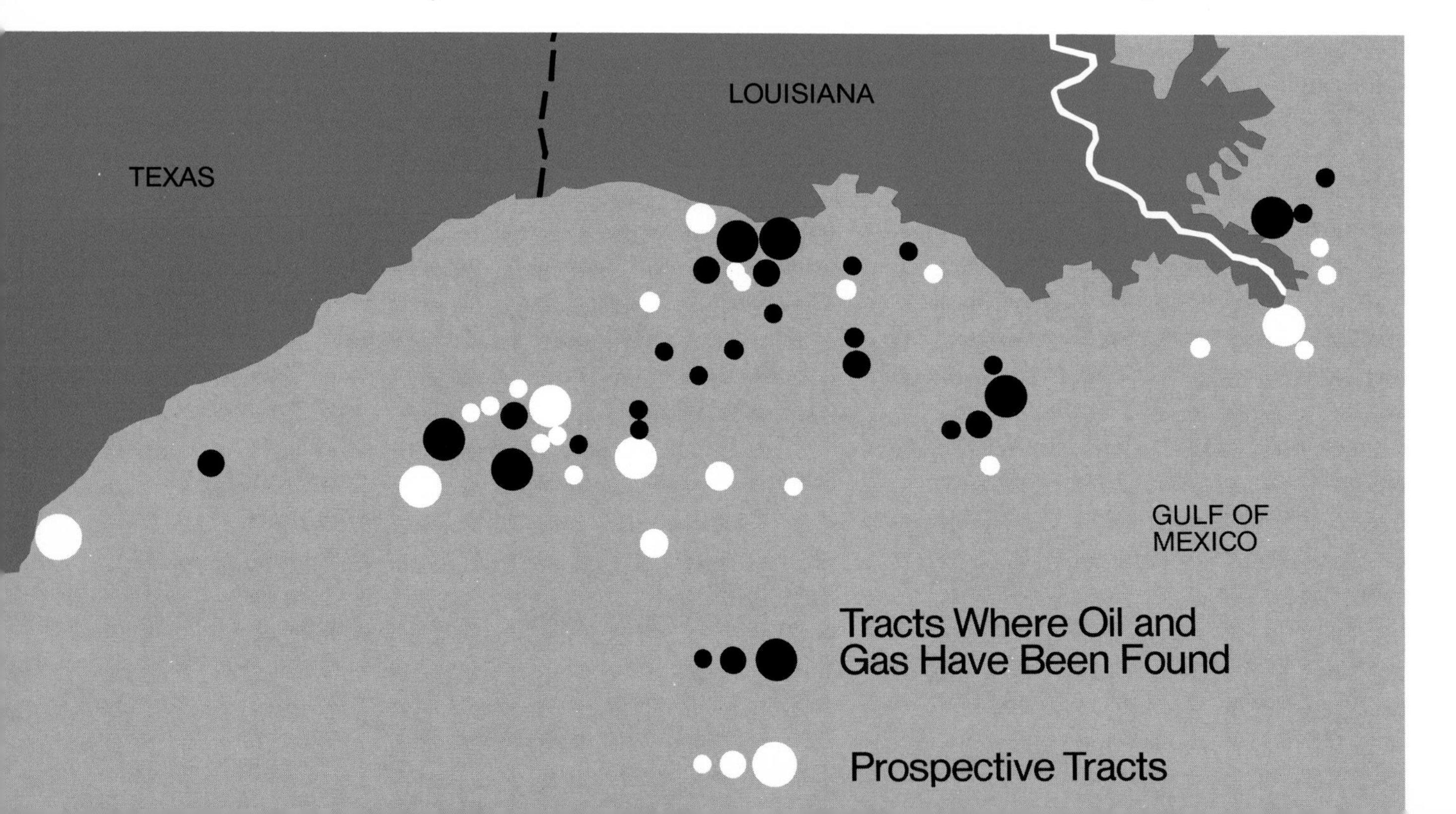

OFFSHORE CITY

Nearly all the conveniences of a work/home away from home are found in offshore platforms like this one in the Gulf of Mexico.

good many dry holes. The field is located 15 miles north of Mobile, Alabama near the village of Chunchula. Union has a 77 percent interest in the 10,000 acre unit in the center of the field, and is the operator. It also has obtained leases in over 60,000 acres in the vicinity of the field.

The discovery well tested 600 barrels of high gravity condensate and almost two million cubic feet of gas per day at a depth below 18,000 feet. Additional successful wells had significantly extended the field by the end of 1976.

Because of unique problems related to the reservoir, a test facility has been installed to determine the best production method for maximum recovery. Later on a full scale natural gas treatment plant and injection system will be built. During 1976 the test facility was producing at a daily rate of around 5,000 barrels of condensate and 12 million cubic feet of natural gas. Both were being sold to waiting markets.

Ray Burke has noted that "we systematically and carefully prepared ourselves for participating in deeper water drilling." For that purpose, he initiated formation of a deepwater technology team. R. W. "Dick" Yarbrough, manager of operations for the Western Region of the Oil and Gas Division, was named chairman.

The team participated with others in the industry in developing a new technique for deep water drilling, using a tension-leg platform with semi-submerged chambers supporting it. An experiment off the southern California coast proved its effectiveness.

Another system, developed by Lockheed under industry sponsorship, was effectively utilized to complete a well using deepwater technology originated to rescue men from trapped submarines. E. E. "Ed" Sands, Jr., manager of operations in the Gulf Region, points to the company's successful use of this system in mid-1976 in completing a well 179 feet underwater and 90 miles from shore in the Gulf of Mexico's Ship Shoal 269 block.

Laying pipeline in deep water also presented a challenge. The Union deepwater technology team participated with industry in an experiment to determine the feasibility of laying pipeline in 1,000 feet of water. In a test under actual conditions, 6,000 feet of pipe were successfully laid in over 1,000 feet of water off Louisiana.

The Gulf Coast has not yet been a candidate for the normal type of secondary recovery. Burke, however, sees a considerable future potential in the larger water drive fields of the Gulf Region. He has enlisted the services of Union's researchers in working on the problem for both onshore and offshore reservoirs of oil and gas.

In another major effort to find new petroleum resources to satisfy mounting domestic demand, Union in the mid-1960's turned to Alaska's Cook Inlet, where it had previously discovered a gas field on the east side of the inlet.

Offshore drilling in Cook Inlet is treacherous, with tides surging as much as 30 feet, currents exceeding six knots and large blocks of ice battering and grinding at everything in their path during the winter.

In spite of these hostile conditions, four new oil fields were discovered in 1965 and 1966, with Union having a substantial interest in three of them. One became the 40,000 acre Trading Bay unit in 1967 as a result of combining acreage interests held by Union, with 41 percent, and six other companies.

Secondary recovery methods were applied almost from the start. Harry Keegan pointed out that Vane Suter (later district manager of the Geothermal Division in Santa Rosa, California) was instrumental in getting the unit project underway. To maintain pressure some 160,000 barrels a day of salt water were taken from the Cook Inlet, filtered, and then injected through specially drilled wells. From 1970 to 1976 total production from the unit was maintained at roughly 110,000 barrels per day, thus demonstrating the effectiveness of the water injection program. The average production of 2,000 barrels of oil per well per day is one of the highest in the U.S.

WINTERIZED *A workman views construction equipment covered with snow and ice in Alaska. Rigors of winter present unusual problems in drilling for oil and gas.*

ON ITS WAY

Tugs start the monopod drilling platform on its way to the Cook Inlet of Alaska from its construction site in Portland, Oregon.

Because of the secondary recovery methods employed, about 40 percent of the oil believed to be present will be recovered. Without it, only about 25 percent recovery could have been expected.

To cope with ice conditions in Alaska's Cook Inlet, a unique platform was designed in 1965 and installed in 1966. It was called a monopod.

When discussing various possibilities with consulting engineers Dick Yarbrough said: "Why don't we build a mushroom?"

That's exactly what the monopod turned out to look like. It was a $12 million one, with only one large support exposed to the ice, rather than multiple legs.

This meant less weight, fewer tons of steel needed to build, and less cost. Yarbrough explained: "You buy a platform like you do potatoes, by the pound."

The single leg is 24½ feet in diameter. Two large tubular sections form a horizontal base on the inlet's floor. The platform goes on top of the leg, with a pontoon system at all four corners providing lateral stability. Through the leg, protected from ice, 32 wells can be drilled.

The monopod was 20 percent cheaper than a four-legged equivalent. But its cost advantage was lost when water was over 100 feet deep or more wells per platform were needed to develop the field. It consequently was used in only one of the Cook Inlet fields.

From virtually no production in 1965, the Cook Inlet is providing over 20 percent of Union's total supply of domestic crude oil, and is making Union Oil the largest producer of oil in Alaska, as it is also of natural gas.

Cook Inlet's crude oil is sweet and low sulfur, ideal for making gasoline, high quality lubricating oil and low sulfur fuel oil. This has a significant and favorable effect on Union's West Coast refineries.

Union's position on Alaska's highly publicized North Slope was not one of very high hopes. By 1976 most of Union's original 1969 investment of $76 million had been charged off against earnings, although some leases were held as still "possible." During 1976, in association with others, one exploratory well was drilled. Hydrocarbons were present, but not sufficient to establish commerciality. Further drilling is required.

Nature was cleverly put to work by Union in 1976 for drilling an additional exploratory well within the Arctic Circle on a man-made ice island.

One of the company's leases on the Beaufort Sea five miles offshore is in 10 feet of water. It was used for a unique test. An area was marked off and snow dikes built around it. Water was pumped into the diked-off area where it froze in winter.

As the process was repeated the ice grew thicker, heavier and sank. Eventually it rested on the bottom as an ice island from which, during about four months of winter, an exploratory well could be drilled. If successful, a permanent drilling platform would be installed.

Union's ice island experiment is of interest to other large oil companies, and six of them have paid a license fee for the technology.

If there was an abundance of oil in the Cook Inlet of Alaska, there was indeed a superabundance of natural gas. To provide a market for it became one of Hartley's early and major decisions: build a Collier ammonia-urea fertilizer plant in the area.

In 1967 a new deep gas zone was discovered beneath the original gas field on the Kenai Peninsula, and another discovery was made in the Peninsula's Beaver Creek area. Union had approximately a 50 percent interest in each.

Union's total of about 100 million cubic feet per day of natural gas production in Alaska is used to supply the city of Anchorage, Collier's ammonia plant at Kenai, and to meet its contract with another oil company for natural gas to repressurize the Swanson River field.

Much of the gas used for repressuring the Swanson River field was in a sense being rented rather than sold. When the repressuring is completed, whatever gas is left is returned to Union to sell, or use again some other way.

While Alaska had far more natural gas than it needed, California did not. W. O. "Bill" Plant, manager of planning and valuation for the Oil and Gas Division, points out that the industry's natural gas reserves and production in California had declined significantly over the past decade. Union's gas reserves in California on the other hand had risen slightly, although its production declined even more than industry. This trend was being reversed by the company as its Union Island field production began coming on early in 1976. It was an important gas discovery, made by Union in 1972 on an 8,000-acre block near Stockton. Much of the development work has been completed, a large utility company has contracted to buy the production, and Union's roughly 50 percent interest in the field will account for about half of its total California natural gas.

UNDER CONSTRUCTION . . .

Barge cranes construct rock walls in preliminary steps toward building oil drilling islands in the placid Pacific off Long Beach, California.

Over the same period crude oil reserves in California for both the industry and Union Oil declined. Although the industry was able to show a small production increase, Union's was down as the natural decline in its older fields outpaced discoveries and development in the latter part of the decade. In the earlier part, however, the reverse was true. Important new production in 1966 came from deep sands near the McKittrick field in the western San Joaquin Valley, and from an additional new development in the Las Cienegas town lot field underlying a residential area in Los Angeles. There were several relatively small oil discoveries, including one in November, 1966 in the Big Mountain field near Simi.

While there were a number of moderately successful onshore developments and discoveries, exploration in California tended to concentrate offshore. One of the first major developments occurred in an offshore Long Beach area where a prolific oil field, East Wilmington, was known to extend.

A contract to develop this energy resource was awarded by the city of Long Beach on competitive bid in 1965 to five companies. The operation became known as THUMS, an acronym for the five equal partners: Texaco, Humble (later renamed Exxon), Union, Mobil, and Shell.

Over 700 wells were drilled from four manmade 10-acre islands in 25 to 40

. . . COMPLETED

This is the completed oil production island for THUMS, a five-company venture. The drilling rigs are concealed in the futuristic high rise buildings. Waterfalls and landscaping complete the beautification project.

feet of water less than one mile offshore. Each required about 160,000 tons of rock and 900,000 yards of sand fill. Each was attractively landscaped, with the drilling rigs camouflaged to resemble tall apartment buildings, and sound proofed. Waterfalls, palm trees and shrubs were included. Once when a rig was being moved, a lady phoned authorities saying an apartment building seemed to be moving. Others have called wanting to rent apartments. The THUMS project has won numerous awards for environmental and scenic adaptation. Secondary recovery operations started early, and currently more than 600,000 barrels a day of brackish water go into the ground to increase production and to combat subsidence.

Total amount spent by THUMS, including islands, all facilities, operating costs and taxes and licenses, has amounted to over $600 million since 1966. About 400 million barrels of oil have been produced over that same period.

THUMS operates under a profit sharing contract. The city of Long Beach and the state of California receive about 96 percent of the profits. This is because large reserves were known to exist prior to awarding the contract to THUMS, so virtually no risk was involved.

Another offshore California project, involving an additional large capital outlay by Union, occurred 11 years later. Union and its partners paid $105 million (Union's 26 percent: $27.3 million) in highly competitive bidding for a 5,800-acre block offshore Huntington Beach. The first well drilled encountered some 250 feet of shallow oil bearing sands. Exploratory drilling is continuing to better evaluate the potential of the structure.

Union also was active in the Santa Barbara Channel in the late 1960's, and continued this active interest into 1976. Aside from the first discovery in 1968 on a block numbered 402, there have been several others whose commerciality remains to be tested. As to block 402, three events of considerable importance happened there early in 1969.

In chronological order they were—

A devastating storm by nature.

A temporary damaging oil spill by accident.

A contaminated ink spill by design.

Over the years Santa Barbara has had more than its share of nature's bounties and natural disasters, including the major 1925 earthquake. One of these disasters struck late in January, 1969 in the form of devastating storms and floods. Lives were lost, tons of debris were scattered on the shoreline, and property damage was in the multi-millions of dollars.

Two days after the storm an accidental oil spill occurred, involving an estimated 10,000 to 20,000 barrels of oil. It happened in the channel some five miles offshore Santa Barbara on a drilling platform belonging equally to four oil companies: Gulf, Mobil, Texaco, and Union. The latter was operating the platform. As heavy seas and tides washed the oil onto the shoreline, the debris from nature's disaster became coated as did sandy beaches, boats, and houses. Birds were affected, a number of which died. But no human lives were lost, there was practically no fish loss, and actual property damage was many millions of dollars

STORM DEBRIS *Devastating storms in southern California late January, 1969 left tons of debris on the beaches, caused millions of dollars in property damage, and some loss of life. Two days later an oil spill off Santa Barbara added to the problem when strong tides washed the oil ashore.*

less than from the storm. No lasting ecological damage resulted. The effect of the oil spill on environmental matters, however, was massive. Many feel it triggered the explosive awareness of the environment not only in the U.S., but world-wide.

The ink spill, as one journalist called it, was of a different and more insidious nature. In reporting the accident the media alternately were factual and inaccurate, objective and then misleading. Omissions of pertinent facts abounded, dire and unfounded predictions of events that would never happen proliferated, and misquotations and exaggerations were frequent. Union had only a 25 percent interest in the venture but received 100 percent of the blame.

Background of the oil spill itself can be briefly summarized. The geologic structures under channel waters were guestimated to contain some two billion barrels of oil, and are extensions of prolific onshore oil trends. The state of California owns everything up to three miles offshore and the federal government owns beyond that. Offshore drilling had taken place without incident in state waters for many years.

In February, 1968 the federal government accepted lease bids totaling $603 million for 363,000 offshore acres from many companies, including a 5,400-acre block numbered 402 for which Union Oil (as operator) and its three equal co-lessees paid $61.4 million. In addition, this group spent $141 million for another 46,000 acres of leases in the Santa Barbara Channel, exploration on which was severely limited until the mid-1970's.

Three successful exploratory wells were drilled on Block 402 in the summer of 1968. A permanent drilling platform, designated Platform A, was tipped into place in 180 feet of water in mid-September of that year. It was somewhat unique in that it utilized a slant rig which permitted the derrick to be inclined 30° from vertical, thus allowing production of shallower reservoirs from fewer platforms. This had both environmental and economic advantages—a rare combination.

From November to January four successful development wells were drilled under procedures approved by federal regulatory authorities, including a variance in the casing program to permit production from shallower zones. The fifth well, A-21, was being drilled under the same procedures and circumstances as the other four. By January 28, 1969 it had reached its objective depth of almost 3,500 feet. A routine "wiper" trip (withdrawal of drillpipe to the surface) was started off the bottom of the hole. Suddenly an uncontainable and powerful stream of drilling mud and gas shot through the drill pipe high into the derrick, roaring as it went, and platform visibility was reduced to almost zero.

After several attempts to control this blowout, the drill pipe was dropped back into the hole and the well head was sealed, 13 minutes after the trouble had started. The flow of gas and mud through the well bore to the surface had now been controlled, but the well bore below the surface had not. Were this an ordinary blowout, the surface sealing would have ended it.

It didn't. Gas first, and then a brownish colored oil, erupted from the sea floor several hundred feet from the platform. The leaking oil and gas were reaching the surface largely through shallow open fractures and seams as a result of subsurface pressures.

John Fraser, vice president of the Oil and Gas Division's Western Region, mobilized for an all-out effort to plug the well. He immediately called in Coots Matthews of the well-known "Red" Adair organization from Houston, Texas, specialists in controlling oil well blow-outs and fires. In addition, two drilling foremen, Ray Adams and Buck Jones, flew over from Union's Gulf Region to add their expertise.

Ten days and 15,000 barrels (about 8 million pounds) of mud later the well was controlled and all flow through the well bore had been stopped. To prevent any recurrence of the flow, cementing operations were commenced. H. T. "Hal" Finney, manager of operations of the Oil and Gas Division's Western Region, reported three days later the well bore of the illfated A-21 well was practically a solid plug of cement, which at that point had replaced most of the mud. Any oil reaching the surface from February 10 on would come from fractures and seeps other than from A-21. It now was possible to abandon the relief well being drilled from a drilling vessel to intersect A-21's well bore if all else had failed.

But even with the well under control, the problems of Union and its three co-lessees were far from over. Right after the accident had occurred, Hartley set in motion a massive companywide mobilization program to deal with the spill's problems, and shortly thereafter announced assumption of responsibility for the cleanup.

Kenny Vaughan, senior vice president of the Oil and Gas Division, coordinated all aspects of Union's activities until the entire job of plugging the well and cleanup had been pretty well accomplished. At its peak this was to involve about 1,000 people.

Bill Stark, chief engineer of the Los Angeles Refinery, was given the job of organizing the beach cleanup during the crucial early weeks, and he bore the brunt of property owner complaints. He recalls that heavy rains and winds after the spill compounded the difficulty of permanent cleanup.

Don Craggs, coastal district operating manager for the Oil and Gas Division, took over from Bill Stark. He and Chad Chadband, southern district operating manager, and Dick Gillen, construction superintendent, devised some ingenious deflecting devices commonly referred to as tents. Some 20 of them—several over 100 feet square—were installed on about 40,000 square feet of the ocean floor to collect seeping oil and carry it to surface containers. It was a very successful innovation.

Bob Bungay, vice president for engineering and construction, was consulting on engineering problems, particularly on booms and skimming devices.

Tom Gaines, coordinator of air and water conservation, had been on the scene since the first day. He coordinated much of the hectic and effective activity that gradually was bringing order out of chaos. A hectic example was when Tom found an associate in his temporary office doing three things at once—talking to an assistant, listening on the phone, and watching pictures of the prior day's operations. And there were many, many others from several different departments who worked long and hard hours before the job was finally done.

BIRD BATHING *Union Oil employees and others worked to clean birds caught in the Santa Barbara oil spill. Research chemist William Gross tenderly cares for one.*

AFTER THE CLEANUP
No effort was spared by Union in its cleanup of Santa Barbara beaches and by July 4 practically all areas had been restored to better than pre-spill conditions. There was no permanent damage to fish and no scientific evidence that seals or whales had been affected.

Literally hundreds of people had ideas on how to stop the seepage. Corporate Communications Director Jerry Luboviski set up a telephone bank in the Los Angeles office to answer the calls, manned largely by knowledgeable research personnel. They also had to analyze and answer written suggestions. Media contacts also were coordinated from Los Angeles, with Fritz Springmann, manager of public relations, assigned to handle all press matters in Santa Barbara.

From the Research Department 16 top men went to Santa Barbara to set up a bird cleaning and care center, led by Al Percy from its products division and Joe Huffman from its instrumentation and electronics group. They worked in teams of two, one man holding the bird and the other washing it. Volunteers brought birds in from the beaches. The washing operation reached an efficiency peak of 10 or so per hour per team. When an oily bird was brought to one of two treating centers, he was dangerous at the front end because of his sharp beak, as some stabbed research fingers bear witness. Then butter was put down the bird's throat as a cleansing laxative, and he became hazardous at the other end. "We got clobbered both ways," as Joe Huffman puts it. Some 1,600 birds went through the two treating centers, and in spite of all the efforts the survival rate was less than 10 percent.

Other wildlife fared far better. There was no permanent damage to fish in

FISH HAVEN *Platform A in Santa Barbara—as with practically all offshore oil drilling platforms—provides an abundance of marine life attached to the structure legs. These provide food and a haven for large schools of fish.*

the area, and there was no scientific evidence that either seals or whales had in any way been affected. In fact, several federal government and California state agencies officially refuted news and magazine articles to the contrary. By fall, there were large schools of fish in the channel, more than before the spill. Both commercial and sport fishing had returned to normal.

Skimming devices, booms, and a variety of dispersants were used, the latter with U.S. government permission, in the early stages to disperse oil patches headed for beaches. Dispersants were applied from both boats and crop-dusting airplanes. Heavy log booms were brought into action, but they were no match for the stormy seas of February 4 and 5 which broke up the offshore oil slick and moved the oil onto the beaches. High tides and strong winds sprayed sea walls, cliffs, and homes.

The massive beach cleaning operation went on over a several month period. No effort was spared, and before the July 4 holiday of the same year practically all the beaches in and around Santa Barbara had been restored to better than their pre-oil spill condition.

The job was accomplished largely by hand labor, using straw as the best of many absorbants tried. Each rock in the breakwater was individually cleaned. Several hundred men worked at these jobs.

During the first four months almost 10,000 loads of debris were hauled away, including roughly 30,000 tons washed ashore by the storm. Homes, piers, and boats were meticulously cleaned, and insurance claims were quickly handled.

Now the main job left to be done was to control the natural seepages. Shortly after the accident, Dr. Lee DuBridge, science advisor to President Nixon (who had made an early on-site inspection), established a special panel of distinguished scientists and engineers. Its report on oil operations in the Santa Barbara Channel made it clear, among other things, that the reservoir into which the wells had been drilled should be depleted as rapidly as possible by further drilling in order to reduce pressures. This recommendation was immediately implemented after receiving approval from Interior Department Secretary Walter J. Hickel. By

Please, let's set the record straight.

During the course of our continued struggle to seal off the oil leak in the Santa Barbara Channel, a statement has been attributed to me by the press, radio and television. A statement which, quite understandably, has generated a certain degree of public outcry.

Were this statement true, I should have nothing to do but shoulder the burden in silence, accepting the response as my due.

The fact is that at no time, anywhere, did I make that insensitive statement charged to me. The Wall Street Journal, acknowledging its error, printed the following letter from me on February 14th:

Editor, The Wall Street Journal:

Since the first moment of the very regrettable incident affecting the Union Oil Company-operated well in the Santa Barbara Channel, the Union Oil Co. has mustered an ever increasing force of men and material to control the well and to clean the ocean and beaches. At the same time, the company has taken steps particularly to care for wild fowl and/or marine life adversely affected by the slick.

It is particularly galling, therefore, in view of this all-out effort, to read, in a page-one story on Feb. 7, a statement attributed as testimony by me before a Senate subcommittee on Feb. 5, 1969, in which I was falsely charged with callously saying:

"I'm amazed at the publicity for the loss of a few birds."

I said no such thing at any time, anywhere, nor did I say it before the Muskie Senate subcommittee. My comments relative to our concern about wildlife, as reported in the official transcript of the proceedings, follow:

"Mr. Chairman, I would like to comment further here: I think we have to look at these problems relatively. I am always tremendously impressed at the publicity that death of birds receives versus the loss of people in our country in this day and age. When I think of the folks that gave up their lives when they came down into the ocean off Los Angeles some three weeks ago and the fact that our society forgets about that within a 24-hour period, I think relative to that the fact that we have had no loss of life from this incident is important.

"We set up, on the third day of the incident, a bird sanctuary, set up with appropriate scientists and cleaning chemicals to try to do our best to save our feathered friends, but I do say to you that relative to the number of deaths that have occurred in this fair city due to crime and all the accidents that do occur—relative to that problem of our nation, this desecration to the offshore area of Santa Barbara, although important and certainly one which we are fully devoted to taking care of, relatively it does seem that we should give this thing a little perspective."

In addition, we have assigned marine biologists and other scientists to assess the effects of the oil on marine life and to determine in what fashion we might be able to expedite a return to a normal balance of under-sea life.

And of course we have not overlooked people. With our three partners in the well—Gulf, Mobil and Texaco—we have arranged for our insurance carriers to set up special offices to quickly handle damage claims to boats or other property.

We have provided more than a score of boats, several airplanes, miles of plastic and wooden booms, thousands of bales of straw, dozens of vacuum trucks, dump trucks and bulldozers and more than 500 men for cleanup operations on land and sea.

It is well nigh impossible to say how deeply we regret this accident. We have operated at all times with procedures approved by our three partners and the Federal regulatory authorities.

Fred L. Hartley
President
Union Oil Company

Los Angeles

(The Journal regrets its inaccurate quoting of Mr. Hartley. —Ed.)

In view of our attitude and these things we are doing, it is most distressing that because I voluntarily and responsibly appeared before a United States Senate Committee to provide information needed for possible legislation, that I—or any other private citizen—should be maligned by manufactured quotations.

For seventy-eight years we have been building with the country. In its economy. And in its communities. We share a great stake in its future.

We are confident that those who have known the company during its long history understand and respect our philosophy and record as a good citizen and a good neighbor. By our actions we hope still to merit that understanding and respect.

President
Union Oil Company of California

year-end the seepages were minimal, far less than the centuries-old seepage in state-owned waters off nearby Coal Oil Point, northwest of Santa Barbara.

Concerned about the media "overkill" on the effects of the spill, and with beaches restored, fish catch not suffering, and the seeping oil almost totally contained, the Santa Barbara Chamber of Commerce undertook an advertising campaign to get the facts out. Oil companies contributed to the program to brighten Santa Barbara's former and favorable image.

One of the most unfortunate and far-reaching of the press' mistakes was the misquoting of Fred Hartley after his voluntary appearance before Senator Muskie's committee in Washington, D.C., on February 5, 1969, at which he pledged the company's full cooperation and responsibility in the cleanup effort.

An experienced reporter from *The New York Times* was covering the hearing, but absented himself at a critical point. Based on hearsay he wrote an article appearing deep inside the February 6 issue of *The New York Times*, and used the now infamous misquote "I'm amazed at the publicity for the loss of a few birds." The February 7 issue of *The Wall Street Journal* used its front page to tell the story without checking it. NBC's David Brinkley likewise used the misquote, without checking it. The *Washington Post* chose to go all out, without checking it, by using colorfully derogatory language. Time magazine used it, without checking it. Scurrilous editorials in newspapers throughout the country condemned Hartley for his alleged insensitivity.

When Hartley first read in *The Wall Street Journal* the statement attributed to him, he knew he had not said it. He quickly got a copy of the official transcript of the hearing to confirm that fact. He prepared a letter to The Journal and sent Luboviski to New York to handle it personally.

On February 12, Luboviski met with Ed Cony, managing editor of The Journal, showed him the transcript and Hartley's letter and asked for its publication and an apology. The Journal ran the letter on February 14 and apologized for its "inaccurate quoting" of Hartley.

Armed with the Journal's retraction, Luboviski called on Clifton Daniel, managing editor of *The New York Times*, and asked for a similar apology. It was forthcoming. That same day he also met with Jim Shepley, editor of Time magazine. Time used the correct quotation in its Letters column but did not apologize for its misstatements.

To make sure that the manufactured quotation was corrected as widely as possible, full-page newspaper ads were taken in major newspapers throughout the United States, Canada and overseas, reproducing Hartley's letter to The Journal and its apology under the heading "Please, let's set the record straight." Reprints of the ad with a covering memo titled "Have you ever been misquoted?" were sent by Luboviski to every newspaper city editor, editorial director and library; to all radio and television stations and to business heads, schools and organizations of all types.

The editorial response was vigorous. Scores of newspapers carried corrected or first-time editorials with the real facts. Numerous letters of apology and support were received. The *Washington Post* did some investigative reporting on how the misquote had occurred and explained the background in an interesting editorial called "F.Y.I."

In spite of the usual prominence given misquotations but only passing mention to corrections, in this case the record was set straight. The misquote no longer appeared, except as an example of bad journalism.

Although damages to homes, boats and other properties were paid for as quickly as possible, approximately 40 law suits resulted. The full brunt of them, and the astronomical $500 million (Union's share) they initially involved, was the legal department's responsibility. Vice President and General Counsel Bert Gibbons, soon to retire, asked his successor-to-be, Doug Gregg, to take over the complex series of negotiations. All of the law suits have been settled, resulting in a very small fraction of the total amount originally sought.

Three independent scientific reports were issued during the first few years after the 1969 oil spill. Each came broadly to the same conclusion: that no permanent ecological or environmental damage resulted. And it is of some interest that several important almanacs of world events in their editions covering 1969 came to somewhat the same general conclusion. None of them listed the Santa Barbara oil spill in chronologies of disasters for that year. On the other hand, two did list under disasters Southern California's devastating storms and floods which immediately preceded, and also followed, the accidental oil spill.

It is worth noting that between the accident and year end 1976 almost 100 million barrels of oil were produced from block 402 without incident, and production is continuing and being helped by selective waterflooding in a secondary recovery operation.

The waterflood being used in the Santa Barbara Channel is relatively small compared to a good many others in numerous older California fields which are helping to reduce normal production declines. In fact, waterflooding is the most common secondary recovery method used in the state, including such large fields as Dominguez and Santa Fe Springs.

Gas injection for repressurization, such as used in California's Coalinga field, also has been successful, but its use as a method declined during the past 10 years. Thermal stimulation, however, has been increasingly used with considerable effectiveness. Steam is periodically injected into new or already existing wells. The steam moving away from the well bores heats the reservoir and reduces oil viscosity so it will flow more easily. When injection is discontinued the oil flows to the well bores and is pumped to the surface. Because this is done on a cyclic basis the technique is called Huff and Puff.

Arch Dawson, vice president for production of the Oil and Gas Division, points out that a good example is in California's south San Joaquin Valley. During 1976 Union's almost 300 shallow thermally stimulated wells, of which 73 were drilled in 1976, reached a high of 6,400 barrels per day of low gravity crude oil that December. This compares with 500 barrels per day without thermal stimulation.

Over the past decade Union has recovered nearly 30 million barrels of this low gravity type crude by steam injection in California. By the end of 1976 there were over 400 wells using this method, thus helping to slow down the decline rate of Union's California crude oil production.

As crude oil prices continued to rise in the mid-1970's, other and more expensive secondary and tertiary recovery methods became economically feasible. These include fire flooding, caustic flooding, and continuous steam drive. In 1973 a task force of operating engineers from the Oil and Gas Division's Western Region and research technicians thoroughly surveyed California's existing oil producing properties to determine the potential of improved recovery techniques. They identified approximately one billion barrels of oil still underground. Roughly half of this could be classified as potential new reserves, recoverable by enhanced recovery methods.

As a first step, the Executive Committee in 1976 approved a five year, 800 well program designed to develop 130 million barrels of these potential reserves by using the continuous steam drive technique. This would significantly increase the level of Union's California crude oil production.

Union's efforts to increase production of heavy oil by this method are limited to facilities for which permits already have been received, at least until environmental regulations are clarified, since the FEA's mandate to increase crude oil production conflicts directly with the EPA's environmental pressures.

Elsewhere in the U.S., Union's secondary and tertiary recovery operations have the same significance as in California and Alaska. One of the most important is the Dollarhide field in west Texas. Additional projects are located in other parts of Texas as well as in Oklahoma and Illinois. In the mid-1960's there were several successful waterfloods in the latter state which for a time contributed to a 22 percent increase in its crude oil production.

All told, Union's secondary recovery operations in the U.S. produced over 100,000 barrels per day in 1976, or almost half of total domestic production. This compares with roughly one-fourth 10 years ago.

Union's crude oil production in Texas increased over the past decade by al-

HUFF 'N PUFF *One of the enhanced recovery methods employed by Union, steam injections increase the amount of oil recovered from a reservoir. Here the operator controls manifold which directs steam from generator to a number of nearby wells.*

most two-thirds, due primarily to the Texas Railroad Commission's decision in 1972 to significantly increase the allocation of crude oil permitted to be produced. There also were a number of relatively small discoveries. Natural gas production in Texas more than doubled over the same period. The Gomez field in Pecos county, discovered prior to the Pure Oil merger, came on production in 1966 as the world's deepest producer at the time. Its depth, almost four and one-half miles, did not quite match Union's 1972 Annie Bruner small gas discovery in Oklahoma's Anadarko basin, in which Union also made several other discoveries. (Several years later another company drilled an exploratory well to a depth of almost six miles.)

In other states there likewise were a number of moderate size discoveries, including Colorado, Mississippi, New Mexico, Oklahoma, and Wyoming. Those in the latter state bear such colorful names as Poison Spider, Rattlesnake, Hell's Half Acre, Kitty, and Quest.

On the Atlantic seaboard a federal lease sale took place in August, 1976 covering acreage offshore New York, New Jersey, and Delaware. Union was awarded one lease, paying $16.3 million for a 100 percent interest in a 5,700 acre block.

While the U.S. government's executive branch was receiving billion dollar lease bonuses from the oil industry in the 1970's, the legislative branch was accusing it of purposely shutting in some of its oil and gas production to wait for higher prices.

After a good deal of unfavorable and uninformed publicity, the National Academy of Sciences as well as the Federal Energy Administration, in two separate reports independently prepared in 1976 and 1975, found no evidence of illegal shutting in.

In addition to crude oil and natural gas there are other sources of hydrocarbon energy. One is shale oil, which has an enormous potential but at significantly higher costs.

As the nation's lack of domestic oil self-sufficiency became more apparent following the OPEC boycott, Union once again turned major attention toward its Colorado oil shale holdings. Recoverable oil from the company's shale land was estimated to be more than double Union's net petroleum reserves at the end of 1975 and would be sufficient to supply for 40 years a plant processing 110,000 barrels of shale oil per day—about one half the daily quantity of crude oil that Union's domestic oil fields produced in 1976.

A process developed at the Research Center in the 1950's under Hartley's direction showed how to unlock the oil from the shale, but cheap foreign oil made doing so uneconomic.

Additional research, plus the soaring cost of imported crude, made it seem feasible to reopen the project in the mid-1970's.

In 1974 the Union Synthetic Fuels Division was formed, with John Hopkins as acting president in addition to his established responsibilities as regional vice president in charge of Union's refining, marketing and transportation operations in the western United States.

The division would be responsible for making environmental studies, preparing an environmental impact assessment, obtaining all necessary permits, and engineering evaluation of the technology developed by Research, plus design, construction and operation of the plant.

Union's acreage is along Parachute Creek, which flows southward into the Colorado River at Grand Valley, Colorado, 15 miles away. This is an area of semi-arid mesas through which streams have cut narrow, steep-sided valleys with sheer cliff faces rising 2,000 to 3,000 feet above the valley floors. There is a shale oil vein called the mahogany zone, approximately 60 feet thick about halfway up a typical cliff face.

Plans called for mining the shale by the room-and-pillar method. A tunnel is driven into the ore vein, with rooms formed as ore is removed. Between one quarter and one third of the ore is left as pillars to support the roof.

Ore processing equipment, most of it underground, is located near the mine portal. Here the ore is crushed to a suitable size for retorting. It then is fed to a retort where heat separates the raw shale oil from the ore. Retorted or spent shale is disposed of in the canyon beneath the plant site.

When first separated from the shale, the oil contains more impurities than a typical crude oil, including many times the amount of nitrogen. Refining the oil to pipeline quality crude oil would be done at a plant located on the valley floor, along with offices, warehouses, shops and other auxiliary facilities.

Union hoped to test the technical, environmental and economic feasibility of the project by building a plant capable of processing 10,000 tons of shale per day which could produce 7,300 barrels of shale oil daily. And, with the process proved on such a commercial scale, it would become one of a series of plants built as demand justified.

Plans provided for revegetating areas where retorted shale is deposited. Experiments had proven this to be feasible and indicated the most effective methods.

By June 1976 the environmental impact assessment had been completed at a cost of over $1 million.

Total cost of the 10,000-ton plant was estimated in early 1976 at about $120 million, this in addition to the $65 million already spent by the company (in 1975 dollars) during 30 years of research and development.

Success of the project depends upon being able to produce oil from shale at a price competitive with low-sulfur fuel oil, for sale to electric utilities, Hopkins says. Because of uncertain future oil prices, the effect of inflation, the risks inherent in a large venture based on new technology, and the many problems involved in obtaining authorizations and permits, Union concluded it still was not justified in proceeding alone.

Some indication of the extent of the problems encountered came in August 1976. At the request of two large companies that had leased federal shale lands, and who already had nearly $200 million invested in less than three years, Interior Secretary Thomas Kleppe suspended for one year lease payments on their Colorado oil shale tracts. He agreed to the suspensions, reported *The Wall Street Journal*, "after the companies complained of a plethora of environmental, legal and technical problems in the development of oil shale leases."

SHALE OIL *Artist's conception of a proposed prototype complex in Colorado to demonstrate the technical, environmental and economic feasibility of Union's process to convert oil shale into shale oil. The raw shale is mined, processed and retorted on this cut into the mountainside at the rich mahogany zone.*

Hartley reflected on an ironic event that had occurred in the early '60's when Union had offered to sell 50,000 barrels of oil from shale daily to a western utility for $3.20 per barrel over a 20-year period. The offer was rejected as the power company then was buying price controlled natural gas at,a price equivalent to $2 per barrel and presumably assumed natural gas always would be available at that price.

"How can you get a non-subsidized program off the ground when you have a price controlled one to compete with?" Hartley asks.

The company's shale program again slowed to low gear, waiting for a government energy policy that would allow development on a firm basis.

Turning from hydrocarbons to another source of energy, geothermal steam, Union's technical know-how, management skills and financial resources transformed a small operation at a geological curiosity into a power source for public utility plants generating enough electricity to supply a city of 500,000.

This dramatic development took place at The Geysers, a geothermal field approximately 90 miles north of San Francisco, near Santa Rosa, California.

It has made Union the world leader in developing geothermal steam resources and The Geysers the largest commercial development of geothermal steam in the world.

Total steam reserves at The Geysers field—including Union's—have been estimated to equal roughly three-quarters of a billion barrels of crude oil, based on a capacity of two million kilowatts. Scientists estimate that from geothermal energy there is the opportunity in the United States to develop up to 20 million kilowatts of electrical generating capacity by the year 2000. This would equal five percent of current U.S. electrical capacity.

The source of geothermal energy is magma, the seething mass of molten rock that forms the earth's core. In some areas it lies comparatively close to the surface. Here it heats the layers of rock above it and any underground water present. It is turned to steam or pressurized hot water. When the latter is able to reach the surface, such phenomena as hot springs, geysers and fumaroles—jets of steam billowing from cracks in the earth—result.

Wells can be drilled to bring the steam or hot water to the surface. Steam, as it occurs in the subsurface at The Geysers, then can be piped to power plants directly to spin turbine blades that drive generators. This is a rare phenomenon.

In most locations hot water occurs. It may be used for heating, and for some industrial purposes, but mostly it is used to create steam by flashing to drive a power plant turbine. The remaining hot water fraction is disposed of. Either way, power plants must be located near producing wells, since steam can be transported only about a mile or so.

Modern geothermal development began at Larderello, Italy, about 40 miles west of Florence. In 1974 The Geysers passed the Italian field as an energy source for power plants and became the largest geothermal power development in the world.

Geothermal heat has been utilized in a score of countries. But only at The Geysers, in Italy, Japan, Mexico and New Zealand have substantial amounts of electrical power been generated.

Starting in 1920 a series of owners attempted to develop The Geysers. In 1956 Magma Power Company and Thermal Power Company obtained a 99-year lease. They were able to produce steam in commercial quantities, and negotiated a 50-year contract for its use with Pacific Gas & Electric Company.

Before the Union-Pure merger, a 12,500 kilowatt generating plant had been put on stream. Dr. Carel Otte, head of Pure Oil's exploration research group, became interested in geothermal developments. A subsidiary, Earth Energy, Inc., was formed with Otte as vice president and general manager. In association with Magma Power, wells were drilled in California's Imperial Valley, hoping to sell steam and to recover potash from hot water-type wells. But corrosion and scaling problems were severe, and the project seemed to be more of a chemical mine than a source of energy. When Union and Pure merged, Union management decided after further expenditures to stop activity in this particular area, although research continued.

But at The Geysers Otte and geologist Dick Dondanville, after examining the Magma-Thermal holdings, decided that the field had the potential of being far more extensive. At the time of the merger, Earth Energy had started negotiations to lease substantial acreage north of the existing development and eventually geothermal rights on 9,785 acres were acquired.

The first well in the new area was successfully completed in June, 1966. Other wells followed, and in June, 1967 a contract was signed with Magma Power and Thermal Power, merging the lease holdings of the two groups to include Union's acreage and about 5,500 acres leased by Magma and Thermal. Union held 50 percent and was to be the operator of the entire field.

In September, 1967, Earth Energy became the geothermal division of Union, with Otte as manager and later vice president and manager.

The existing Magma-Thermal sales contract applied to steam from the reserves they contributed to the operation, which were dedicated to PG&E. Those Union brought to the joint venture were not. A sales contract covering them had to be negotiated.

At this point brilliant field work and decisive management made possible rapid development of this geothermal resource.

PG&E had been contracting for a power plant only after sufficient wells had been drilled to assure it a 30-year supply of steam. Drilling, obtaining permits, materials assembly, and construction time meant years of delay. But should it be possible to demonstrate that sufficient steam would be available by drilling only a few wells, getting plant construction underway would not have to await the drilling of all wells.

By adapting natural gas technology to geothermal systems, Otte's reservoir group developed techniques for measuring steam reserves and predicting longevity through drilling only a few wells. The drilling department, under Manager of Operations Del Pyle and Superintendent Don Ash, did a monumental job of modifying existing tools and techniques to meet and conquer the harder rock and higher temperatures encountered in geothermal drilling.

Union management and financial strength then made their decisive contribution.

Hartley had visited New Zealand geothermal projects and could recognize the superior situation at The Geysers. He and Senior Vice President Kenny Vaughan recommended, and the executive committee approved, an all-out, multi-million dollar exploratory drilling campaign for 1969–70 to establish that huge reserves existed.

They did.

PG&E was interested. Its engineers and consultants finally were convinced that practical estimates of reserves could be made without drilling all wells before committing to a power plant and ordering equipment. This permitted the inclusion of geothermal power in the utility's long-range plans. A sales contract was signed in May, 1970. It included the price provisions of the existing Magma-Thermal contract, plus two important new features.

Union guaranteed that wells drilled would be sufficient to provide, for one year, enough steam to operate the power plant being built. Partial failure to do so would mean that Union would pay a partial portion of the plant's cost. Complete failure at any time during the year would mean payment of the entire plant cost, well over $10 million at the time.

Hartley's and Vaughan's recognition, as engineers, that a satisfactory basis for the guarantee had been established, and their willingness to take the gamble, were basic factors in accelerating commercial development at The Geysers.

When Union became operator of The Geysers field in 1967, steam was being supplied to three PG&E plants with a generating capacity of 54,000 kilowatts. Plans called for reaching 1,600,000 kilowatts by 1980. This would mean that 18,400,000 barrels of low-sulfur oil a year would not be needed to generate electricity, during a time when the nation was confronted with a shortage of energy.

By May, 1975 generating capacity had reached just over 500,000 kilowatts, but it was evident that the 1980 goal would not be attained, due to environmental and government-imposed delays.

It was taking the California Public Utilities Commission as long as three years to authorize plant construction, with at least another year's delay before it could be operating.

Local authorities compounded the problem, delaying authorization of well drilling or plant construction on environmental grounds. In one instance, Sonoma County insisted on an Environmental Impact Report prepared by an outside consultant. A 2,000-page statement just prepared by the federal government covering its holdings in the same general area would not do. This cost Union $48,000. And final approval of the project was not forthcoming until mid-1976, over a year after the report was received.

Securing satisfactory lease titles also presented problems when separate parties owned surface and mineral rights. Assistant General Counsel Sam Snyder had the solution: obtain leases from both parties and escrow royalties until the courts determine who is entitled to them.

By 1976 additional drilling had brought the total operation to over 8,700 gross proven acres with an additional 12,000 being considered productive. Union had drilled 123 gross wells with an average depth of 6,000 feet, the deepest being 9,609 feet. The average well had taken 45 days to drill, produced 150,000 pounds of steam per hour with an average temperature of 350° Fahrenheit, and cost $500,000. However, by 1976 per well costs had risen to over $650,000. To

ELECTRICITY FROM STEAM *The Geysers geothermal field is developed in a cluster concept around the generating plant (A). Steam wells (B) one to two miles deep tap steam which is transported by pipelines (C) from wellheads to the central generating plant where turbines convert it to electrical energy. Mufflers (D) will vent steam if a sudden power shutdown occurs. Transmission lines (E) carry electricity from the generating plant to the interconnected electrical system of the public utility.*

supply a 110,000 kilowatt generating plant required steam from 16 wells.

In 1970 work was resumed in California's Imperial Valley, where recent developments gave new hope for success.

In Mexico, just 20 miles south of the border, a geothermal reservoir with less saline brines was discovered by another company and there were some indications that the reservoir might continue northward. Union acquired lease holdings in the Heber area, near the border.

A geothermal reservoir also was discovered on 2,000 acres about two miles north of Brawley.

Several wells were drilled in both areas. Each showed potential for being a sizable field, and development work continued.

Elsewhere in the West, 11 successful wells had been drilled by December, 1975 on 100,000 acres leased in the Redondo Creek area north of Albuquerque, New Mexico. Tests were started to determine the field's actual potential.

Union, with Magma, drilled four exploratory wells on leases near Brady, Nevada. Some 3,000 acres were under lease in the Long Valley area, east of Mammoth Lakes, California; 11,830 acres in Millard county, Utah, and extensive acreage north of Vale, Oregon.

Union's geothermal expertise also was being applied internationally. In 1971 the government of The Philippines was referred to Union, as the leader in geothermal development, by the U.S. government-owned Overseas Private Investment Corporation for assistance in the development of their geothermal potential.

This led to the formation of Philippine Geothermal, Inc., a 100 percent Union-owned subsidiary, in September, 1971. It contracted with the Philippines National Power Company to explore and develop geothermal resources, delivering steam to generating plants built by the company.

The price of steam was set based on estimated exploration and development costs, with an escalator clause providing that it would increase or decrease with the world price of crude oil.

In June, 1972 the Tiwi Field was discovered on 44,000 acres of the Bicol Peninsula, Luzon Island, about 240 miles southeast of Manila. In January, 1975 a second field in the Los Banos area was discovered within about 50 miles of Manila. The commercial potential of both fields was established and a number of wells drilled.

Generating plants were ordered in 55,000 kilowatt units by the Philippine government. Eight had been ordered by the end of 1976, the first to be operational by early 1978 and the rest by 1980.

Meanwhile price increases by OPEC had sent the price of crude oil to dizzy heights. The Philippine government understandably felt that it could not afford to have OPEC decisions govern the cost of power from a Philippine natural resource, so Philippine Geothermal's contract was renegotiated by mutual consent.

Union thus became the operator of a major geothermal development abroad as well as at home.

The history-making rapidity with which Union created new technology and developed The Geysers field astounds geothermal scientists. And the President of the United States, Gerald Ford, was sufficiently impressed to visit The Geysers area on a snowy day in April, 1975 accompanied by Hartley, Otte, and PG&E officials.

Still another source of energy, uranium, is being developed as the principal activity of one of Union's wholly owned subsidiaries, Minerals Exploration Company, which also explores for and produces hard minerals. It had been dormant for years as holder of small mining claims for Union.

E. H. "Ned" Eakland, who had both mining and financial experience, was named president in 1967. William R. "Bill" Moran, formerly a Union Oil geologist, was named vice president and general manager.

By late 1969, Minerals Exploration made its first significant discovery, a nickel deposit near Mt. Windarra in western Australia, jointly with two large U.S. mining companies. It lay close to a similar sized deposit discovered by Poseidon, Ltd., an Australian company, to which Union sold its interest in 1972.

A joint venture led to the discovery of a sulfur deposit on Union Oil lands in March 1970, but commerciality was not established.

Minerals Exploration's biggest venture is in uranium. It has a 65 percent interest in a $45 million uranium mining and milling project in Sweetwater County, Wyoming, about 34 air miles northwest of Rawlins.

It is estimated that the deposits consist of about 15 million tons of uranium ore containing approximately 15 million pounds of uranium oxide.

If all necessary permits are obtained on a timely basis mine preparation and mill construction will begin in mid-1977 and continue for approximately 15 months. Mining of ore is expected to begin by late 1977 and mill start-up is scheduled for late 1978.

The mill will operate continuously over an expected minimum life of 15 years and is expected to produce approximately one million pounds of uranium oxide per year, sufficient to supply the energy needed to operate two typical nuclear power plants. A midwestern utility already has contracted with Union to take 50 percent of the mill's output.

The total operating work force, when the project is on stream in late 1978, is expected to be approximately 290.

Minerals Exploration also plans development of uranium prospects in other western states.

Its other activities are far flung. In 1975, acting as operations manager for a U.S.-Canadian-French consortium, it began a search for phosphates in the South Pacific.

During the middle 1970's work in the Republic of Mexico concentrated on the evaluation of a former high-grade gold-silver producer in the state of Guerrero. By 1976 underground exploration had indicated more than five million tons of sulfide ore containing recoverable quantities of silver and zinc, with by-product values of gold, copper, and lead. Difficult metallurgical problems are under study by various metallurgical consultants in both the United States and Mexico.

High	Low	Stock	Div	P/E	Sales 100s	High	Low	Last	Chg
15⅝	14	TucsnG	1.08	8	196	15¼	15⅛	15⅛ –	⅛
12¼	9⅞	TwenCen	.50	8	122	10⅞	10⅜	10⅞ +	⅝
17¾	16⅜	TwinDs	.80	7	10	16½	16¼	16¼ –	⅛
24½	17⅞	TycoLab	.40	13	123	[illegible]	21⅜	21¾ +	½
24⅜	20⅜	TylerCp	.60	7	61	[illegible]	23¼	23½ +	¼
		– U-U-U –							
27½	20⅛	UALInc	.60	26	260	21½	21	21 +	¼
20⅛	18⅜	UGICp	1.40	8	54	20	19⅞	20 +	[illegible]
31½	28⅞	UGI pf	2.75	..	z200	30⅛	30⅛	30⅛ –	⅛
15½	14⅛	UMCInd	1	8	130	14⅞	[illegible]	14⅜	¼
2⅜	1¼	UMET Tr		..	8	1½	1½	1½	....
17¾	14	UOP	.35e	10	123	15¼	14½	14¾ +	⅛
37¼	31¼	UVInd	1.50	[illegible]	47	36⅝	36⅛	36⅝ +	¼
22¾	20½	UARCO	1.30	[illegible]	[illegible]	20⅞	20¾	20⅞	....
13⅝	11	Unarco	.60	4	14	12½	[illegible]	[illegible]	½
32⅜	28¼	UnilLt	1.06e	6	1	33	33	33 +	⅝
50¾	47¼	UniNV	2.07e	6	4	50	50	50 +	⅜
13⅞	11⅝	UnBancp	.84	10	126	12⅛	12	12⅛	....
66⅝	57⅝	UCamp	1.80	13	579	63½	63	63½ +	1¼
62⅜	56⅜	UnCarb	2.80	8	549	60¾	60⅛	60½ +	⅛
8¾	7¼	UnCmrce		19	50	8¼	8	8¼ +	¼
7¾	6	UnionCp		12	40	6½	6¼	6¼ –	¼
16½	15	UnElec	1.36	8	222	15⅜	15⅛	15¼	....
42	38½	UnEl pf	3.50	..	z400	40	39¾	40 +	1½
53	50½	UnEl pf	4.50	..	z230	52	51¼	51¼	....
31	29⅛	UnEl pf	2.72	..	9	29⅝	29⅜	29⅝	....
87	83¾	UnEl pf	7.44	..	11	86	85	85 +	½
93	88	UnEl pf	8	..	1	88¾	88¾	88¾ –	1
5⅞	4⅝	UnFidel		6	10	5	5	5	....
59¼	53⅝	UnOCal	2.10	8	257	58⅛	57⅝	58 +	¼
76⅜	70¼	UOCa pf	2.50	..	1	74⅞	74⅞	74⅞ +	⅜
51¾	48	UPacCp	1.70	13	342	51½	51	51½ +	¼
17½	16⅞	UnPac pf	.47	..	2	17¾	17¾	17¾ +	¼
10⅜	9¼	Uniroyal	.50	16	227	10	9⅞	9⅞	....
89½	82⅛	Uniroyal pf	8	..	z130	85½	85⅜	85½	....
10⅛	8⅛	[illegible]		8	38	8⅞	8¾	8¾ –	¼
14⅞	12½	UnBrand pfA		..	9	13	12¾	13 +	⅜
11⅛	10	UnitCp	.80e	..	174	10¾	10½	10⅝ +	¼
30½	25⅝	UnEnRs	1.72	6	96	28½	27⅞	28 –	⅜
13⅛	11	UFinCal	.24	6	60	11⅞	11¾	11¾	....
14⅜	11¾	UnGrnty		6	61	12½	12⅛	12⅛ –	⅛
27⅝	26	UIllum	2.44	9	48	26⅛	25⅝	25⅝ –	⅜
25¼	23¾	UnIllu pf	2.20	..	z500	24½	24¼	24¼ –	¼
24⅛	19⅛	UnitInd	.70	8	11	23½	23⅜	23½ –	⅛
5½	4⅝	UnitInn	.14	7	69	5⅝	5½	[illegible]	¼
13⅞	12¾	[illegible]rBk	1.04	8	18	13	12⅞	13	....
13⅛	10½	[illegible]tMM		..	260	12	11⅝	11¾ +	¼
39⅝	31¼	[illegible]Nuclr		11	222	36	35⅛	35⅝ +	⅜
4⅜	2¾	UnPkMn		50	14	3⅛	2⅞	3 +	⅛
13⅝	11¾	UnRefg	.56	9	35	13⅜	13⅛	13⅜ +	⅜
18⅛	15⅞	USFoS	1.26e	..	8	16½	16½	16½ +	⅛
54⅞	47¼	USFidG	2.76	10	221	53	52	52½ +	⅛
26⅜	23¼	USGyps	1.60	12	85	25½	25⅛	25¼ +	¼
28⅞	26¼	USGy pf	1.80	..	8	28	27½	27¾	....
8⅜	6⅜	USHom	.16	9	150	7¼	7	7¼ +	¼
8¾	6½	USInd	.40	9	205	7	6¾	6⅞	....
12⅝	9⅝	USLeasg	.32	5	229	10⅝	9⅞	10½ +	⅝
4	2⅝	US Rty		..	22	3¾	3⅝	3⅝ –	⅛
27	22¾	USShoe	1.20	7	23	23⅞	23⅝	23⅞ +	⅛

Last	Chg
0⅛ +	¾
6¼ +	¼
3⅞ +	⅛
3¼ +	⅛
6⅜	......
9⅞ +	⅛
4⅜ –	⅛
3½	......
1¼	......
4⅜ +	⅛
6⅛	......
0¼	......
6⅛ –	⅜
7⅛ +	¾
3½	......
6½	......
6⅜	......
4⅜ +	⅛
9⅜ –	⅛
8¼ –	⅛
2¾	......
7 –	⅛
9⅜ +	⅛
7⅝ +	⅞
4¾ +	¼
3 –	⅛
2⅝ +	¼
6½ +	⅛
1⅞	......
2⅞ –	⅛
9⅝ +	⅛
4 +	¼
6⅜ –	⅛
6⅛ –	⅛
5¾ –	¼
9⅛	......
8⅛	......
8 +	⅛
2	......
5 +	½
3½ +	½
1¾ +	½
8½ –	⅛
5¾ +	⅛
2 –	1
2⅞ –	¼
6¾ –	¼
5½ +	½
9¾ +	¼
6¾ –	⅛
8⅝ +	¼
3½ +	⅛
2⅝ –	⅜
4⅛ –	¼
0 +	⅜
3½ +	⅛
5⅛ –	⅛
5¾	......
7½ +	½

High	Low	Stock
50	46⅜	VaEP
108¾	104	VaEP
31¾	30¼	VaEP
6⅜	5¼	Vornad
27⅜	24⅝	VulcnM
21	17	Wachov
56¾	47½	Wach
[illegible]	4	WachRt
15⅜	13⅛	WalMar
17⅞	15⅞	Walgrn
28⅞	25⅜	WlkrA
21⅜	18¾	WallBus
24¼	20½	WallMu
[illegible]	33⅜	WaltJim
12½	11½	WaltJ
42⅜	36⅛	WaltJ
[illegible]	5	WardFd
8¾	6½	Warnac
21	17¾	Wrnc
31½	28½	WarnS
29¾	26¼	WrnCor
58	52	WrnC
[illegible]	9½	WrnerC
31¾	27⅝	Warner
23⅛	21	WashGs
20¾	16¾	WashNa
21¾	18½	WashSt
25⅝	20½	[illegible]Wa
15	12	WasteM
24½	18¼	WatkinJ
7¾	6¼	WayGos
19½	18	WayG
6⅛	4⅝	WeanUn
18⅜	15⅛	Wea pf
10⅛	8¾	Weathrd
10¾	8	WebbDe
27½	24¾	WeisMk
28⅞	26¾	WellsFg
11¾	9½	WellFM
57	54	WtPP
41	35¼	WtPtPe
27½	26¼	WstctTr
10⅜	8	WnAirL
30½	27⅜	WnBnc
18¼	14⅛	WnNoA
18⅞	14	WnPacI
19	17¼	WnPubl
20½	17⅞	WUnion
53½	50¾	WnUn
65	61½	WUTI
27¼	26	WUTI
18⅝	16¼	WestgEl
48½	46½	Westg
32¼	26	Wstvaco
23½	22	Weybrg
46½	38½	Weyerhr
64½	54½	Weyr

CHAPTER NINETEEN

The Bottom Line: People and Money

AFTER ALL THE WORK IS DONE, all business boils down to people and money.

At Union Oil money has had two masters over the past decade: the money managers who direct all financing, and the corporate planners who develop forecasts and budgets. The two work closely together.

Money management is exclusively the Treasury Department's sphere, reporting through Bill Craig as treasurer to Senior Vice President Charles F. Parker. As defined by Craig it is "having adequate amounts of money available when and where the company needs it, at the lowest cost obtainable." Treasury directs all financing and cash management, the latter involving putting idle cash to work until needed for projects.

Corporate planning reports through Tom Sleeman as vice president to Senior Vice President Claude S. Brinegar. As Sleeman puts it, "Corporate planning focuses on the company's long term objectives and establishes challenging but achievable goals for its operating groups."

After corporate goals are approved by the Executive Committee, each profit center develops its own strategic (10 year), tactical (three year) and one year plans. All involve forecasts and budgets for profits and capital expenditures.

Union Oil's capital expenditures totaled over $5 billion from 1965 through 1976, as reported by Philip Blamey, comptroller. They exceeded the combined capital expenditures of Union and Pure for all the years they were in existence prior to their merger. They were also more than double the company's net earnings during the same period. In 1976 the capital expenditure budget reached an all-time high of over $800 million, an almost 20 percent increase over 1975 and well over three times the amount a decade earlier.

As R.E. "Bob" Dalbeck used to say before he retired in 1974 as comptroller

THE BOTTOM LINE

Superimposed on the figures of oil workers is a partial listing of a day's transactions on the New York Stock Exchange. Together they personify "the bottom line"—the successful melding of people and money in a corporate enterprise.

BICENTENNIAL MEETING *Chairman and President Fred L. Hartley opens the 1976 annual meeting of shareowners at Union Oil Center. In honor of the Bicentennial, early flags of the nation were draped along the walls and the meeting opened and closed with patriotic music.*

and budget director, profit planning involves the last step to the bottom line. In 1976 Union's earnings were the second highest in the company's history at $269 million, an increase during the Hartley years of 174 percent, about the same as for the industry. Union's cash dividends on common shares increased by 133 percent over the same period, compared to a somewhat lesser percent for the industry.

The most important single source of capital is funds (cash flow) from operations. During the past decade they amounted to just over $5 billion. Deciding on the best financing method of the dozen or so available often presents problems. But as Parker sums it up, "We balance all factors, decide how much is needed if any, what types are available, and what types we can live with. Then we look at the market to see what is available at what cost."

With capital expenditures of $686 million and funds from operations of $656 million in 1975, Union's planners raised the $30 million difference and retired other debt by selling $150 million of 8⅜ percent 10-year debentures in June, 1975.

When 1976 planning indicated a level of capital expenditures of more than $800 million, it was conservatively assumed about $150 million more would be needed if funds from operations were no greater than in 1975. So a $150 million 30-year debenture was authorized. When it appeared that investors, now less worried about double digit inflation, were willing to lend money at 8⅝ percent interest, the issue was increased to $200 million and promptly sold in March, 1976.

Some foreign operations were financed in foreign currencies. In 1971 Union established the Union Overseas Finance Corporation because of the U.S. gov-

RALLY 'ROUND THE ICE CREAM STAND *The Culpepper Minute Men, a quartet of college students, play rousing tunes at the entrance to Union Oil Center following the Bicentennial year annual meeting. The ice cream stand was created to illustrate an annual report insert explaining the free enterprise system.*

ernment's effort to reduce the unfavorable balance of payments.

With the value of foreign currencies fluctuating as compared to the dollar, substantial realized and unrealized gains/losses on foreign exchange resulted as foreign currency loans continued. Union took a $24 million pre-tax loss from this source in 1974, largely on an unrealized basis. Fortunately that year's earnings were nevertheless the highest ever. There was a small gain in 1975 from foreign exchange, followed by a small loss in 1976.

By the end of 1976 Union's foreign currency obligations totaled less than $25 million, only 3 percent of the company's long-term debt. The latter had increased by more than $630 million to $925 million during the decade, or over 200 percent, this being lower than the rest of the industry.

Use of commercial paper as a short term borrowing technique was one of Union's most significant financial developments over the decade. While it was short term in function it saved Union millions of dollars in lower interest rates, at the same time giving a timing flexibility to long term financing.

A wholly owned subsidiary company was formed in 1969 in connection with the issuance of commercial paper. Its assets were retail credit card receivables which were purchased for cash from Union by the subsidiary, later named Union Oil Credit Corporation. It issues commercial paper from time to time at relatively low interest rates to raise the cash needed for such purchases.

In 1976 alone approximately $1.5 billion in commercial paper was issued at one time or another, most of which was repaid during the same year on a "roll over" basis. At the end of 1976, the outstanding balance was under $25 million.

Another aspect of Union's money management is keeping cash from being idle, even for a day. One strategy is the zero balance concept. After the merger, Union had many bank accounts throughout the country with idle cash, because most of its operating facilities need quick access to money. But these accounts were not earning any interest, so most of them were consolidated into several special accounts in Los Angeles carrying zero balances.

Outlying offices write checks against these special accounts, and the total amount of checks presented for payment to each of them is cleared daily by charging Union's general account. If the latter needs additional funds they are deposited immediately.

The "zero balance" concept also was applied to Union's dividend account to take advantage of the "float," the time lapse between issuance of a check and its being returned through the banking system to Los Angeles for payment. The funds needed to pay the shareholders' checks earned interest in the meantime, often several days.

In Japan, a financing problem arose in 1968 in connection with Union's 33 percent ownership of Maruzen Oil Company, Ltd., Japan's third largest oil company. A Japanese government regulation subsequently limited the amount of foreign ownership in a petroleum refining company to 20 percent.

Hartley and Parker visited Japan and worked out a solution by which Union's 13 percent excess shares were put in a trust controlled and administered by Japanese trust companies in Japan.

In the retail credit field a significant development took place in the late 1960's called revolving credit. If customers wanted to pay only a portion of their monthly statement they could do so, but with a service charge applied to the unpaid balance. L.B. "Roy" Houghton, who retired as treasurer in 1972, recalls that Union was one of the first oil companies to adopt this, although department stores and other merchandisers were already using it. Customer service charges offset to a considerable extent the relatively high cost of credit card operations.

Quite aside from internal money management and corporate planning are the company's external relations with the financial community, including security analysts. During the decade some two dozen financial and operating presentations were made by company officers to various groups of the financial community,

LEARNING THE BUSINESS *A Union Oil chapter of Desk and Derrick, composed of women employees of the oil industry, visit The Geysers geothermal operations where C. F. Budd, Jr., geothermal district manager, explains what's happening.*

explaining to them the company's progress and goals.

In addition to the money managers putting idle cash to work, some idle lands were put to work by the Real Estate Division created in 1973 under the presidency of Fred M. Anderson. There were surplus lands no longer needed for operations. To sell them would involve large taxable gains, but to trade them for a package of wide-spread service station sites or other operating properties involved no capital gain. During the past decade numerous transactions of this kind were made.

Union had entered into a real estate development operation the same month Hartley became chief executive officer. Several months earlier a subsidiary, Moreland Investment Company, was formed to acquire the Strathearn Cattle Company which owned land in the Simi Valley of California. Union held a 47 percent interest. In 1968 Union bought out the other shareholders. Delay in freeway construction has limited increase in land values in the area, but a small portion of it is being sold for avocado and citrus orchards to cover the holding costs of the remaining acreage, which has longer term profit potential.

The Simi Valley project has not yet created significant profits. But another project made a profit not once, but twice. Someone else's bad luck and Union's foresight made it possible.

In 1966 Union sold, after reserving mineral rights and service station sites, approximately 600 acres of land in Orange County, California, most of which had been owned by it for about 70 years. The total value on Union's books was a little over $100,000. It was sold for $11 million in cash. That was the first profit.

Macco Realty Company, a subsidiary of Penn Central, had bought the land for residential development, having borrowed most of the purchase price from institutional lenders. Their arrangements with Macco provided that if the latter defaulted, Union would buy back any undeveloped land over a period of time at the 1966 sales price.

Caught in the web of Penn Central's financial collapse, Macco did default in 1971 after developing only 65 acres. So Union's Real Estate Division, forced to

MAKING BEAUTIFUL MUSIC *Employees at Union Oil Center who enjoy singing formed the Unionaires of 76 in 1971. They are shown in a performance at Disneyland, one of a continuing series of appearances before civic and business groups in southern California.*

step into Macco's shoes, began periodically to buy back the undeveloped land, and resell it at 1971-1976 prices, which had appreciated considerably since 1966. And that was the second profit.

In the early 1970's Union bought 125 acres with nearly a mile of ocean frontage north of Santa Barbara in the Goleta area. The Goleta Water District, which later adopted a "no growth" policy, refused to supply water for this and other large parcels in the vicinity. As a result, the land had to be leased for cattle grazing to pay interest and taxes on the investment.

Moreland Development Company, which was formed in 1971 as a wholly owned subsidiary, over the past several years has built business parks in the California cities of Simi, Brea and Ventura. According to Jay Gordon, Moreland's president, it appears that the Ventura development probably will be completed in five years instead of the estimated eight.

Another substantial project of Moreland Development Company was started in May, 1975. Some 600 acres of already zoned residential land in southern Orange County, California were purchased and the first unit of 274 lots went on sale in the latter part of 1976.

While real estate operations over the past decade had been helping Union's profits somewhat, changes in U.S. and foreign income taxes had been hurting them badly.

Virtual elimination by Congress of the U.S. percentage depletion allowance on crude oil starting in 1975 and natural gas starting in the last half of 1976 hit the hardest. This was on top of a cut in the depletion allowance six years before from 27½ percent to 22 percent. L.D. "Lew" Lawrence, general manager of the tax department, calculated that the cost to Union for 1975 was over $50 million and for 1976 was over $80 million.

"It is incredible," said Fred Hartley in a letter to employees, "that historical tax incentives would be removed at the very time that the industry has its greatest need for capital to finance the search for critically needed petroleum reserves."

INDUSTRIAL PARK *The sign identifies the entrance to the San Buenaventura Business-Industrial park in Ventura, California, an 80-acre site on rolling hills overlooking the Pacific Ocean. The park is a project of Moreland Development Company, a subsidiary of Union Oil.*

ENERGY SAVERS *U.S. Department of Commerce representative Eric Silberstein (left), presents a special citation to Union for the company's energy conservation program which saved enough energy to supply the equivalent electrical needs for 65,000 homes. Accepting are Paul Grandle (center), chairman of the energy conservation task force, and Fred L. Hartley, chairman and president.*

Ironically, no other extractive industries from coal and uranium to gravel, peat and sand lost depletion.

Another tax blow in the early 1970's was the harsher foreign and U.S. tax treatment of the company's foreign extraction operations. The aggregate tax rates in the two overseas areas where most of Union's foreign production comes from have reached a level half again higher than the U.S.'s 48 percent.

In 1966 Kenny Vaughan and Ray Burke asked H.A. "Fritz" Skinner, then comptroller of the exploration and production division, to work with Union's insurance division, which reported to Corporate Secretary Bob Niven, to find a cheaper and more effective way to handle insurance matters.

What evolved was an innovative and cost saving self insurance program. The first big step was to self insure the Blue Water rig in the Gulf Division. From there, Union self insured Alaska platforms in the Cook Inlet as well as those in the Gulf. By 1976 many other significant risks were under the self insurance program. J.A. "Jim" McCullough, named manager of insurance in 1970, points out that by 1970 purchase premiums had been reduced by over $5 million annually, largely as a result of self insuring most operating assets.

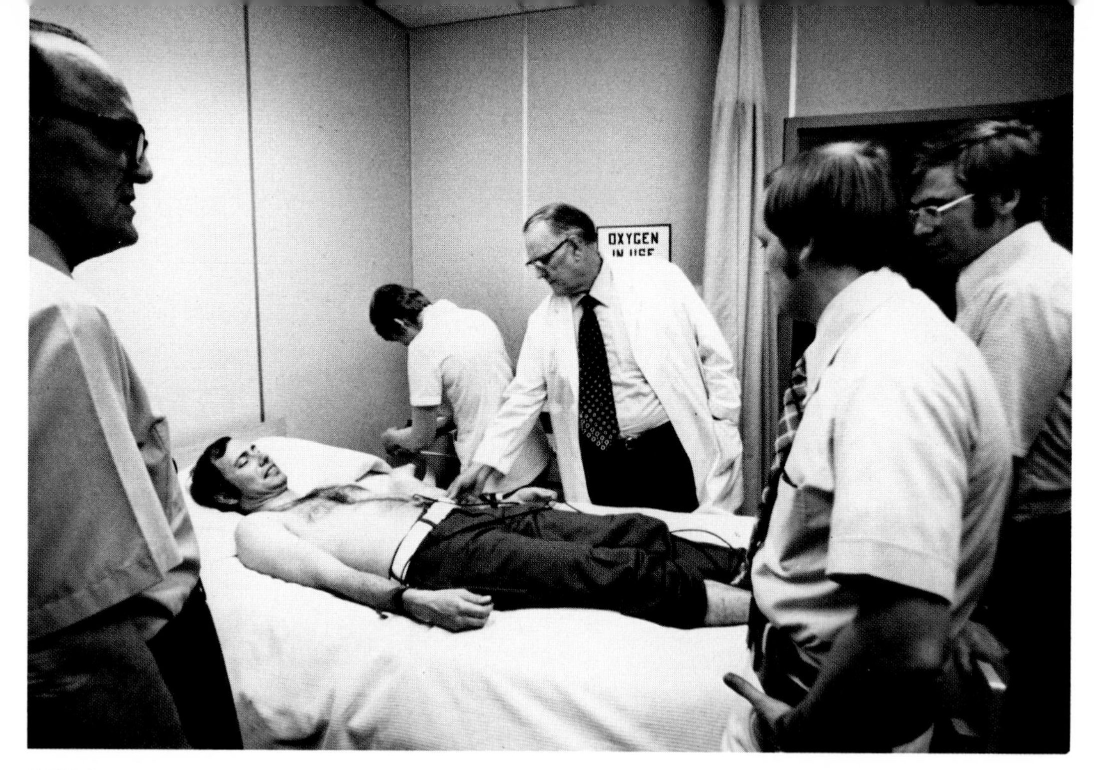

LIFE SAVING TECHNIQUES *Chicago Refinery employees review emergency life saving training program with Dr. Allan Skoog (center).*

People are one of Union Oil's most valuable assets. Talented people. Dedicated people. Motivated people.

So in the first decade of Fred Hartley's presidency, as the company grew, Union's employee benefit plans got better all the time.

"Practically every plan has been modified two or three times," Paul Doyle, vice president, corporate industrial relations, points out. "There has been no stagnation in that period."

By 1976 Union was spending roughly 40 percent of its base payroll for employee benefits. In 1965 the figure was 30 percent.

The employees retirement plan is one where significant changes took place. The company has paid the entire cost since 1970, when employee contributions were eliminated. Benefits also were broadened. An employee no longer has to wait for the normal retirement age of 65 to retire, but can do so at age 62 without the former reduction factor. Also spouses are entitled to a 50 percent survivor annuity when an employee becomes 55 years old.

Significant improvements in the medical plan also took place, with considerably broader coverage, including maternity benefits and improved co-insurance and deductibility provisions. Additionally, the company in 1976 paid over two-thirds of the plan's total cost as compared with one-fifth in 1965.

Other long standing employee benefits have improved over the past decade, including broadening of disability income and liberalization of holidays and vacations.

Under the leadership of Corporate Medical Director Dr. Richard Call, the medical department over the past decade has been organized on a worldwide basis. In 1974 the medical department employed a full time industrial hygienist-toxicologist. Specific exercise and anti-smoking programs tailored to the employees' needs and capacities also are available, and a successful program on alcoholism was initiated.

As an equal opportunity employer during the past decade, Union has been following an affirmative action program to assure compliance. In a letter to employees Hartley stated Union's position: ". . . our policy is one of equal opportunity for all with respect to hiring, promotion and all personnel handling practices and policies. There shall be no discrimination because of race, creed, color, age, handicap, or sex."

J.P. "Joe" Johnson is Union Oil's coordinator of minority and urban affairs. He has a law degree and is a former Los Angeles police officer. One of his jobs is to find individuals with the best training and growth potential. To do this, he has to move among minority groups.

Johnson evolved a simplistic but successful method: he sometimes gets his hair cut several times a week at minority area barber shops. His reasoning: they are the best places to find out about the local community. Johnson says the method has one drawback: explaining his high cost of haircuts as a business expense!

Between 1965 and 1976 the average pay of all employees more than doubled over the $8,100 in 1965. At the end of 1976 there were almost 16,000 Union Oil employees. This was a 6 percent decrease under 1965.

BLACK HISTORY *Union Oil has participated in Los Angeles' annual Festival in Black since 1969. Viewing the company's display of black history are Los Angeles Mayor Tom Bradley; Joe Odoms, research; Mrs. Jessie Mae Beavers, and Joe Johnson, coordinator of minority and urban affairs.*

INTERNATIONAL PEACE ARCH

A symbol of fraternity that straddles the western end of the unfortified U. S.-Canadian border at Blaine, Washington, The International Peace Arch was built by workmen of the two countries in 1921 as a reminder that the peoples of two great nations can live side-by-side in peace.

MONUMENT TO FREEDOM

A granite monument stands at a Union Oil service station in Blaine, Washington, commemorating the 45th anniversary of the International Peace Arch. Union Oil President Fred L. Hartley presided at the dedication of the monument upon whose face is inscribed: "In recognition of the concord between free nations for which the Peace Arch stands—freedom to live, freedom to work, freedom to worship, freedom to reason and invest—this monument is set by the 103,000 shareowners of a private enterprise—Union Oil Company of California—in its 76th year, June 5, 1966."

TOURNAMENT OF ROSES *H. W. "Hoot" Bragg, area commercial sales manager, officiated as president of the 1968 Pasadena Rose Parade after working on various Tournament committees for nearly 20 years. Rose Parade Queen Linda Strothers and the late Everett Dirksen, U. S. Senator from Illinois who served as grand marshall, stand with him before parade begins.*

In addition to higher pay and improved benefits, employees continued to share in the company's profits. One method is the newest of Union's benefit plans, Employee Stock Ownership Plan (ESOP). It is made possible by the federal government's decision to provide a small investment tax credit to any company which will use the amount of that credit to buy its own stock on the open market for its employees. It became effective in 1975.

The other profit sharing arrangement was started some 20 years earlier. For many years employees contributed to the plan, called Union Oil Employees Profit Sharing Plan, on a voluntary basis. The company contributed a percentage of its pre-tax profits, but only contributing employees shared in those contributions. Shortly after the Pure Oil merger, contributions by employees were no longer required for membership. Using the funds contributed, a bank acting as trustee buys Union Oil stock on the open market on almost a daily basis. In 1976 the company contributed approximately $7.5 million to the Plan.

The Union Oil Employees Profit Sharing Plan is Union's largest shareowner, holding for its approximately 12,000 employee members roughly 2.2 million shares at the end of 1976, or 5½ percent of Union's total outstanding stock. No individual shareholder has owned as much as even one percent since the company purchased Daniel K. Ludwig's more than four million shares (14 percent) for $146 million at $35.50 per share in February, 1965.

In addition to the profit sharing plan, Union has approximately 135,000 other shareowners. This is an increase of eight percent since 1965.

During the Hartley years per share quarterly dividends more than doubled, from 25 cents to 52½ cents, the increase being somewhat better than the oil industry average. The price of Union's common shares on the New York Stock Exchange over the same period was up by 65 percent, as compared with 15 percent for the Dow Jones Industrial Average.

In 1965 slightly more than 10.2 million shares of $2.50 cumulative convertible preferred stock were issued to 42,000 shareholders of the former Pure Oil Company in connection with the merger. Since then roughly two-thirds of the preferred shares have been converted into common shares by one-third of the preferred shareholders.

Part of the responsibility for success is sharing good fortune with other people. Art Stewart, Bob Niven and Bob Hedley had this in mind when they helped to form Union Oil's charitable foundation. Union's contributions to it during the past decade have included properties and securities with a low tax basis and high market value, plus cash.

Almost half of the Foundation's contributions goes to support education, partly for students at both graduate and undergraduate levels in fields closely related to Union's interests, and another part to children of employees and dealers for undergraduate scholarships. Over the past decade more than 2,000 scholarships of all kinds were awarded by the Foundation to deserving students.

The other half of the Foundation's contributions goes to hospitals, publicly supported community welfare agencies, and civic enterprises in the company's operating areas.

To encourage support of colleges and universities by employees, their contributions between $20 and $1,000 are matched by the Foundation on an annual basis.

Union Oil also has recognized its corporate responsibility in the area of political contributions. It has firm official policies against illegal or unethical contributions in the U.S. or foreign countries for political purposes, or for the promotion of favored government treatment.

Equally important is the responsibility for making legitimate contributions to candidates for political office in the U.S. Shortly after he became chief executive officer, Hartley was the prime mover in creating a totally non-partisan political fund to which management employees may contribute on a completely voluntary basis.

The Political Awareness Fund (PAF), as it is named, is administered by a committee of three middle management employees, chaired by H.P. "Hal" Shawlee, manager of civic affairs. Upon recommendation of those who contribute to the fund, the committee determines contributions to be made. They subsequently are reported to all contributors and all proper government agencies. In those states where corporate political contributions are permitted, the company itself makes the contributions.

Board of Directors

December, 1976

*Claude S. Brinegar
Senior Vice President,
Union Oil Company

*Ray A. Burke
Senior Vice President,
Union Oil Company

Robert Di Giorgio
Chairman, Chief Executive Officer,
Di Giorgio Corporation

William H. Doheny
Personal Investments

Prentis C. Hale
Chairman of the Executive Committee,
Carter Hawley Hale Stores, Inc.

*Fred L. Hartley
Chairman and President,
Union Oil Company

T. C. Henderson
Vice President,
Union Oil Company

Donald P. Jacobs
Dean, Graduate School of Management,
Northwestern University

*William S. McConnor
Senior Vice President,
Union Oil Company

Henry T. Mudd
Chairman, Chief Executive Officer,
Cyprus Mines Corporation

Peter O'Malley
President, Los Angeles Dodgers, Inc.

*Charles F. Parker
Senior Vice President,
Union Oil Company

Arthur C. Stewart
Personal Investments

*Member of the Executive Committee

union

CHAPTER TWENTY

The End. And the Beginning

A COMPANY IS SOMETHING LIKE A SHIP.

To follow a chartered course it needs all the science of navigation and an able crew.

But most of all, it needs a strong hand at the helm.

Union Oil has been fortunate in having such men. Each seemed aptly fitted to the challenge of his voyage.

When the young company was first formed in 1890 it needed money and prestige. Its first president furnished both. He was Thomas R. Bard who had come west for his health. Later he was to serve as a United States Senator from California.

When what was needed was a high determination to find oil combined with an entrepreneur's willingness to take risks, Lyman Stewart took the helm. And held it for 20 years.

Among other things, he had an extraordinary gift: the foresight to find land where his nose smelled oil. And the courage to acquire it long before it could be developed.

He also had the stubbornness and the savvy to keep control of Union out of the reach of its many suitors who wooed with money and promises. He saw the young company through its very early growing pains, never, it would seem, in any doubt as to its ultimate success.

When California was about to come into its own as the world's leading producer of oil, Lyman's son Will succeeded to the presidency. He had quit school, preferring to work in the oil fields. And he led Union into the era of some of its richest California oil strikes.

He remained president for 16 years until his death in 1930, seeing the burgeoning company through critical resistance to take-over by larger oil companies. Like his father, Will had the backbone and the vision to keep Union independent.

THE END AND THE BEGINNING

Union Oil Center was dedicated in 1956 as the building that freedom built, a symbol of our free, competitive system which has produced the greatest social and economic benefits in the history of mankind. It represents the efforts of the past and the hope of the future. Fred L. Hartley, ninth president of Union Oil, is in the foreground.

He also pioneered in founding some of the early and more significant company benefits for employees.

Then the depression threatened the very life and survival of Union Oil. Hard driving, desk pounding Leonard Pressley St. Clair was its president. He cut costs to the bone while religiously maintaining dividends.

After the depression and the St. Clair years, the board of directors sought a man to give the company new shape and thrust. They found him sitting on their own board: Reese Hale Taylor.

All six foot three of him came in from the presidency of Consolidated Steel Company, knowing little about oil. But he knew something else: how to raise capital and how to motivate people and get them moving in the same direction.

It seemed that from the very morning he arrived at headquarters before 7 o'clock in the morning and started asking questions things began to happen, things that were significant to the new forward thrust of the company.

He tapped new sources of capital in the east, and launched Union on an era of vital expansion of its capacity to find oil and refine it into multiple products.

He modernized most of Union's refineries and added new ones as productive hardware for the coming growth.

He pushed research and emphasized the need to have new and better products and processes in the competitive market.

He enlarged Union's service station system, styling them to fit into the communities in which they did business.

He first articulated an intensive and extensive quality philosophy for Union, defining it as the "Tiffany of oil companies."

He created a corporate advertising campaign for the company that was among the first to espouse the cause of free enterprise.

Before he was through, he had turned a parochial oil company into a maverick regional oil company, with a strong share of market and a quality reputation.

Cy Rubel came to the presidency of Union Oil twice. First, when Reese Taylor moved up to chairman of the board to make room for him.

Rubel was one of the great international petroleum engineers. He had cut his teeth in exploration and brought a worldwide, sophisticated knowledge of oil finding to his job. He knew the importance of finding new sources of oil, and pushed Union's exploration into the Gulf of Mexico and Louisiana.

He had a low key, homespun personality and demonstrated an intuitive understanding of people. As a result, he had a great "come together" effect on the company, a calming, almost healing influence after some of the previous tempests.

Notwithstanding, he was a shrewd executive who knew how to set a plan, map a strategy to implement the plan, take it to market and see it through.

Rubel was excellent at running Union's capacities to explore for, find, refine and market oil at full throttle. His were growth years.

When he became 65 he retired, and went fishing.

But he was called back from his fishing when Reese Taylor died suddenly in 1962.

He led the company again as president, while the executive vice president—

Fred Hartley—was being prepared for Rubel's job. When he felt Fred had all the requirements, Cy went fishing again.

Hartley came to his new challenge with an in-depth training. He had gone through most of the chairs: day laborer, refining, research, marketing, administration.

As a result he brought a toughness of mind, a knowledge and understanding to his job which were exactly right for his time.

He knew Union could not survive as a regional company. So one of his first important official acts was to make the Pure Oil merger.

Hartley also knew Union needed access to new sources of oil beyond the well-worked fields of the past. He built a bridge to explorations in Alaska, the Far East and western Europe, and established a successful international division of exploration and production.

Yet—along with the rest of the industry—he faced troubles at home. For the first time the country had been struck by an oil boycott of middle eastern producing countries. And domestically the very success of the industry in finding and supplying the energy the country needs had made it suspect and vulnerable.

Proposals were made in Congress to dismember the large integrated oil companies into one or two of their four basic functions and/or to prohibit them from engaging in any other energy activity except oil and gas. Can this happen? No one can say for sure.

As Fred Hartley ended the decade in 1976 as chief executive officer, and as Union Oil completed its 86th year as a company, one thing can be predicted with historical certainty.

Whatever the weather ahead, Union Oil will have a strong hand at the helm.

Index